INTRODUCTORY ELECTRIC CIRCUITS

INTRODUCTORY ELECTRIC CIRCUITS

JOHN B. WALSH, M.S., P.E.

ASSISTANT DIRECTOR
COLUMBIA UNIVERSITY ELECTRONICS RESEARCH LABORATORIES

FORMERLY ASSISTANT PROFESSOR OF ELECTRICAL ENGINEERING
COLUMBIA UNIVERSITY

KENNETH S. MILLER, Ph.D.

PROFESSOR OF MATHEMATICS
NEW YORK UNIVERSITY

McGRAW-HILL BOOK COMPANY, INC.

NEW YORK   TORONTO   LONDON

1960

INTRODUCTORY ELECTRIC CIRCUITS

II

68020

THE MAPLE PRESS COMPANY, YORK, PA.

PREFACE

This book has been written to bridge the gap between traditional texts and ultrasophisticated treatises. Even in presenting what is essentially still a classical selection of material, it reflects the important advances made in electric-circuit theory during the past 20 years. The authors believe that the more modern approach clarifies and leads to a better understanding of the subject matter.

The text commences with a thorough treatment of d-c circuits. This is more than a mere review of material already learned. It serves two purposes. For one, it presents d-c circuit theory, per se, from a unified point of view. Furthermore, the treatment of d-c circuits is used as a framework in which may be developed many notions of general circuit analysis (loop and node), topology, and duality. Such concepts are fairly simple to present to a student when referred to d-c circuits, whereas they are more difficult to introduce along with a-c circuits, where the student is already struggling on unfamiliar ground.

Direct-current circuit theory is followed by a presentation of a-c circuits from what is believed to be the proper point of view: namely, as a problem in differential-equation theory. The notion of complex impedance is introduced as a tool which is fortunately available for solving constant-coefficient differential equations when a certain class of forcing functions (sinusoids) is present. The discussion of transients in Chap. 3 not only serves as an introduction to a-c circuit analysis but also provides a background for the presentation of the Laplace transform in Chap. 10.

Several topics related to the steady-state analysis are given: general analysis, network theorems, and an introduction to the analysis of active networks. In this latter case the proper form of Thévenin's theorem is stressed. Power and energy considerations are given detailed attention.

There then follow chapters on elementary two-terminal and two-terminal-pair networks. Here the transformer is discussed, and the relationship between real and ideal transformers is carefully developed. Circle diagrams are treated by a new method. Three-phase circuits are the subject of an entire chapter. A chapter on Fourier analysis serves as a bridge between conventional steady-state analysis and the Laplace transform.

v

Finally, the Laplace transform is treated, not only as a tool for the solution of transient problems but as part of a more general approach to circuits from the point of view of complex frequency (a notion which is briefly introduced in Chap. 3). This point of view is essential to an understanding of linear systems as they are used today. Then, except for the appendixes, a brief chapter on the matrix analysis of networks completes the text.

It is felt that the inductive approach, developing general methods from a study of particular cases, with the consequent emphasis on motivation, is very important at this elementary level. Toward this end many of the illustrative examples have been chosen to point out at each step why additional development of a topic is merited. In the opinion of the authors the illustrative examples form an important part of the text. Besides the point just mentioned, they are used to illustrate the less obvious applications of the material presented and to show methods of dealing with apparent exceptions (or even to introduce such exceptions) which could be discussed otherwise only with confusing circumlocution.

In some of the topics treated, special situations or apparent exceptions to statements made in the body of the text occur. Such difficulties usually disturb only the better student, whereas a full discussion of every apparent anomaly would certainly confuse the average student. In such cases brief footnote remarks are used to clarify the subtleties without disrupting the trend of the discussion. It is not always expected that the average student will appreciate the significance of the footnotes without additional discussion.

In spite of the use of differential equations, no previous knowledge of the subject on the part of the student is presumed. However, we do assume that the student has studied the differential and integral calculus. A familiarity with basic physics is also assumed, not because many of the principles are explicitly used, but because a study of that subject matter provides the student with a proper background for the study of electric circuits.

It is a pleasure to acknowledge the assistance of L. E. Blumenson, J. Bose, H. Dern, and L. H. O'Neill of the Electronics Research Laboratories of Columbia University, all of whom read portions of the manuscript and offered helpful comments for the improvement of the text.

John B. Walsh
Kenneth S. Miller

CONTENTS

CHAPTER 1

DIRECT-CURRENT CIRCUITS

At one time it was necessary to preface every elementary textbook on electrical engineering with a dissertation on the importance of the field. This is no longer necessary. Radio and television are familiar to all, and most persons have at least heard of radar. The nationwide integrated telephone system is a household and business servant; electric power service extends to the most remote corner of the country. New uses of electricity are developing faster than a single mind can comprehend them.

In spite of the apparent diversity of these manifold developments, electrically they are very similar. It is this similarity with which this book is concerned. Each of the above-mentioned devices may be considered as a collection of elements connected by wires. Such an interconnected group of elements is an electric *network* or *circuit*.† Electric-circuit analysis considers the electrical behavior of electric circuits as distinct from their mechanical properties, thermal properties, etc. These other characteristics are not unimportant—they are just not the subject of circuit analysis.

In the next few sections we shall undertake a brief review of some of the basic concepts which are important to circuit analysis. It is presumed that none of these concepts is entirely new to the reader. They are presented so that they may appear in their proper perspective as part of a unified theory of circuit analysis. The study of electric circuits proper follows this review (Sec. 1.5).

1.1. Basic Concepts. The fundamental substance of electricity is *electric charge*. We do not know what the essential nature of charge is, any more than we know that of mass, or force, or energy. It is known that two kinds of charge exist, termed, rather arbitrarily, *positive* charge and *negative* charge. While we do not know the essential nature of charge, we can adequately define and accurately describe the *effects* of charge, and this is all that is really necessary to circuit analysis. Thus, charges exert forces on each other; like charges repel and unlike charges

† We need not be concerned here with the subtle distinction between *network* and *circuit* (see Sec. 1.5).

attract.   The force between two charges was determined experimentally by Coulomb and is described by *Coulomb's law*, which states that, if two point charges† of strength Q_1 and Q_2 are spaced r meters apart in a medium of infinite extent, the force exerted by one charge on the other is directed from one point charge to the other and has a magnitude F given by

$$F = \frac{1}{4\pi\varepsilon}\frac{Q_1Q_2}{r^2}. \tag{1.1}$$

Here F is measured in newtons.   The factor ε is a parameter whose value depends on the medium in which the charges are located; termed the *dielectric constant* or *permittivity* of the medium, it is expressed in units of farads per meter.   The 4π in Eq. (1.1) is a factor arising from the mks rationalized system of units used in this book.‡   In this system the unit of charge is the *coulomb*.   Like other units such as mass, length, and time, which are defined through certain practical considerations stemming from Newton's law, the unit of charge is defined through the basic law for charges, namely, Coulomb's law.   Two equal like charges of one coulomb placed one meter apart in a vacuum experience mutually repulsive forces of 9×10^9 newtons.   (In the rationalized mks system of units $\varepsilon = 36\pi \times 10^9$ farads/m for a vacuum, and for all practical purposes the same value holds for air.)

The fact that charges exert forces on each other gives rise to the concept of *electric fields*.   An electric field is said to exist in a region wherein a test charge experiences a force.   The magnitude of the electric field intensity is hypothetically measured by placing a test charge q (sufficiently small as not to disturb the field) in the field and measuring the force experienced by the charge.   The magnitude of the electric field intensity $\mathcal{E}$ is defined as the ratio of the magnitude of the force to the magnitude of the test charge.   Accordingly, the unit of electric field intensity is the newton/coulomb.   The direction of the electric field intensity is taken as the direction of the force acting on a positive test charge.   It follows from Eq. (1.1) that the magnitude of the field intensity $\mathcal{E}$ resulting from a point charge Q is

---

† A *point charge* is one which occupies a region whose dimensions are negligible compared with r.

‡ Although much discussion has attended the selection of units for general use in electrical engineering, the mks (meter-kilogram-second) system is that finally adopted by the International Electrotechnical Commission in 1940.   The question as to the choice of a rationalized or an unrationalized system was not originally settled by that commission but has since been resolved in favor of the former.   Since the rationalized system is used throughout this book, it is sufficient to comment that all the commonly used units—volt, ampere, ohm—are units of the rationalized system.

$$\mathcal{E} = \frac{F}{q} = \left(\frac{1}{4\pi\varepsilon}\frac{Qq}{r^2}\right)\frac{1}{q} = \frac{1}{4\pi\varepsilon}\frac{Q}{r^2} \tag{1.2}$$

where r is the distance between the test charge q and the charge Q.

Since an electric field exerts a force on a charge, energy (derived from an externally applied force) is required to move a charge against a field. The external mover must supply energy if the charge is moved in a direction contrary to that of the field; it acquires energy if the charge is moved in the direction of the field.† The work done by the external mover (and hence stored in the field) is given by

$$W_{AB} = -\int_A^B F \cos\theta\, d\lambda \tag{1.3}$$

where W_{AB} is the work in joules done moving the charge from A to B, F is the magnitude of the force exerted on the charge by the field, $d\lambda$ is a differential element of path length, and θ is the angle between the direction of the field and the direction of $d\lambda$, measured positively from the direction of the force F to the element $d\lambda$. The minus sign occurs because the external force on the charge is equal in magnitude and opposite in sense to the force of the field.

The value of the integral in Eq. (1.3) is dependent on the size of the charge moved in the field. In order to have a measure of the field which is independent of the size of a test charge, we define the *potential rise* V_{AB} from point A to point B as equal to the work per unit charge stored in the field in moving a positive charge q from A to B. From Eq. (1.3),

$$V_{AB} = -\int_A^B \frac{F}{q}\cos\theta\, d\lambda = -\int_A^B \mathcal{E}\cos\theta\, d\lambda. \tag{1.4}$$

The unit of potential rise is the joule/coulomb, commonly termed the *volt*.

It is sometimes convenient to consider not the potential rise from point to point but rather the absolute potential at a point. This may be done only if a point of zero potential is defined. It is customary to define the potential of the "point at infinity" as zero. The potential V_B of the point B is accordingly the work per unit charge required to move a test charge from infinity to B:

$$V_B = -\int_\infty^B \mathcal{E}\cos\theta\, d\lambda. \tag{1.5}$$

Thus

$$V_{AB} = V_B - V_A. \tag{1.6}$$

† A philosophical question may be raised as to where the energy added to a system of charges is stored: in the charges or in the field? This parallels the similar question of where the potential energy of a raised mass is stored: in the mass or in the gravitational field? For present purposes it is convenient to consider the potential energy associated with moving the charge as stored in the field. This convention should be carefully noted, as otherwise confusion may result.

In most practical cases the origin of electric fields as arrays of charges is overshadowed by the nature of the devices used as voltage sources. We are usually presented with a device having two or more terminals between which various differences of potential may exist. Actually, the terminals of such devices do carry charges. This fact is probably most obvious in the case of electrochemical cells but is none the less true in the case of various rotating machines.

In treating electric circuits it will be sufficient to consider our sources of potential difference—usually called simply *voltage sources*—to be two-terminal devices between whose terminals there exists a difference of potential. The terminals are designated as positive $(+)$ and negative $(-)$ to show which terminal is at the higher potential. The designation of the relative potentials of a pair of terminals is termed the *polarity* of the terminals. When necessary, several of these two-terminal devices can be connected to provide the equivalent of a multiterminal voltage source (Fig. 1.1). Occasionally there is reason to mark the terminals of a voltage source as $+$ and $-$ and then state that the potential difference is, say,

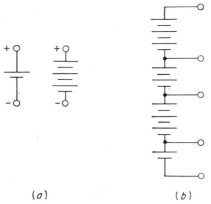

(a) (b)

FIG. 1.1. Representation of voltage sources. (*a*) Two-terminal; (*b*) multi-terminal.

-10 volts. This convention, which often causes confusion, merely means that the terminal marked $+$ is actually 10 volts negative with respect to that marked $-$; that is, the potential rise from $-$ to $+$ is actually a negative rise, and thus a positive drop, of 10 volts. This point will be reemphasized subsequently.

A flow of electric charges is an electric *current*. Current may be the flow of charged particles moving in a vacuum, as in the case of vacuum tubes; it may be the flow of charged particles in liquids or gases, or in semiconductors; commonly it is the flow of free electrons in metals. Current is measured as the rate of flow of charge; hence the unit of current is the coulomb/second, termed the *ampere*. A flow of charge at the rate of one coulomb per second comprises a current of one ampere. The positive direction of current is taken as that of the flow of positively charged particles. In wire circuits the flow of charge is mainly that of the negative charge carried by electrons; thus, the positive direction of current flow is opposite to the actual direction of electron flow.

In circuit theory, as contrasted with field theory or physical electronics, we are commonly concerned only with the total current entering the terminals of a device and not with the detailed flow of charge within the device.

A point not commonly stressed is that the electrons in a conductor actually move quite slowly—it is the fact of conduction which travels at the speed of light. (Analogously, water may flow slowly through a pipe, yet when the water is turned on at one end of a filled pipe it comes out the other end almost immediately, the delay depending on the speed of a pressure wave in water.) In fact, as the charge on an electron is -1.60×10^{19} coulombs and as there are 5×10^{22} free electrons per cubic centimeter of copper, the mean velocity of the electrons in a No. 10 wire (0.2587-cm diameter) wherein a steady current of 1 amp exists is only 2.4×10^{-3} cm/sec.

1.2. Ohm's Law. In 1826, George Simon Ohm discovered that if a source of voltage is impressed on a metallic circuit, at a fixed temperature, the resulting current is given by the relation

$$I = \frac{V}{R} \qquad (1.7)$$

where I† is the current in amperes, V is the potential difference impressed on the circuit in volts (commonly referred to as the "voltage"), and R is a measure of the "resistance" of the circuit to the flow of charge. A circuit in which one ampere exists when a voltage of one volt is impressed on it is said to have a *resistance* of one *ohm*. (For convenience, "ohm" is often designated by capital Greek omega, Ω.)

This well-known relationship, known as *Ohm's law*, is of basic importance in electrical engineering. It is to be noted, however, that well-known though it be, Ohm's law is not an obvious relationship. Indeed, it does not hold for circuits made of many materials. Fortunately, it applies to many materials used in practice. Hence, as we shall see, the validity of Ohm's law permits many circuits to be analyzed on a *linear*‡ basis.

In real circuits we generally encounter elements having large values of resistance interconnected by wires having low values of resistance. In drawing diagrams of such circuits, called *schematic diagrams*, it is convenient to consider the circuits as being made up of *resistors* connected by resistanceless wires. Resistors are two-terminal circuit elements which are characterized by the single parameter, resistance.§

† I is the initial letter of the French *intensité*.

‡ If, in Eq. (1.7), R is independent of V and I, we say that the relationship is *linear*. If R depends on V or I, then the relation is said to be *nonlinear*. (A more formal definition of linearity is given in Chap. 3.)

§ It will subsequently be seen that other parameters may be necessary to characterize real resistors. In such cases it will prove useful to hypothesize *ideal resistors*, characterized by only their resistance, as distinguished from real, or physical, resistors.

The resistance of the real wires is accounted for by showing appropriate additional resistors in the schematic diagram. Since the circuit which is analyzed is always to some degree an approximation or idealization of the real circuit (for example, insulators are nearly always considered to have "infinite resistance"), the resistance of the real wires is frequently neglected (see Fig. 1.2).

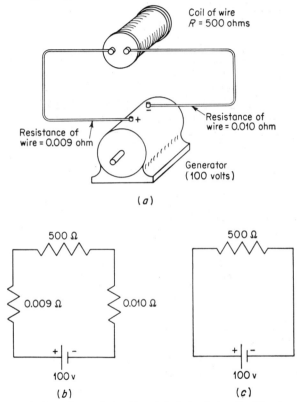

FIG. 1.2. Representation of a real circuit. (a) Actual circuit; (b) schematic diagram; (c) simplified schematic diagram.

In the circuit of Fig. 1.2 the resistance of the wires may be included in the 500-ohm resistor of Fig. 1.2c. This leads to a value of

$$500 + 0.009 + 0.010 = 500.019 \text{ ohms.}$$

If this number is meaningful, it implies that the value of the 500-ohm resistor (that is, the value of the resistance of the 500-ohm resistor) is known to six significant figures. This is unlikely.

1.3. Energy Relations. Equation (1.4) expresses the amount of energy per unit charge stored in a field by moving a charge from A to B. If, then, a charge dq moves from A to B, the amount of energy du stored in the field is, from Eqs. (1.3) and (1.4),

$$du = V_{AB}\, dq \qquad (1.8)$$

or

$$\frac{du}{dq} = V_{AB}.$$

Alternatively,

$$\frac{du}{dt} = \frac{du}{dq}\frac{dq}{dt} = V_{AB}\frac{dq}{dt}. \qquad (1.9)$$

Now dq/dt, the rate of flow of charge from A to B, is the current I_{AB}; and du/dt is the rate of increase of energy in the field, or the power input P_{AB} to the field. Thus

$$P_{AB} = V_{AB}I_{AB}. \qquad (1.10)$$

The unit of P is the joule/second, commonly termed the *watt*.

A note on the physical mechanisms associated with Eq. (1.10) is in order. Charge may be transported from A to B by simple mechanical force. Since the electrons or ions (which con-tain the elemental charges) have mass, it is possible to release into a field a charged par-ticle having a kinetic energy. If the charge is positive and its path carries it from a region of low potential to a region of high potential, the (kinetic) energy of the particle will be con-verted into electrostatic energy of the field until the velocity of the particle becomes zero. Unless some means is provided to restrain the particle when it stops, the field will accelerate the particle toward the region of lower potential, thereby converting electrostatic energy back to kinetic energy.

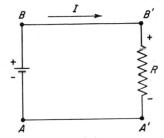

FIG. 1.3. Pertaining to power dissipation in a resistor.

In an electric cell, electrochemical processes force electrons and positive ions to opposite poles of the cell, thus setting up an electric field. If the electrons are drawn from the negative terminal (and returned to the positive terminal), charge flows through the cell, giving rise to a current. The positive direction of flow through the cell is from negative to positive terminal. According to Eq. (1.10), energy is stored in the field. What, precisely, is meant by this statement? This situation is typified by an electric cell across whose terminals a resistor of value R is connected (see Fig. 1.3). The conductor AA' is at a positive potential relative to BB'. A free charge placed anywhere in the vicinity of the circuit will experience a force; thus, an electric field exists in the vicinity of the circuit *and not merely in the cell or in the resistor.*

When equilibrium is reached, the voltage rise from A to B (or from

A' to B') is constant, and the current I, by Ohm's law, is V/R. The cell delivers energy to the field at a rate VI. What happens to this energy? It must be remembered that the potential difference across the resistor accelerates the negatively charged free electrons in the resistor and hence the electrostatic energy of the field is converted to kinetic energy of electrons. The average velocity of the electrons is such that the energy loss from the field initially used to impart kinetic energy to electrons is equal to that lost by the electrons through collision with the molecules of the resistor. The kinetic energy is accordingly transformed to thermal energy, manifested as heat which raises the temperature of the resistor.

The point of view adopted here, that the chemical energy of the cell creates a field which in turn causes a current in the resistor, is more appropriate than the common viewpoint that "the battery forces current through the resistor."

It is often more convenient to measure the rate at which a voltage source delivers energy not by measuring the current through the voltage source but by measuring the current in the external circuit. This is indeed the same current save for a difference in reference; the current I_{AB} in the source (see Fig. 1.3) is the current I_{BA} in the resistor. Thus, Eq. (1.10) may be recast as

$$P_{AB} = V_{AB}I_{AB\text{(source)}} = V_{AB}I_{BA\text{(resistor)}}. \tag{1.11}$$

Since the power delivered by the source is the power dissipated in the resistor, we may complete our shift in viewpoint by stating that the power dissipated† (or, simply, power loss) in a resistor (or, to use a more general term, in a *load*) is equal to the product of voltage across, and current in, the load, where the relative directions of current and voltage are as shown in Fig. 1.3. When the load is simply a resistor we may express the voltage in terms of the current by using Ohm's law and write Eq. (1.11) as

$$P = IV = I^2R = \frac{V^2}{R}. \tag{1.12}$$

The subscripts have been dropped for simplicity.

1.4. Signs and Conventions. A source of great confusion not only to beginning students but also to the more advanced is the matter of signs which should be associated with various differences of potential. This difficulty stems largely from two causes: (1) a necessary use of "negative" currents and (2) the *indiscriminate* employment of voltage rises and voltage drops in the same circuit. The first of these two difficulties may be clarified by the following discussion.

---

† Strictly speaking, power is not dissipated; energy is. Power is the time rate of energy flow. The usage "power dissipation" is, however, well established.

Consider the resistor shown in Fig. 1.4a. Consider a current flowing in the direction of the arrow as positive. Such a current will result in a potential difference having the polarity indicated. From Ohm's law,

$$V = IR. \tag{1.13}$$

The situation here is quite straightforward—a current having the direction shown is associated with a voltage having the polarity shown, and the values of current and voltage are related by Eq. (1.13). On the other hand, it is not always clear in practical cases what direction the current actually has. Then the symbols in Fig. 1.4 are taken merely as *reference direction* and *reference polarity*, and the current and voltage are considered as algebraic (signed) quantities in Eq. (1.13). Thus, if

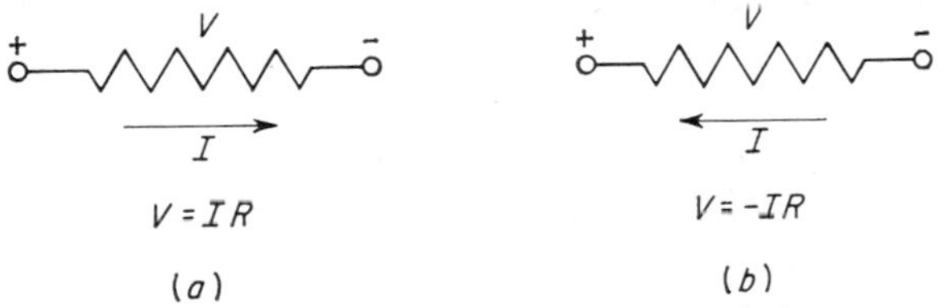

FIG. 1.4. Polarity conventions for Ohm's law.

in Fig. 1.4a a current of 1 amp were directed from right to left, I would have the value -1 amp, and if R were, say, 2 ohms, V would be

$$V = (-1) \times 2 = -2 \text{ volts}. \tag{1.14}$$

The minus sign means merely that the terminal marked "$+$" is at a potential 2 volts *lower* than that marked "$-$."

Reference potentials and directions are merely that: references. They are not necessarily *assumed* potentials and directions. This is illustrated by Fig. 1.4b wherein the current direction and voltage polarity cannot both actually be as shown. But does this imply that they are inconsistent? Inconsistent with respect to what? They are inconsistent with respect to Eq. (1.13). The difficulty may be removed by writing

$$V = -IR. \tag{1.15}$$

Now if a current of 1 amp actually is directed from left to right in a 2-ohm resistor, I is -1 amp, but Eq. (1.15) shows that V is $+2$ volts, and the terminal marked "$+$" is indeed positive with respect to that marked "$-$."

Thus it is seen that in order properly to specify the relation among V, I, and R we must specify a reference direction for current, a polarity for the voltage, and the proper algebraic form of Ohm's law.

The other mentioned difficulty arises largely from the use of various contradictory or inconsistent conventions in a single problem. Sometimes, the symbol E is used to represent a voltage rise and V a voltage drop. (Thus $E_{AB} = -V_{AB}$.) At other times E is associated with energy sources and V with energy sinks. When these two conventions are intermixed in a single problem, confusion reigns. Accordingly, this double convention is not used in this text; rather, E is generally used to

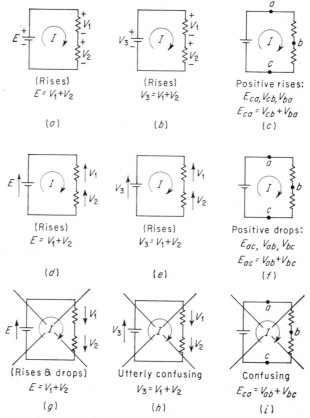

FIG. 1.5. Various polarity conventions used in circuit diagrams.

designate potential differences across sources (frequently termed electromotive forces, or emf's) and V for potential differences across resistors, as in Fig. 1.4a.

In drawing circuit diagrams, various methods of designating currents and potential differences are used. Plus and minus signs are used for voltage, with subscripts where necessary, to distinguish among various voltages. Often, the relative location of the + and − signs is symbolized by arrows. Here again need for caution arises because the arrows may be pointed in the direction of either the voltage rise or the voltage drop; generally the arrow points in the direction of rise. Currents are usually designated by arrows pointing in the direction of positive current flow. A double subscript is often used, both for current and voltage. Here again one must be careful to distinguish between the use of voltage rises and voltage drops.

The various symbolic conventions mentioned are shown in Fig. 1.5. Generally, that shown in Fig. 1.5a will be used in this book.

1.5. Direct-current Circuits. Having completed our brief review, we turn to the study of circuits themselves. Circuits are made up of two-terminal *elements*. For the time being, the only elements we shall consider are sources of constant potential, sources of constant current, and resistors. Circuits composed of such elements are called *direct-current (d-c) circuits*. In theory, this definition precludes circuits wherein

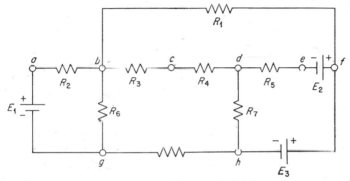

Fig. 1.6. Sample circuit to illustrate definitions of terms.

the voltage may be switched off or on,† since such voltage sources are not constant. In practice, after closing switches, we wait a sufficient length of time for the currents in the circuit to become constant. Our d-c analysis applies to these constant (final) values of current. What constitutes a "sufficient time" will be discussed later under the heading "transient analysis."

It must be borne in mind that the elements which we encounter in practice are never constant voltage or current sources or fixed resistors. However, the large majority of real circuits may be represented to a suitable degree of accuracy by such idealized elements. Such an idealized representation of a circuit is much easier to analyze than the actual network having nonconstant parameters.

When the terminals of two or more elements are connected, the point of connection is called a *node*. Each element is referred to as a *branch*. A *network* consists of two or more interconnected elements. (One-

---

† Indeed, in theory, no real circuit is a direct-current circuit, because at some time it was assembled, and attaching the last wire constituted closing a switch. We may disregard such pedantic quibbling for the present.

element networks have no practical consequences. Also, "dangling" elements in networks need not be considered.)

A loop which cannot be formed from smaller loops is a *mesh* (see Sec. 1.9). A *circuit* is a network which contains at least one loop. The foregoing definitions are illustrated in Fig. 1.6. The elements *ab*, *bc*, *bg*, *bf*, etc., form the branches. The letters *a*, *b*, *c*, etc., designate the nodes. Typical loops are *abga*, *abfdhga*, *bcdefhgb*. The loops *abga*, *bcdhgb*, *defhd*, and *bfedcb* are also meshes.

1.6. Kirchhoff's Laws. The fundamental circuit laws used in electric-circuit analysis are *Kirchhoff's laws*. These are:

1. *Kirchhoff's current law:* The algebraic sum of all the currents entering a node is zero. This follows from the observation that charge cannot accumulate at a node.
2. *Kirchhoff's voltage law:* The algebraic sum of the potential differences around any loop is zero. It is also frequently stated: The sum of the potential rises around a loop equals the sum of the potential drops. This law follows from the fact that the difference of potential between any two points is independent of the path between the points along which it is measured.

These two laws, coupled with Ohm's law, enable us to solve any d-c circuit problem. By "solve" we mean, in general, that, if all the voltage sources and values of resistances are specified, the current in each branch and the voltage drop across each branch must be determined. Frequently, of course, the problem is less general, but if the general problem can be treated, a fortiori the others may be solved.

The application of Kirchhoff's laws to a circuit may best be illustrated by means of an example.

Example 1.1. Determine each branch current and the voltage drop across each branch in the circuit of Fig. 1.7*a*.

Solution. To solve this problem we first assign voltage polarities and current directions to each branch and identify the nodes (Fig. 1.7*b*). Observe that the reference polarities for V_5 and I_5 have been assigned in accordance with Eq. (1.15) rather than Eq. (1.13). This is done only by way of illustration and is not what ordinarily would be done.

We then write Ohm's law for each resistive branch,

$$V_2 = 10I_2$$
$$V_3 = 20I_3$$
$$V_5 = -30I_5$$
$$V_6 = 40I_6,$$

Kirchhoff's current law for each node,

a
$$I_1 - I_2 = 0$$
b
$$I_2 + I_3 - I_5 = 0$$

c $I_5 - I_6 = 0$
d $I_4 - I_3 = 0$
e $I_6 - I_4 - I_1 = 0,$

and finally Kirchhoff's voltage law for each loop (here the voltage drops are summed around each loop),

abdea $V_2 - V_3 + 50 - 100 = 0$
bcedb $-V_5 + V_6 - 50 + V_3 = 0$
abcea $V_2 - V_5 + V_6 - 100 = 0.$

It is observed that we have 12 equations but only 10 unknowns: six branch currents

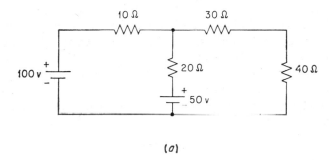

(a)

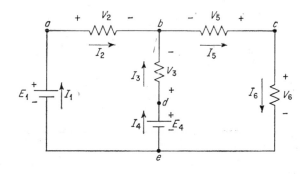

(b)

Fig. 1.7. Circuit for Example 1.1. (a) Original circuit; (b) branch currents and voltages designated.

and four branch voltages. Solution of these equations leads to

$$V_2 = \quad 23.91 \text{ volts}$$
$$V_3 = -26.08 \text{ volts}$$
$$V_5 = -32.61 \text{ volts}$$
$$V_6 = \quad 43.48 \text{ volts}$$
$$I_1 = I_2 = \quad 2.391 \text{ amp}$$
$$I_5 = I_6 = \quad 1.087 \text{ amp}$$
$$I_3 = I_4 = - \quad 1.304 \text{ amp}.$$

The foregoing method may be extended to a circuit of any degree of complexity, but it is clear even from this simple example that such an approach leads to a multitude of simple equations. Some simplifications may be made immediately. Nodes a, d, and c in the example are superfluous, and thus I_1, I_3, and I_5 need not be considered different from I_2, I_4, and I_6, respectively. However, we have still spent time writing down more equations than necessary. What is needed is an efficiently organized method of attacking circuit problems.

There are two such organized methods: the mesh-current method and the node-voltage method. These two methods will be explained in the next two sections.

1.7. Loop-current Analysis of Circuits. In the loop-current analysis of circuits *loop currents* are taken as the unknown variables, rather than the branch currents. Loop currents are hypothetical currents which follow closed paths in a circuit. They are so chosen that any branch current may be specified as the sum of loop currents. The technique of applying the loop-current method is most readily demonstrated by means of an example.

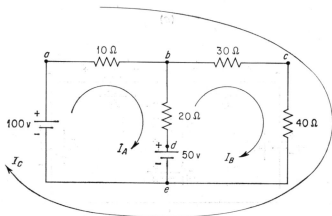

FIG. 1.8. Circuit for Example 1.2.

Example 1.2. Solve Example 1.1 using the loop-current method.

Solution. Here we select as variables the loop currents I_A, I_B, and I_C (see Fig. 1.8). Each of the branch currents may be represented as the sum of loop currents. Thus

$$I_1 = I_A + I_C$$
$$I_3 = -I_A + I_B$$
$$I_5 = I_B + I_C.$$

Applying Kirchhoff's voltage law (taking voltage rises as positive) for each loop (and including Ohm's law) gives

eabde	$100 - 10(I_A + I_C) - 20(I_A - I_B) - 50 = 0$
edbce	$50 - 20(I_B - I_A) - 30(I_B + I_C) - 40(I_B + I_C) = 0$
eabce	$100 - 10(I_A + I_C) - 30(I_B + I_C) - 40(I_B + I_C) = 0$

which become, after some trivial algebraic manipulations,

$$50 - 30I_A + 20I_B - 10I_C = 0$$
$$50 + 20I_A - 90I_B - 70I_C = 0$$
$$100 - 10I_A - 70I_B - 80I_C = 0.$$

We thus have three simultaneous equations on three unknowns. However, we observe that these equations are not independent. That is, we can obtain the third by adding the first two. Since this is the case, we may arbitrarily select the value of one of the variables and still satisfy the set of equations. Let us set $I_C = 0$.† Since only two unknowns I_A and I_B now exist, we need only two equations. We use the first two of our set to write

$$50 - 30I_A + 20I_B = 0$$
$$50 + 20I_A - 90I_B = 0$$

or

$$50 = 30I_A - 20I_B$$
$$50 = -20I_A + 90I_B.$$

These equations may be solved to yield

$$I_A = 2.391 \text{ amp}$$
$$I_B = 1.087 \text{ amp}$$

whence

$$I_1 = I_2 = I_A + I_C = 2.391 + 0 = 2.391 \text{ amp}$$
$$I_3 = I_4 = -I_A + I_B = -2.391 + 1.087 = -1.304 \text{ amp}$$
$$I_5 = I_6 = I_B + I_C = 1.087 + 0 = 1.087 \text{ amp}$$

and

$$V_2 = 10I_2 = 10 \times 2.391 = 23.91 \text{ volts}$$
$$V_3 = 20I_3 = 20 \times (-1.304) = -26.08 \text{ volts}$$
$$V_5 = -30I_5 = (-30) \times 1.087 = -32.61 \text{ volts}$$
$$V_6 = 40I_6 = 40 \times 1.087 = 43.48 \text{ volts}.$$

In the above example, by replacing the branch-current variables with loop-current variables we have been able better to organize our work. More important, a careful study of what we have done enables us to arrive at the end result with less lost effort.

First it should be pointed out that, although we wrote only equations based on Kirchhoff's voltage law, the only currents entering a node are the loop currents, which also leave every node they enter. Thus Kirchhoff's current law is automatically satisfied at each node.

When writing the loop equations, it is observed that the coefficient of each current term is the total resistance traversed by that current in the loop under consideration. For example, in loop A, the coefficient of

† This is done merely for convenience. We may assign any numerical value to I_C and still get the same answer for I_1, I_2, etc. Or, if desired, one can assign an arbitrary value to I_A (or I_B) and our problem can still be solved, yielding the same numerical values for I_1, I_2, etc., as originally obtained. The reader may verify these statements by actual calculations. (While one of the variables may be chosen arbitrarily, this does not mean, in general, that *any* variable may be selected. A knowledge of matrix theory is necessary to determine under what conditions a particular variable may be specified.)

I_A is $10 + 20 = 30$ ohms.   The coefficient of I_B is -20 ohms because I_B traverses loop A in a sense opposite to that of I_A.

These remarks lead us to observe that we may write loop equations for a λ-loop network in the general form

$$
\begin{aligned}
E_1 &= R_{11}I_1 + R_{12}I_2 + \cdots + R_{1\lambda}I_\lambda \\
E_2 &= R_{21}I_1 + R_{22}I_2 + \cdots + R_{2\lambda}I_\lambda \\
&\cdot\cdot\cdot\cdot\cdot\cdot\cdot\cdot\cdot\cdot\cdot\cdot\cdot\cdot\cdot\cdot\cdot\cdot\cdot\cdot\cdot \\
E_\lambda &= R_{\lambda 1}I_1 + R_{\lambda 2}I_2 + \cdots + R_{\lambda\lambda}I_\lambda.
\end{aligned}
\tag{1.16}
$$

In this set of equations

E_i is the algebraic sum of the voltage sources in loop i, voltage rises being taken positive.

R_{ii} is the sum of the resistances in loop i and is called the *self-resistance* of loop i.

R_{ij} is the resistance common to loops i and j.   It is positive if I_i and I_j traverse it in the same direction, negative if I_i and I_j traverse it in the opposite direction, and zero if I_i and I_j do not both traverse it.   Clearly, $R_{ij} = R_{ji}$.   It is called the *mutual resistance* between loops i and j.

Example 1.3.   Write the loop-voltage equations for the circuit of Fig. 1.9.
Solution.   We may write the result directly as

$$
\begin{aligned}
2 + 7 &= (1 + 2)I_1 - 2I_2 &&\quad + 0I_3 &&\quad + 0I_4 \\
0 &= -2I_1 &&\quad + (2 + 3 + 4)I_2 + 0I_3 &&\quad - 4I_4 \\
3 - 7 - 6 &= 0I_1 &&\quad + 0I_2 &&\quad + (5 + 6)I_3 - 5I_4 \\
6 &= 0I_1 &&\quad - 4I_2 &&\quad - 5I_3 + (5 + 4 + 7)I_4
\end{aligned}
$$

or, on simplifying,

$$
\begin{aligned}
9 &= 3I_1 - 2I_2 + 0I_3 + 0I_4 \\
0 &= -2I_1 + 9I_2 + 0I_3 - 4I_4 \\
-10 &= 0I_1 + 0I_2 + 11I_3 - 5I_4 \\
6 &= 0I_1 - 4I_2 - 5I_3 + 16I_4.
\end{aligned}
$$

There do exist other possible loops, such as $abcfjhgda$ or $adefjhgda$.   Equations written for such loops would not be independent but would merely be combinations of those we already have.   This matter will be treated more fully in Sec. 1.9.

Several observations may be made concerning the equations just written.

1. Some loops may have no voltage sources (for example, loop 2).
2. A single voltage source may appear in more than one loop equation (for example, the 6-volt and 7-volt sources).
3. Some loops have no common branch (for example, loops 1 and 4).
4. R_{ij} may be zero even for loops having a common branch if that common branch is occupied only by a voltage source (for example, $R_{13} = 0$).

The solution of the set of simultaneous equations may be carried out by successively eliminating variables or by using determinants. The method of determinants is explained in Appendix A, wherein is also included the numerical solution of the foregoing example.

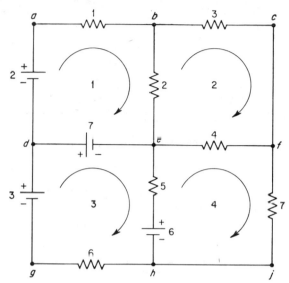

Fig. 1.9. Circuit for Example 1.3.

1.8. Node-voltage Analysis. A companion method to that of loop-current analysis is the method of node-voltage analysis. In this method we write, explicitly, Kirchhoff's current law for each node (and automatically satisfy the voltage law).

Until recent years this method was not generally taught, primarily because it is most easily systematized when sources of constant current, rather than sources of constant voltage, occur in the circuit. A *constant-current generator* (sometimes referred to simply as a *current source*) is a two-terminal device which maintains the same current regardless of the resistance network connected across its terminals. Its terminal voltage, of course, may vary, depending on the network across terminals. Such ideal devices do not exist in reality† but are closely approximated by many devices encountered in practice. For example, a voltage source in series with a high resistance R_1 approximates a constant-current source, provided that the external resistance R_2 connected across the terminals of the combination is small compared with the resistance R_1

---

† There is often raised an aesthetic objection to constant-current generators: "How can they maintain a constant current when the load is an open circuit?" This is no more serious an objection than "How can a constant-voltage source maintain its voltage when the load is a short circuit?"

(see Fig. 1.10). Certain vacuum tubes may be analyzed as constant-current generators. Finally, as shown in Sec. 1.13, a real voltage source may be represented by a current source shunted by a resistor.

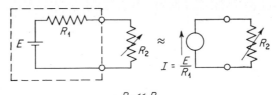

$$R_2 \ll R_1$$

FIG. 1.10. Practical constant-current generator.

In applying the node-voltage method of analysis, it is convenient to deal with the reciprocal of resistance, called *conductance*, rather than with resistance itself. In terms of conductance, Ohm's law is written as

$$I = GV \qquad (1.17)$$

where G is the conductance in *mhos* (reciprocal ohms).

A node voltage is the algebraic value of the voltage difference between the node and an arbitrarily selected reference node (the zero node) which is assigned the potential of zero volts.

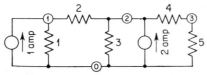

The application of node-voltage analysis will be illustrated by means of an example.

FIG. 1.11. Circuit for Example 1.4. Values on resistors are conductance.

Example 1.4. Find the node voltages for the circuit of Fig. 1.11.

Solution. Writing the current law for each node and combining with the form of Ohm's law given by Eq. (1.17) yield

1
$$\begin{aligned} 1 &= I_{12} + I_{10} \\ &= 2(V_1 - V_2) + 1(V_1 - 0) \end{aligned}$$

2
$$\begin{aligned} 2 &= I_{21} + I_{23} + I_{20} \\ &= 2(V_2 - V_1) + 4(V_2 - V_3) + 3(V_2 - 0) \end{aligned}$$

3
$$\begin{aligned} 0 &= I_{32} + I_{30} \\ &= 4(V_3 - V_2) + 5(V_3 - 0) \end{aligned}$$

0
$$\begin{aligned} -1 - 2 &= I_{01} + I_{02} + I_{03} \\ -3 &= 1(0 - V_1) + 2(0 - V_2) + 5(0 - V_3). \end{aligned}$$

In the above equations we have used I_{10}, I_{20}, I_{30} to indicate only the current through the resistors. Simplifying these equations, we have

$$\begin{aligned} 1 &= 3V_1 - 2V_2 \\ 2 &= -2V_1 + 9V_2 - 4V_3 \\ 0 &= -4V_2 + 9V_3 \\ -3 &= -V_1 - 2V_2 - 5V_3. \end{aligned}$$

Again we have an extra equation (the last is the negative of the sum of the first three). The remaining set of three equations may be solved for the node voltages, from which branch currents and branch voltages may be obtained if desired.

The node analysis may be expressed in the more general terms

$$I_1 = G_{11}V_1 + G_{12}V_2 + \cdots + G_{1n}V_n$$
$$I_2 = G_{21}V_1 + G_{22}V_2 + \cdots + G_{2n}V_n$$
$$\cdots \cdots \cdots \cdots \cdots \cdots \cdots \cdots \cdots \cdots$$
$$I_n = G_{n1}V_1 + G_{n2}V_2 + \cdots + G_{nn}V_n.$$

(1.18)

In the foregoing set of equations

I_i is the current *from current sources* entering the node i.

V_i is the potential of the ith node, with respect to the node designated zero.

G_{ii} is the sum of all conductances terminating on the ith node. It is known as the *self-conductance* of node i.

G_{ij} $(i \neq j)$ is the negative of the conductance connecting the ith and jth nodes. It is called the *mutual conductance* between the ith and jth nodes. It follows that $G_{ij} = G_{ji}$.

We give another example to illustrate the above terminology.

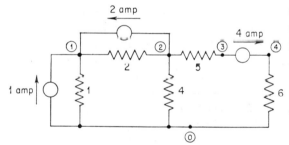

FIG. 1.12. Circuit for Example 1.5. Conductances are in mhos.

Example 1.5. Write the node equations for the circuit of Fig. 1.12.
Solution. The equations may be written directly as

1	$1 + 2 = (2 + 1)V_1$	$- 2V_2$	$+ 0V_3$	$+ 0V_4$
2	$-2 = -2V_1$	$+ (2 + 4 + 5)V_2$	$- 5V_3$	$+ 0V_4$
3	$-4 = 0V_1$	$- 5V_2$	$+ 5V_3$	$+ 0V_4$
4	$4 = 0V_1$	$+ 0V_2$	$+ 0V_3$	$+ 6V_4.$

An equation for node zero would be superfluous (see Sec. 1.9).

Observe from the above example the following:

1. A node may be supplied with current by more than one current source (for example, node 1).
2. A single-current generator may be the current source for two nodes (for example, nodes 1 and 2).
3. Two nodes connected only through a current generator have zero mutual conductance (for example, nodes 3 and 4).

1.9. Network Geometry. In the preceding examples the following questions have always been implicitly raised. What is the minimum number of equations (loop or node) that must be written? If the correct number of equations is written, what assurance is there that they are truly independent, that is, that one equation is not a linear combination of several of the others? In order to give an answer to these questions we must have recourse to network geometry.

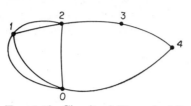

FIG. 1.13. Circuit of Example 1.5 redrawn from network-geometry point of view—graph of Fig. 1.12.

Network geometry is the study of the properties of the circuit diagram without regard to the nature of the individual elements. Thus, from a network-geometry point of view it is sufficient to redraw Fig. 1.12 as in Fig. 1.13. Figure 1.13 is called the *graph* of Fig. 1.12. In this simple discussion we shall limit ourselves to the consideration of *mappable*

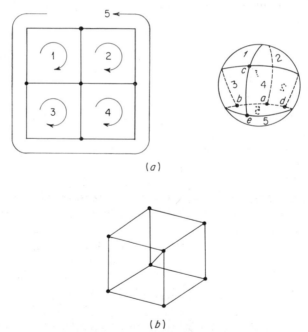

(a)

(b)

FIG. 1.14. Examples of mappable and nonmappable networks. (a) Mappable network; (b) nonmappable network.

networks. A mappable network is one which can be drawn on the surface of a sphere, all crossing lines being connected. Figure 1.14 shows a simple network mapped on a sphere. It also shows a simple nonmappable network.

A *mesh* is a loop which cannot be subdivided into other loops. (This definition is meaningless for nonmappable networks. Also, this definition explains why we use a sphere, rather than a plane, in defining a mappable network. Referring to Fig. 1.14a, it is not clear from the first drawing that loop 5, *adeba*, is a mesh.) Observe that what is a mesh may depend on how we draw the circuit. Figure 1.15a and b represents the same circuit. However, in Fig. 1.15a the meshes are *abcfa*, *bdfcb*, *befdb*, and *abefa*, whereas in Fig. 1.15b they are *abcfa*, *befcb*, *bdfeb*, and *abdfa*.

If we let

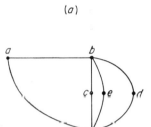

B = the number of branches
N = the number of nodes
m = the number of meshes
λ = the number of independent loop equations which may be written
n = the number of independent node equations which may be written

then the essential relations which may be drawn from network geometry are

$$\lambda = m - 1 \qquad (1.19)$$

and

$$n = N - 1. \qquad (1.20)$$

(b)

Fig 1.15. Alternative graphs of the same circuit.

Equation (1.19) follows from the fact that one loop equation may be written for each mesh, but the mth equation may be obtained by adding all the other equations. Also, if we attempt to write other loop equations not using meshes (as, for example, loop *aceba* in Fig. 1.14) then it is found that each such equation is made up of the sum of the equations for each mesh included in the loop. A similar argument applies to Eq. (1.20).

Equation (1.19) indicates that in writing loop equations, if the meshes are chosen as the loops and if no equation is written for the "outside" mesh (for example, mesh 5 in Fig. 1.14), then the resulting set of equations will be both necessary and sufficient to determine all the currents flowing in the network. Similarly, Eq. (1.20) indicates that, if one node be chosen as a reference node and if current equations be written for all the other nodes, the resulting set of equations will be necessary and sufficient to determine the node voltages.

One other immediately useful result may be obtained from network geometry. The variables in a circuit are the branch voltages and branch currents. Hence, there are $2B$ variables. For each branch we have a relation (Ohm's law) between V and I. Thus, there are B such relations.

We may also write λ Kirchhoff's voltage-law equations and n Kirchhoff's current-law equations. From physical considerations, then, the number of variables must equal the number of equations. Thus

$$2B = B + \lambda + n \tag{1.21}$$

or

$$B = \lambda + n. \tag{1.21a}$$

For a given circuit, then, this relationship† enables us to determine readily whether fewer loop equations or node equations are required for a solution.

When dealing with nonmappable networks, the concept of *mesh* is nonexistent, and so a different procedure for writing a necessary and sufficient set of loop equations must be employed. Elegant extensions of network geometry to nonmappable networks do exist, but it suffices here to note that the loop equations will be independent if successive loops each include at least one branch which was not previously used, for this assures that no equation may be obtained by linear combinations of others (see Chap. 11). It should be noted that Eq. (1.21a) applies also to nonmappable networks.

1.10. Networks Having Both Voltage and Current Sources. The methods of analysis utilized so far have considered networks wherein the sources were either all voltage sources (loop analysis) or all current sources (node analysis). It frequently happens that networks are encountered which contain both current and voltage sources. These give rise to difficulties because if a loop analysis is attempted it is observed that the voltage drops across current sources are also unknown, whereas if a node analysis is attempted it is seen that the currents through voltage sources are unknown.

Two methods of attacking this problem exist. One involves the use of Thévenin's and Norton's theorems (explained later) to convert current sources to voltage sources, or vice versa. This may always be done, although the application is not always obvious. The second, using a more direct approach, will be explained here.

We first consider the loop analysis of a circuit which contains current sources as well as voltage sources. The difference of potential across each current source is not known, but each current source introduces one extra constraint on the mesh currents: The sum of the currents through the current source must equal the value of that current source. Thus, although there are more unknowns, there are more equations, and the number of equations exactly equals the number of unknowns. The symmetry of the array of mesh equations is, however, destroyed.

† This relationship may also be derived from topological considerations alone. Euler derived it by considering polyhedra, where m was the number of faces, N the number of corners, and B the number of edges. Then $B = m + N - 2$.

The application of this method of analysis will be illustrated by means of an example.

Example 1.6. Determine the currents in each element and the potentials of nodes 2 and 3 in the circuit of Fig. 1.16 by the loop-current method.

Solution. The potential difference across the current source is unknown, and so we call it V_c. Writing the mesh equations, we have

$$5 = 21I_1 + V_c$$
$$0 = 7I_2 - V_c.$$

There also exists the additional constraint that

$$6 = -I_1 + I_2.$$

Solving these three equations simultaneously, we find that

$$I_1 = -4\tfrac{1}{9} \text{ amp}$$
$$I_2 = 1\tfrac{8}{9} \text{ amp}$$
$$V_c = 13\tfrac{2}{9} \text{ volts.}$$

Using these values it follows immediately that

$$V_2 = V_c = 13\tfrac{2}{9} \text{ volts}$$
$$V_3 = 4I_2 = 7\tfrac{5}{9} \text{ volts.}$$

It is similarly possible to perform a node analysis on a circuit which contains voltage sources as well as current sources. The current through each voltage source is not known, and so each voltage source introduces an extra unknown. However, each voltage source introduces an additional constraint on the node potentials by fixing the difference of potential between two nodes. Thus, the number of independent equations continues to equal the number of unknowns.

These points will be illustrated by applying node analysis to the circuit previously considered.

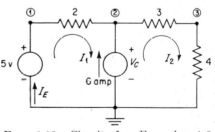

FIG. 1.16. Circuit for Examples 1.6 and 1.7.

Example 1.7. Determine the currents in each element and the potentials of nodes 2 and 3 in the circuit of Fig. 1.16 by node analysis.

Solution. The current provided by the voltage source (entering node 1) is unknown and is designated I_E. The node equations are

$$I_E = V_1(\tfrac{1}{2}) \quad + V_2(-\tfrac{1}{2})$$
$$6 = V_1(-\tfrac{1}{2}) + V_2(\tfrac{1}{2} + \tfrac{1}{3}) + V_3(-\tfrac{1}{3})$$
$$0 = \quad\quad V_2(-\tfrac{1}{3}) \quad + V_3(\tfrac{1}{3} + \tfrac{1}{4}).$$

We also have the additional constraint that

$$V_1 = 5.$$

Solving the above four equations yields

$$V_1 = 5 \text{ volts}$$
$$V_2 = 13\tfrac{2}{9} \text{ volts}$$
$$V_3 = 7\tfrac{5}{9} \text{ volts}$$
$$I_E = -4\tfrac{1}{9} \text{ amp.}$$

From these it follows that the current through the 3- and 4-ohm resistors is $1\tfrac{8}{9}$ amp.

The use of mixed analyses such as the foregoing requires that we modify Eq. (1.21a) relating the number of equations required to specify completely the equilibrium conditions on a network. For a loop analysis of a circuit containing current sources, Eq. (1.21a) becomes

$$\lambda' = B - n + c \qquad (1.22)$$

where

λ' = the number of equilibrium equations
c = the number of current sources

and the other terms have been previously defined. Also, for a node analysis of a circuit containing voltage sources,

$$n' = B - \lambda + v \qquad (1.23)$$

where

n' = the number of equilibrium equations
v = the number of voltage sources.

1.11. Duality. It may already have been observed by the reader that Eqs. (1.16) and (1.18) appear to have a certain similarity. Indeed, we may speculate about the significance of two sets of numerically identical equations, one of which represents the equilibrium equations of a network on a loop basis, and one the equilibrium equations of a (different) network on a node basis. This leads to the concept of the principle of *duality*. Two networks are said to be duals if the loop equations characterizing one have the identical form as the node equations characterizing the other. From this definition it is clear that the number of meshes in one network must equal the number of nodes in the other. It also follows that the following pairs of quantities may be considered as duals:

Current	Voltage
Branch current	Branch voltage
Mesh	Node
Loop current†	Node-pair voltage (node-to-node voltage)
Mesh current	Node potential (node-to-datum voltage)
Number of loops	Number of node pairs
Short circuit	Open circuit

† Obvious correspondences between loop currents and node-pair potentials may be obtained only when the loops are meshes or are chains of meshes. When the loops are chosen arbitrarily, the dual node pair may have no physical significance.

Current source	Voltage source
Reference node	Outside mesh
Parallel paths	Series paths
Conductance	Resistance

It should be noted that only mappable networks have duals. This follows from the fact that the concept of *mesh* is undefined for unmappable networks. Figure 1.17 illustrates a network and its dual. A brief examination will show how the dual pairs listed above occur. (For the purposes of duality, it is necessary to consider a mesh as being the area included by the branches outlining the mesh rather than as the branches themselves.)

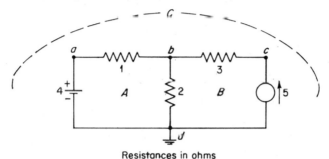

Resistances in ohms

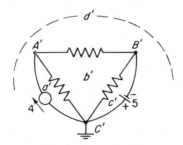

Conductances in mhos

FIG. 1.17. A network and its dual.

The concept of duality is quite useful in network analysis. Once a network is analyzed, the analysis of its dual is readily accomplished. Also, many general network relations (for example, Thévenin's and Norton's theorems) have dual forms, and their utilization is facilitated by using the principles of duality. Rather than give artificial examples of this point, applications of duality will be pointed out as they occur.

1.12. Simple Network Theorems. Frequently networks are encountered which are so simple that use of a general method of analysis is not warranted. Also, it is not always desired to find every branch current and voltage but rather the current or voltage in one particular branch. In such cases the analysis is often simplified by using elementary properties of networks in order that a preliminary reduction of the circuit may be performed. Some of these network-reduction techniques are illustrated below.

1. When resistors are connected in series across a source of potential, the ratio of the voltage drop across one resistor to the total voltage drop is equal to the value of that resistor divided by the total resistance. The proof of this statement is a trivial application of Kirchhoff's laws and is left as an exercise for the reader.

Example 1.8. Determine the voltage drop across R_3 in Fig. 1.18.
Solution. We have immediately

$$V_3 = \frac{R_3}{R_1 + R_2 + R_3} E = \frac{2}{2 + 3 + 4} 10 = 2.22 \text{ volts.}$$

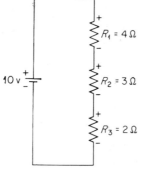

2. The equivalent resistance of several resistors in parallel is given by

$$\frac{1}{R_{eq}} = \frac{1}{R_1} + \frac{1}{R_2} + \frac{1}{R_3} + \cdots . \quad (1.24)$$

This follows from the definition of conductance. The equivalent conductance of several resistors in parallel is equal to the sum of the individual conductances.

In particular, for two resistors in parallel,

FIG. 1.18. Circuit for Example 1.8.

$$R_{eq} = \frac{R_1 R_2}{R_1 + R_2}. \quad (1.25)$$

3. When two resistors are connected in parallel the current flowing through them divides as follows:

$$I_1 = \frac{R_2}{R_1 + R_2} I, \qquad I_2 = \frac{R_1}{R_1 + R_2} I \quad (1.26)$$

where I is the total current and I_1 and I_2 are the currents through R_1 and R_2, respectively.

The equivalent parallel resistance of the two resistors is

$$\frac{R_1 R_2}{(R_1 + R_2)};$$

hence the voltage drop across them is $I R_1 R_2 / (R_1 + R_2)$. Dividing this expression by the resistance of each branch yields Eq. (1.26).

The generalization of 3—that the ratio of the current through one of a set of parallel resistors to the total current equals the ratio of the conductance of the resistors to the total conductance—is the *dual* of 1.

Example 1.19. Determine the current in R_3 (see Fig. 1.19).
Solution. By use of Rules 2 and 3 we may immediately write

$$I_3 = \frac{E}{R_1 + \dfrac{R_2 R_3'}{R_2 + R_3'}} \frac{R_2}{R_2 + R_3'} = \frac{10}{1 + \dfrac{2 \times 4}{6}} \frac{2}{6} = 1.43 \text{ amp.}$$

4. Two useful sets of relations are the wye-delta (Y-Δ) and delta-wye (Δ-Y) transformations. They are also frequently referred to as pi-tee (π-T) or star-mesh transformations.

Three resistors can be arranged in a three-terminal network in either of the two ways shown in Fig. 1.20. Figure 1.20*a* shows the Y arrangement (T or star), and Fig. 1.20*b* shows the Δ configuration (π or mesh). If one is able to make measurements at the three terminals of the network, it is impossible to tell *from these measurements alone* what is the configuration of the circuit. Thus it is possible to have two circuits, a Y and a Δ,

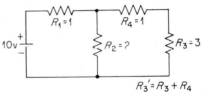

$$R_3' = R_3 + R_4$$

Fig. 1.19. Circuit for Example 1.9

which appear (from measurements made at the terminals) to be the same network. In circuit analysis, then, it is possible to replace a Y network by its equivalent Δ, or vice versa, and this is frequently done to reduce the complexity of circuits to be analyzed.

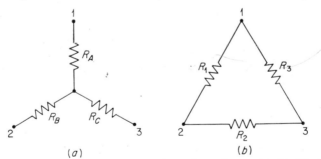

(a)   (b)

FIG. 1.20. Three-terminal network configurations. (a) Y; (b) Δ.

To determine the elements of a Y which is equivalent to a given Δ, we proceed as follows. If the resistance between various pairs of terminals is measured, for the two networks, it is clear that for the Y

$$
\begin{aligned}
R_{12} &= R_A + R_B \\
R_{23} &= R_B + R_C \\
R_{31} &= R_C + R_A
\end{aligned}
\tag{1.27}
$$

and for the Δ

$$R_{12} = \frac{R_1(R_2 + R_3)}{R_1 + R_2 + R_3}$$

$$R_{23} = \frac{R_2(R_3 + R_1)}{R_1 + R_2 + R_3} \qquad (1.28)$$

$$R_{31} = \frac{R_3(R_1 + R_2)}{R_1 + R_2 + R_3}.$$

In order that the Y be equivalent to the Δ, R_{12}, R_{23}, and R_{31} for each must be the same. Equating Eqs. (1.27) and (1.28) and solving for R_A, R_B, and R_C, we find

$$R_A = \frac{R_1 R_3}{R_1 + R_2 + R_3}$$

$$R_B = \frac{R_1 R_2}{R_1 + R_2 + R_3} \qquad (1.29)$$

$$R_C = \frac{R_2 R_3}{R_1 + R_2 + R_3}.$$

The inverse problem, that of finding the elements of a Δ equivalent to a given Y, may be carried out most readily in terms of conductances. In that case we find

$$G_1 = \frac{G_A G_B}{G_A + G_B + G_C}$$

$$G_2 = \frac{G_B G_C}{G_A + G_B + G_C} \qquad (1.30)$$

$$G_3 = \frac{G_C G_A}{G_A + G_B + G_C}.$$

It is observed that Eqs. (1.30) are the duals of Eqs. (1.29), and so they need not be separately derived. The forms of each of these equations are such that they may easily be remembered as the "product of the two adjacent over the sum of all three."

Example 1.10. Determine the current I in the circuit of Fig. 1.21. *Solution.* First replace the Δ, *abc*, by the equivalent Y (Fig. 1.21*b*).

$$R_A = \frac{4 \times 3}{4 + 2 + 3} = 1.333\ \Omega$$

$$R_B = \frac{4 \times 2}{4 + 2 + 3} = 0.889\ \Omega$$

$$R_C = \frac{2 \times 3}{4 + 2 + 3} = 0.667\ \Omega.$$

The current may then be determined by the method of Example 1.9:

$$I = \frac{10}{1.667 + \dfrac{1.333 \times 6.389}{1.333 + 6.389}} \cdot \frac{1.333}{1.333 + 6.389} = 0.624\ \text{amp.}$$

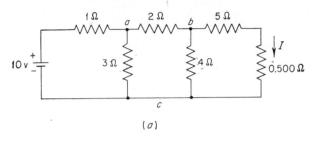

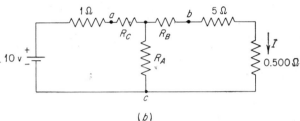

FIG. 1.21. Circuit for Example 1.10.   (a) Original circuit; (b) after simplification.

1.13. General Network Theorems.   The network relationships presented in the previous section are simple and obvious rules.   There also exist several very important but less obvious general network theorems which are extremely useful in circuit analysis.   These will be stated here without proof, as they will be proved later in Chap. 5 in a more general setting.

I. *The Principle of Superposition.*   In a network containing several sources, the current (or voltage) in any branch may be obtained by determining the current (or voltage) in that branch resulting from each source acting independently, and then algebraically adding the individual values in a branch to find the total current (or voltage).

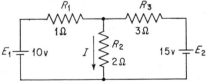

FIG. 1.22. Circuit for Example 1.11.

Example 1.11.   Determine the current flowing in the center arm of the T (see Fig. 1.22).

Solution.   Replacing E_2 by a short circuit (that is, by a voltage source whose value is zero) we may determine the current in R_2 by the method of Example 1.9.

$$I_2' = \frac{10}{1 + \dfrac{2 \times 3}{5}} \frac{3}{5} = 2.73 \text{ amp.}$$

Similarly, replacing E_1 by a short circuit,

$$I_2'' = \frac{15}{3 + \frac{2}{3}} \frac{1}{3} = 1.36 \text{ amp.}$$

Thus,

$$I_2 = 2.73 + 1.36 = 4.09 \text{ amp.}$$

II. *The Reciprocity Theorem.* The current in any loop in a circuit (say loop 1) caused by a voltage source in another loop (say loop 2) is the same as the current in loop 2 caused by the same voltage in loop 1, provided that no other voltage sources exist in the circuit.† Alternatively, an ideal voltage source and an ammeter may be interchanged in a circuit without changing the reading of the ammeter.

Example. 1.12 The circuit shown in Fig. 1.23a is known as a Kelvin double bridge. It is used for the measurement of low resistance. In the analysis of this bridge it is necessary to determine what value of resistance would be measured at the terminals *ab* if the battery were short-circuited and the galvanometer removed. As an example we shall determine this resistance.

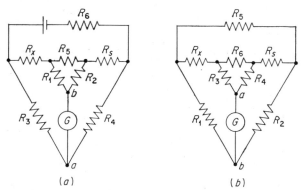

Fig. 1.23. Kelvin double bridge (Example 1.12). (*a*) Original circuit; (*b*) redrawn.

Solution. At balance, no current flows in the galvanometer. In measuring the resistance R_{ab} between *a* and *b* we essentially place a voltage source between *a* and *b* and determine the current which flows. Now, if a voltage source is placed between *a* and *b* no current will flow through R_6, by the reciprocity theorem. Hence, R_6 does not affect the value of R_{ab}. Also, it can be shown that at balance $R_1 R_4 = R_2 R_3$ and $R_1 R_s = R_2 R_x$, so that if we redraw the circuit, as in Fig. 1.23b, it follows from considerations of symmetry that R_5 now plays the role previously occupied by R_6. But, again by reciprocity, no current is produced in R_5 by a voltage source placed between *a* and *b*. Thus R_5 has no effect on the value of R_{ab}. If we replace R_5 and R_6 by open circuits, then we may write by inspection

$$R_{ab} = \frac{(R_1 + R_x + R_3)(R_2 + R_s + R_4)}{(R_1 + R_x + R_3) + (R_2 + R_s + R_4)}.$$

The reciprocity theorem is actually only of limited usefulness in circuit

† If there are many voltage sources in the circuit, a generalization of the reciprocity theorem must be employed. In such cases the *component* of total current in loop 1 caused by the voltage in loop 2 is equal to the *component* of total current in loop 2 caused by placing the source in loop 1. The generalization is not particularly useful for simplifying circuit calculations.

analysis. It is a particular consequence of the reciprocal property of networks discussed later.

III. *Thévenin's Theorem.* Very often we are confronted with a network consisting of voltage and current sources and resistors, wherein we wish to know not the currents and voltages in the whole network but only the current and voltage at two terminals of that network. The two "terminals" may be any two points in the network. Sometimes they are clearly identified as terminals, for example, the points of a power distributing system into which an appliance is connected. At other times they may just be arbitrary points, as we shall see in later examples.

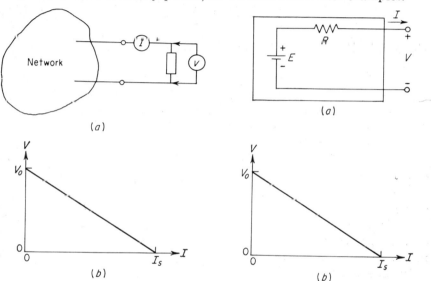

FIG. 1.24. (a) Two-terminal network; (b) output voltage vs. current.

FIG. 1.25. (a) Simple circuit; (b) output voltage-current relation.

If we connect a load across these points and simultaneously measure the current through and the voltage drop across the load, we in general obtain results of the form shown in Fig. 1.24. The load generally considered is a variable resistor. There is no need that it be such, however. Any means of varying the output voltage and current is acceptable. We may instead use a voltage source whose magnitude is variable; the current will still be determined only by the network itself. (Similarly, a variable current source could be used.) This important point may not yet be obvious, but it will become apparent during the subsequent discussion.

Examining the graph relating the output voltage and current, we see that it has the same form as that of the simple network shown in Fig. 1.25a, a resistor in series with a voltage source. Clearly,

$$V = E - IR. \tag{1.31}$$

Observe that nowhere in this expression does the form of the load appear. For any particular value of current the output voltage is determined only by the parameters of the network within the box. Nonetheless, we have not created a paradox, for the load does determine one of the quantities V or I so that the other, as determined by the network, satisfies the current-voltage relation of the load. We cannot independently specify both load current and voltage.

If we select the value of E and R for the simple network so that

$$E = V_o \tag{1.32}$$

$$R = \frac{V_o}{I_s} \tag{1.33}$$

where V_o is the open-circuit (no load) voltage of the original network and I_s is the short-circuit current, then the graph of V against I for the simple network is the same as that for the original network. Thus we say that the networks are equivalent in that measurements made at the two terminals of either network† do not enable us to distinguish between the networks. This is inherent in *Thévenin's theorem*, which states: Any two-terminal network may be replaced, insofar as measurements made at the two terminals are concerned, by an equivalent network consisting of a voltage source in series with a resistor. The value of the equivalent voltage source is the voltage measured across the two terminals of the original circuit with an ideal (infinite resistance) voltmeter—the so-called open-circuit voltage. The equivalent resistance is equal to the ratio of the open-circuit voltage to the short-circuit current (the current measured by a zero-resistance ammeter). If the circuit contains only independent sources, this resistance is also equal to that resistance measured between the two terminals when all the voltage sources are replaced by short circuits, and the current sources by open circuits.‡ This resistance is called the *internal resistance* of the circuit.

Example 1.13. Determine the variation of I as R is varied in Fig. 1.26.

Solution. The circuit to the left of terminals ab may be replaced by its Thévenin equivalent. The open-circuit voltage across terminals ab is equal to that across cb and is

$$V_o = 10 \frac{2}{2+1} = 6.667 \text{ volts.}$$

---

† We shall later see, though, that one network may become hotter than the other.

‡ In some circuits, particularly those containing electron devices, the magnitude of a source is proportional to the voltage drop across some branch. In these circuits it is improper to determine the equivalent resistance by replacing the voltage sources by short circuits; rather, the equivalent resistance must be determined from the ratio of open-circuit voltage to short-circuit current. Failure to observe this fact results in many erroneous analyses.

The short-circuit current from a to b is

$$I_s = \frac{10}{1 + \frac{2 \times 4}{2 + 4}} \frac{2}{2 + 4} = 1.428 \text{ amp.}$$

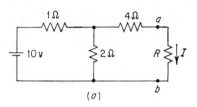

Whence

$$R_0 = \frac{6.667}{1.428} = 4.667 \ \Omega.$$

Thus,

$$I = \frac{V_o}{R + R_0} = \frac{6.667}{R + 4.667} \text{ amp.}$$

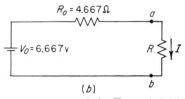

In many practical circuits it is found that the graph of voltage against current is not a straight line. This means that the circuit is *nonlinear*. Still, it is possible to make use of Thévenin's theorem

Fig. 1.26. Circuit for Example 1.13. (a) Original circuit; (b) equivalent circuit.

in analyzing such circuits if we operate the device in such a manner that the current or voltage is never allowed to enter the nonlinear region. An example of such an application will be given.

Example 1.14. The voltage-current graph of a certain d-c generator is as shown in Fig. 1.27a. The generator is always used so that the current is less than 10 amp.
  a. Find the Thévenin equivalent.
  b. Determine the output current when the load consists of a 10-amp current generator in parallel with a 4-ohm resistance (see Fig. 1.27b).
  Solution. a. From Eq. (1.31) it is seen that the equivalent resistor is the negative slope of the volt-ampere characteristic. Thus

$$R = -\frac{100 - 80}{0 - 10} = 2 \ \Omega.$$

V_o is the open-circuit voltage and is 100 volts. Thus the equivalent circuit consists of a 100-volt source in series with a 2-ohm resistor, provided that the current does not exceed 10 amp.
  b. We may solve this by drawing the circuit as in Fig. 1.28. Clearly, $I_1 = -10$ amp, and so we write for loop 2

$$100 - 2(I_2 - 10) - 4I_2 = 0$$
$$I_2 = 20 \text{ amp.}$$

It may appear that we have violated the constraint on output current, which was not to exceed 10 amp. However, the current I_2 is not the output current; the output current is $I_1 + I_2$ which here is just equal to 10 amp. The constraint is on the total output current, not on a component of the current.

IV. *Norton's Theorem.* Norton's theorem is the dual of Thévenin's theorem. It states that a two-terminal network is equivalent to a current source in parallel with a resistor. The current source has a value equal to the short-circuit current, and the value of resistance is determined as in Thévenin's theorem.

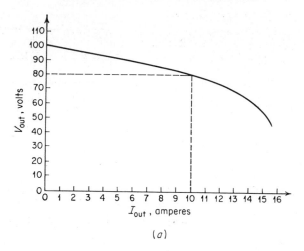

(a)

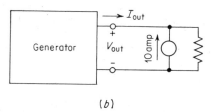

(b)

FIG. 1.27. Generator for Example 1.14.   (a) Voltage-current curve; (b) conditions of problem.

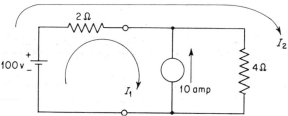

FIG. 1.28. Equivalent circuit of Fig. 1.27b.

In particular, a voltage source having a series internal resistance may be replaced by a current source, $I_0 = V_o/R_0$, in parallel with the same resistance. This fact is frequently used in converting voltage sources to current sources before performing a node analysis.

Example 1.15. In Fig. 1.29a determine the potential of point a with respect to point b.

Solution. Converting the voltage sources to current sources, we have

$$I_1 = \frac{E_1}{R_1} = \frac{5}{2} = 2.5 \text{ amp}$$

and

$$I_2 = \frac{E_2}{R_2} = \frac{8}{4} = 2.0 \text{ amp.}$$

The circuit of Fig. 1.29b then reduces to that of Fig. 1.29c, where

$$R = (\tfrac{1}{2} + \tfrac{1}{4} + \tfrac{1}{5})^{-1} = 1.05.$$

Thus

$$V_{ab} = IR = 4.50 \times 1.05 = 4.72 \text{ volts.}$$

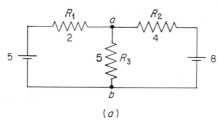

(a)

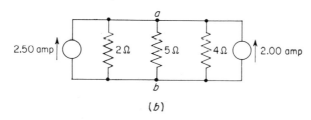

(b)

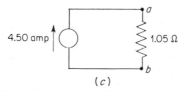

(c)

Fig. 1.29. Circuit for Example 1.15. (a) Original circuit; (b) voltage sources replaced by current sources; (c) reduced circuit.

It should be noted that an ideal voltage source, if replaced by a current source, will result in an infinite current source shunted by zero resistance. This is usually difficult to manipulate. However, real voltage sources have some resistance, though it may be small, so that this is not a practical difficulty. Also, various "dodges" may be used such as placing in series with the voltage source two hypothetical resistors of equal magnitude, one positive and one negative, and using only one of the resistors when converting to a current source.

Consideration of "equivalent" current and voltage sources enables one to see more clearly the limitation on the term "equivalent." With a low-resistance voltage source most of the energy provided by the battery is dissipated in the external circuit. In the equivalent current source, on the other hand, most of the energy is dissipated in the internal conductance. Thus, although measurements at the two external terminals fail to distinguish between the two equivalent circuits, the current-source equivalent certainly becomes hotter than the voltage-source equivalent.

V. *Maximum Power Transfer.* If a variable resistor is connected to a two-terminal network containing energy sources, maximum power will be transferred to the resistor when its value is made equal to the internal resistance of the circuit. When the external resistance is equal to the internal resistance of the circuit, the external resistance is said to be *matched* to the circuit.

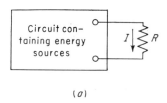

(*a*)

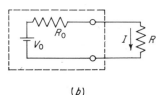

(*b*)

FIG. 1.30. Circuit for maximum-power-transfer theorem. (*a*) Actual circuit; (*b*) equivalent circuit.

As a result of Thévenin's theorem, we need only show this for equivalent circuits consisting of voltage sources in series with internal resistances. Then (Fig. 1.30) the power dissipated in R is given by

$$P = I^2R = \left(\frac{V_o}{R_0 + R}\right)^2 R. \tag{1.34}$$

This will be a maximum when the derivative dP/dR is zero,

$$\frac{dP}{dR} = V_o{}^2 \left[\frac{1}{(R_0 + R)^2} - \frac{2R}{(R_0 + R)^3}\right], \tag{1.35}$$

and this is zero when $R = R_0$, proving the theorem.

The theorems presented above are very powerful and useful tools in circuit analysis, as can be seen even from the few elementary examples considered above. After practicing his knowledge on the exercises at the end of this chapter, the reader should be in a position to analyze efficiently any d-c circuit. In subsequent chapters we shall proceed to the study of *alternating-current* (a-c) circuits.

EXERCISES

1.1. A positive charge of 1 coulomb is placed at the North Pole of the earth and a similar charge is placed at the South Pole of the earth. Determine the repulsive force between these charges and express the result in tons. The polar radius of the earth is 3960 miles.

1.2. (a) In atomic physics a commonly used unit of energy is the *electron volt*. This is the amount of energy acquired by an electron when it moves through a potential difference of one volt. What is the number of joules in an electron volt?

Ans. 1.602×10^{-19} joule.

(b) Develop an expression for the velocity of an electron in terms of its energy measured in electron volts.

1.3. The resistance of copper varies with temperature according to the law

$$R(t) = R_0 \frac{234.5 + t}{234.5 + t_0}$$

where t is the temperature (°C) and t_0 is the temperature at which the resistance R_0 is measured. As a "rule of thumb" the temperature rise of small resistors is 50°C per watt dissipation per square inch of surface. This is, of course, the temperature after equilibrium is reached. Let R_0 be 100 ohms at room temperature (20°C). Develop an expression relating the voltage across and the current through this resistor, assuming 1 in.² of surface area. Assume that thermal equilibrium has been reached. How does this relation compare with Ohm's law?

1.4. For the circuit shown in Fig. 1.31 find the current in each branch and the voltage across each branch by (a) the direct application of Kirchhoff's laws to the circuit; (b) the loop-current method; (c) the node-voltage method.

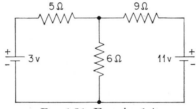

FIG. 1.31. Exercise 1.4.

1.5. Find the branch currents and voltage drops in the circuit shown in Fig. 1.32 by (a) the loop-current method; (b) the node-voltage method.

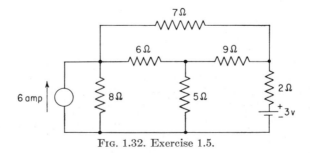

FIG. 1.32. Exercise 1.5.

1.6. Prove Theorem 1 of Sec. 1.12.

1.7. Prove Eqs. (1.30).

1.8. Solve Exercise 1.4 by use of the superposition theorem.

1.9. Solve Exercise 1.5 by (a) converting the current source to a voltage source and using the loop-current method of analysis; (b) converting the voltage source to a current source and using the node-voltage method of analysis.

1.10. Prove Norton's theorem.

1.11. The output voltage of a certain generator, with no load connected, is found to be 100 volts. The short-circuit current is 20 amp. A 10-ohm resistor is connected across the terminals of this generator.

(a) Assume that the generator is equivalently a voltage source in series with a resistor. What power is dissipated in the resistor? What power is dissipated internally in the generator?

(b) Assume that the generator is equivalently a current source in parallel with a resistor. What power is dissipated in the resistor? What power is dissipated internally in the generator?

(c) Repeat (a) and (b) with a 5-ohm resistor instead of the 10-ohm resistor.

1.12. Determine the current I in the circuit shown in Fig. 1.33. [HINT: Assume a value for I and find the voltage needed; then prorate the value of I.]

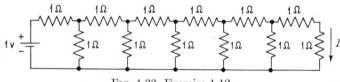

FIG. 1.33. Exercise 1.12.

1.13. Determine the current in R_0 in the circuit shown in Fig. 1.34 when it is adjusted so that the current in R_1 is one-half the current in R_0. If R_0 is adjusted so that the battery current is 20 amp, what is the current in R_0?

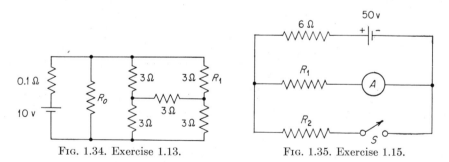

FIG. 1.34. Exercise 1.13.   FIG. 1.35. Exercise 1.15.

1.14. An electric trolley line 12 miles long is driven by generators at each end. One generator has a terminal voltage of 500 volts, and the other has a terminal voltage of 550 volts. The total resistance of the circuit (wire and track) is 0.07 ohm/mile. The trolley car draws a current of 600 amp. If it is located at the point where the voltage is minimum, where is the point, what is the voltage, and how much current is supplied by each generator?

1.15. In the circuit in Fig. 1.35 the ammeter A reads 5.0 amp with S open; with S closed it reads 2.5 amp. Determine R_1 and R_2.

1.16. Each of n points is joined to each other by a resistor having a resistance r. Any two points are connected to a battery having an internal resistance R and an emf E. Show that the current I in the battery is

$$I = \frac{2E}{2r + nR}.$$

1.17. (a) Six wires form a regular tetrahedron. The resistance of each wire is R. Find the resistance between two apexes of the tetrahedron.

(b) Twelve 1-ohm resistors form the edges of a cube. Determine the resistance between one corner of the cube and the other that is most remote.

1.18. Find the currents in each branch of the circuit shown in Fig. 1.36.

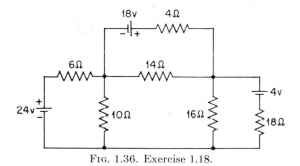

Fig. 1.36. Exercise 1.18.

1.19. A voltage divider used to give several currents and voltages in a radio receiver is shown in Fig. 1.37.

(a) Determine R_1, R_2, R_3, R_4.

(b) What power is dissipated in each resistor?

(c) If the 200-volt tap becomes disconnected, what changes occur in the power dissipations of the resistors?

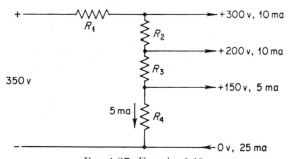

Fig. 1.37. Exercise 1.19.

1.20. A single-strand telegraph wire has a resistance of R ohms/mile. When installed, it also has a leakage conductance to ground of G mhos/mile. Let R_o be the resistance measured between one end of the wire of length l and ground when the far end of the wire is open-circuited. Let R_s be the resistance between one end of the wire of length l and ground when the other end is short-circuited to ground. Assume that the ground has no resistance. Prove that

$$R_c = \sqrt{R_o R_s}.$$

where R_c (the "characteristic resistance") of the wire is the resistance of a very long ("infinite") cable measured between one end and ground.

1.21. In the circuit shown in Fig. 1.38 find the proper position of the sliders so that the current through the galvanometer G (assumed resistanceless) is (a) zero; (b) 100 ma.

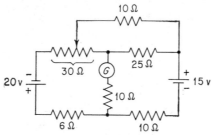

FIG. 1.38. Exercise 1.21.

1.22. Why is the power output of a generator not equal to I^2R, where R is the internal resistance of the generator and I the current through it?

1.23. In the circuit shown in Fig. 1.39, what is the value of R_{12}, when the loops are selected as indicated?

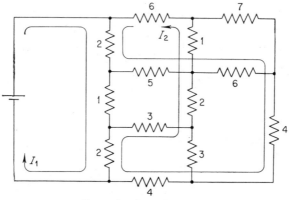

FIG. 1.39. Exercise 1.23.

1.24. The loop currents shown in Fig. 1.40 traverse each and every element. Why are they inadequate to solve the network?

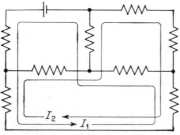

FIG. 1.40. Exercise 1.24.

1.25. Determine the current-voltage relationship at the terminals of each of the circuits shown in Fig. 1.41. For each circuit, determine the simplest equivalent circuit based on (*a*) voltage source; (*b*) current source.

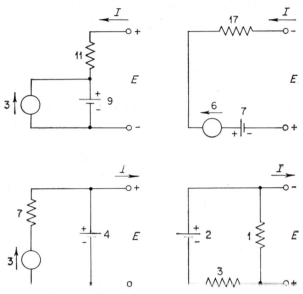

FIG. 1.41. Exercise 1.25.

1.26. Solve for the branch currents and voltages in the network illustrated in Fig. 1.42.

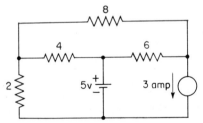

FIG. 1.42. Exercise 1.26.

CHAPTER 2

CIRCUITS WITH ENERGY STORAGE

In Chap. 1 we analyzed circuits which contained constant-current and -voltage sources, that is, sources which did not vary with time. In many, indeed in most, cases occurring in practice the potential differences of the voltage sources (or currents of the current sources) *do* vary with time. When such is the case, the branch currents and voltages are determined not only by the resistances in the circuit but also by elements whose principal characteristic is to store energy, either in an electric or in a magnetic field. These elements are called *capacitors* and *inductors*. Their action is to store energy during one period of time, releasing it at another. Thus their presence may influence profoundly the behavior of circuits having time-varying sources. This chapter will show how to include the effects of these new parameters in setting up the equilibrium equations of circuits.

2.1. Capacitors and Capacitance. A *capacitor*† is a two-terminal circuit element whose principal characteristic is to store energy in an internal electric field. It consists of two conductors, each connected to one terminal, separated by a dielectric. Some typical capacitors are illustrated in Fig. 2.1. The symbol for a capacitor is shown in Fig. 2.2.

Capacitance is a parameter which is a gross measure of the nature of the *electric* field between the two conductors. It is defined for two conductors carrying equal and opposite charges as the ratio of the magnitude of the charge to the difference of potential between the conductors. That is,

$$C = \frac{Q}{V} \tag{2.1}$$

where C is the capacitance in farads between the two conductors carrying charges of $+Q$ and $-Q$, respectively, between which there exists a potential difference of V volts.

If we place a capacitor in a closed circuit (see Fig. 2.3) and cause a current i to flow in that circuit, the amount of charge on each conductor at time t will be given by

$$q = \int_0^t i \, dt + q_0 \tag{2.2}$$

† Still called, by some, a *condenser*.

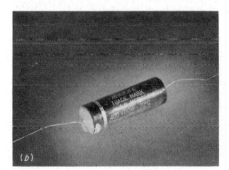

FIG. 2.1. Capacitors and their construction. (a) Precision variable air capacitor. (*Courtesy of General Radio Company.*) (b) Paper dielectric capacitor. This consists of two strips of thin aluminum foil separated by oil-impregnated paper dielectric, rolled into a convenient-sized unit. (*Courtesy of Aerovox Corporation.*) (c) Electrolytic capacitor. One electrode is an aluminum strip. An oxide coating on this strip forms an extremely thin dielectric, with resulting high capacitance. A liquid electrolyte forms the other dielectric. Blotting paper is used to carry most of the electrolyte and lends mechanical stability to the assembly. The other aluminum strip is merely to provide a contact to the electrolyte. (*Courtesy of Columbia University Electronics Research Laboratories.*)

where q_0 is the initial charge at $t = 0$.† This relationship follows from the definition of current as the rate of flow of charge. Thus, the potential difference between the conductors will be given by

$$v = \frac{q}{C} = \frac{1}{C} \int_0^t i\,dt + \frac{q_0}{C} = \frac{1}{C} \int_0^t i\,dt + v_0 \tag{2.3}$$

where v_0 is the difference in potential at $t = 0$. Since the conductor receiving positive charge will be at a higher potential than the other, it follows that the polarity designations shown in Fig. 2.3 are correct.

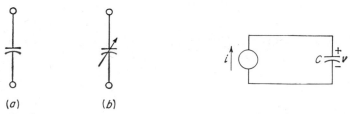

(a)   (b)

FIG. 2.2. Symbols for capacitance. (a) Fixed; (b) variable.

FIG. 2.3. Charging a capacitor.

Frequently the inverse relation is required. That is, the voltage across the capacitor is known and the current is to be determined. The desired relation is found by differentiating Eq. (2.3) with respect to time,

$$\frac{dv}{dt} = \frac{1}{C} i \qquad \text{or} \qquad i = C \frac{dv}{dt}. \tag{2.4}$$

2.2. Symbols and Conventions for Sources. Voltage and current sources are usually designated on circuit diagrams by one of the symbols shown in Fig. 2.4. An important feature of these symbols is their polarity designations. Reading too much into such polarity signs frequently leads to confusion; they should be regarded only as *reference polarities*. If, for example, the voltage has the form

FIG. 2.4. Symbols for time-varying voltage and current sources.

$$e(t) = E_m \cos \omega t \tag{2.5}$$

the terminal marked $+$ is positive relative to that marked $-$ for $0 < \omega t < \pi$, but the $+$ terminal is negative relative to the $-$ terminal for $\pi < \omega t < 2\pi$. Similar remarks apply to the arrow used with the symbol for a current source.

In order that the various conventions associated with signs and

† One must be careful when evaluating expressions such as Eq. (2.2) to specify precisely what is meant by $t = 0$. Particularly when switches are operated at $t = 0$ it is important to be consistent in evaluating quantities just before $t = 0$ (designated $t = 0-$) or just after $t = 0$ (designated by $t = 0+$).

polarities be clearly understood, it is well at this time to refer back to Sec. 1.4 to review the subject of signs and symbols used in marking circuit diagrams.

2.3. Energy Stored in a Capacitor. Since a capacitor affects circuits by virtue of the energy stored in its electric field, it is useful to have an expression for the amount of energy stored, even though we only occasionally make explicit use of such an expression.

From Eq. (1.10) it follows that p, the rate at which energy is delivered to a two-terminal circuit, is

$$p = vi \qquad \text{watts.} \tag{2.6}$$

Therefore, the total energy U delivered to a circuit between time t_0 and time t is

$$U = \int_{t_0}^{t} p \, dt = \int_{t_0}^{t} vi \, dt \qquad \text{joules.} \tag{2.7}$$

Now, from Eq. (2.4), $i = C \, dv/dt$, so that

$$U_C = \int_{t_0}^{t} Cv \frac{dv}{dt} \, dt = \int_{v(t_0)}^{v(t)} Cv \, dv = \tfrac{1}{2}Cv^2 \Big|_{v(t_0)}^{v(t)} \tag{2.8}$$

$$U_C = \tfrac{1}{2}C[v^2(t) - v^2(t_0)] \qquad \text{joules.} \tag{2.9}$$

If we start with an uncharged capacitor and raise its voltage to V, that is, $v(t_0) = 0$ and $v(t) = V$, then

$$U_C = \tfrac{1}{2}CV^2. \tag{2.10}$$

Since there is no mechanism for dissipating this energy, it must all be stored in the electric field of the capacitor. (This may also be demonstrated by showing that a charged capacitor connected across a resistor delivers $\tfrac{1}{2}CV^2$ joules to the resistor. See Exercise 3.12.)

2.4. Inductors and Inductance. An *inductor* is a two-terminal circuit element whose principal characteristic is to store energy in a magnetic field. Although any piece of wire is an inductor, inductors usually consist of coils of wire so arranged as to have a strong magnetic field. The coils also frequently have cores of iron or other ferromagnetic material in order to increase the strength of the magnetic field (see Fig. 2.5). The symbol for inductance is simply a coil (see Fig. 2.6).

An inductor is described by its *inductance*. Inductance is a parameter which is a gross measure of the nature of the *magnetic* field surrounding the current-carrying conductor. In such a magnetic field a *flux linkage* is said to exist when one line of flux links the current once; if the line links the circuit n times there are n flux linkages (Fig. 2.7). The total number of flux linkages Λ is frequently expressed as $\Lambda = N\Phi$, where N is the number of turns (loops) in the circuit and Φ is the average flux

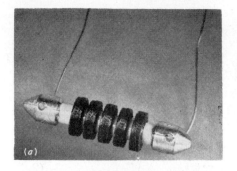

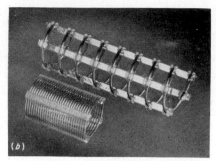

Fig. 2.5. Typical inductors. (*a*) Radio-frequency choke, 2.5 mh. (*Courtesy of Columbia University Electronics Research Laboratories.*) (*b*) Air-core coils. The plastic rods provide mechanical stability. (*Courtesy of Barker and Williamson.*) (*c*) Iron-core filter choke, 8 henrys. (*Courtesy of Columbia University Electronics Research Laboratories.*) (*d*) View of iron-core filter choke with protective cover removed. (*Courtesy of Columbia University Electronics Research Laboratories.*)

linking each loop† (Fig. 2.7*c*). Since for linear materials (see Sec. 1.2) Φ is proportional to the current I which gives rise to the flux, Φ/I is constant and hence Λ/I ($= N\Phi/I$) is a constant, depending only on the geometry of the circuit. This latter constant is defined as the inductance L of the circuit,

Fig. 2.6. Symbol for inductance.

$$L = \frac{\Lambda}{I}. \qquad (2.11)$$

The unit of inductance is the weber/amp, commonly termed the *henry*.

Two categories of inductance are usually distinguished: *self-inductance* and *mutual inductance*. The self-inductance L of a circuit is defined as the ratio of the total flux linkages developed by the current flowing in the circuit, to that current. The mutual inductance M_{12} (Fig. 2.8)

---

† Dimensionally, flux linkage is equal to flux, since the number of turns is dimensionless. That is, $N\Phi$ is the total flux linking N turns. The unit of flux, and thus of flux linkage, is the *weber*.

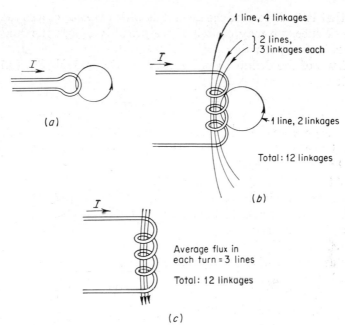

(a)

(b)

(c)

Fig. 2.7. Examples of flux linkages. These drawings are symbolic and are not meant to be accurate descriptions of the actual magnetic fields. (*a*) Single flux linkage in a simple circuit; (*b*) multiple linkages in a four-turn circuit; (*c*) simplified equivalent of (*b*).

between two circuits, say 1 and 2, is the ratio of that portion of the flux linkages due to current in coil 2 which links coil 1, to the current in coil 2. The mutual inductance M_{21} is defined similarly. The generalized reciprocity theorem enables us to show that $M_{12} = M_{21}$. (This is not at all obvious and is one of the most important consequences of this theorem. The proof is too extensive for inclusion here.)

The voltage across an inductor may be derived from Faraday's law, which states that in a coil linked by a changing flux λ a voltage e is induced such that

$$e = -\frac{d\lambda}{dt}. \qquad (2.12)$$

(Faraday's law is frequently expressed in the form

$$e = -N\frac{d\Phi}{dt} \qquad (2.12a)$$

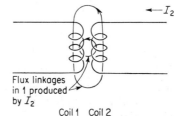

Fig. 2.8. Mutual inductance.

where Φ is the average flux linking the N turns of the coil.)

Undue significance should not be attached to the minus sign, which is really only a reminder of the fact that the polarity of the induced voltage is such that it *tends* to produce a current which would oppose the change in flux. Hence, we may omit it if we properly assign the current and voltage reference polarities.

By virtue of the definition of inductance [Eq. (2.11)], Eq. (2.12) may be written

$$v = \frac{d}{dt}(Li) = L\frac{di}{dt}. \tag{2.12b}$$

Here we use a v rather than e because we wish to regard the difference of potential across the terminals of the inductor as a simple voltage drop, rather than be concerned with the nature of the induced voltage. This difference in viewpoint has a simple parallel. It was agreed to assign the symbol E to energy sources and V to loads. Usually, then, the symbol E is associated with a battery. When a battery is connected to a battery charger, it might seem more appropriate to associate the symbol V with it. Similarly, a magnetically induced voltage is a generated voltage with which e is usually associated. It is more fruitful, however, to consider an inductor as being a load, with which we associate

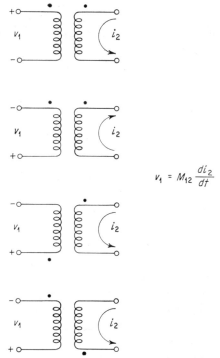

$$v_1 = M_{12}\frac{di_2}{dt}$$

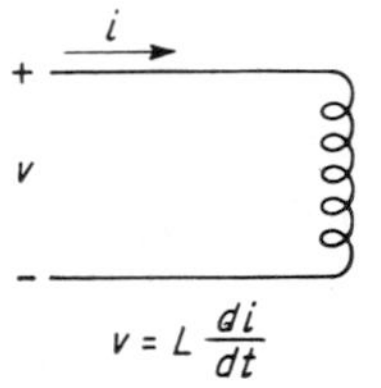

FIG. 2.9. Polarities of voltage and current in an inductance.

FIG. 2.10. Polarities associated with mutual inductance.

the symbol v. Since an increasing current has a positive time derivative, the polarity of the voltage drop across the inductor must be as shown in Fig. 2.9, because this polarity opposes any increase in the current.

The voltage induced as a result of mutual inductance is expressed similarly as

$$v_1 = M_{12}\frac{d}{dt}i_2. \tag{2.13}$$

Here some difficulty may arise in designating polarities unless an indication is placed on the circuit diagram as to how the coils are wound. This designation takes the form of two dots, one on the end of each coil, in such a way that the polarity of the voltage of mutual inductance in a coil is the same as the polarity of the voltage of self-inductance in that coil, provided that the two currents flow through the coils in the same direction relative to the dots. This rather wordy explanation is more readily seen by means of the illustrations in Fig. 2.10.

In general, there will be currents flowing in both coils, so that voltages both of self- and mutual inductance appear. In that case the situation is as shown in Fig. 2.11. Here several different combinations of current

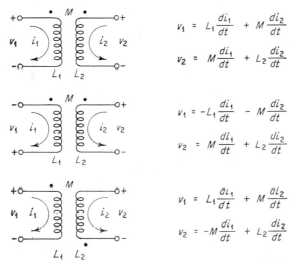

$$v_1 = L_1 \frac{di_1}{dt} + M \frac{di_2}{dt}$$

$$v_2 = M \frac{di_1}{dt} + L_2 \frac{di_2}{dt}$$

$$v_1 = -L_1 \frac{di_1}{dt} - M \frac{di_2}{dt}$$

$$v_2 = M \frac{di_1}{dt} + L_2 \frac{di_2}{dt}$$

$$v_1 = L_1 \frac{di_1}{dt} + M \frac{di_2}{dt}$$

$$v_2 = -M \frac{di_1}{dt} + L_2 \frac{di_2}{dt}$$

FIG. 2.11. Current-voltage relationships in coupled coils.

and dot polarities are shown to point out various arrangements which might be met with in actual circuits. (Again, Sec. 1.4 should be carefully reviewed.)

The inverse problems associated with inductance, that is, finding the currents which flow when known voltages are applied, should be considered separately for self-inductance and for mutual inductance.

In the case of self-inductance, we may integrate Eq. (2.12b) with respect to time and obtain

$$i = \frac{1}{L} \int_0^t e \, dt + i_0 \qquad (2.14)$$

where i_0 is the current in the coil at $t = 0$.† In most cases $i_0 = 0$, because the problem is usually presented as applying a voltage to an inductor by means of a switch, through which no current may flow before $t = 0$, and current through an isolated inductor cannot jump instantly in zero time at the instant the switch is closed, for if this occurred, the induced voltage would be infinite, which is contrary to

† The comments in the footnote on page 44 also apply here.

facts observed in actual practice. There are cases, however, typical of which is that illustrated in Fig. 2.12, where $i_0 \neq 0$.

With mutual inductance, the inverse problem is that of finding the two currents produced by two voltage sources. This cannot be solved trivially. Rather, it involves solving a set of simultaneous differential equations on two unknowns (the two currents). Such sets of equations are exhibited in Fig. 2.11. The solution of such sets of equations is discussed in Chaps. 3 and 4. It is sufficient here to note that the solution contains $i_1(0)$ and $i_2(0)$, the currents in each coil at $t = 0$.

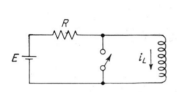

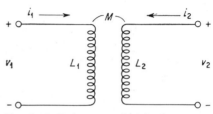

FIG. 2.12. Circuit wherein $i_0 \neq 0$. (The switch is closed at $t = 0$.)

FIG. 2.13. Reference polarities for energy storage in mutually coupled coils.

2.5. Energy Stored in Inductors. The energy stored in the magnetic field of an inductor can be calculated in a manner similar to the calculation of the energy stored in a capacitor. Starting from Eq. (2.6),

$$p = vi \qquad \text{watts} \qquad (2.6)$$

where v is the voltage drop, it follows that

$$U = \int_{t_0}^{t} p \, dt = \int_{t_0}^{t} vi \, dt \qquad \text{joules.} \qquad (2.15)$$

Since, from Eq. (2.12b), $v = L \, di/dt$,

$$U_L = \int_{t_0}^{t} L \frac{di}{dt} i \, dt = \int_{i(t_0)}^{i(t)} Li \, di \qquad \text{joules.} \qquad (2.16)$$

$$U_L = \tfrac{1}{2}Li^2 \Big|_{i(t_0)}^{i(t)} = \tfrac{1}{2}L[i^2(t) - i^2(t_0)] \qquad \text{joules.} \qquad (2.17)$$

Thus, if we start with an inductor in which no current exists and force through it a current I, the energy stored in the associated magnetic field is

$$U_L = \tfrac{1}{2}LI^2 \qquad \text{joules.} \qquad (2.18)$$

The situation involving mutually coupled coils is less obvious. Consider the circuit of Fig. 2.13. No dot polarities are shown so that the situation may be considered general. Then

$$v_1 = L_1 \frac{d}{dt} i_1 \pm M \frac{d}{dt} i_2$$

$$v_2 = \pm M \frac{d}{dt} i_1 + L_2 \frac{d}{dt} i_2. \qquad (2.19)$$

(Either both $+$ or both $-$ signs are to be used.) The power into terminals 1 is $v_1 i_1$, and that into terminals 2 is $v_2 i_2$, so that the total power input to the network is given by

$$p_{in} = v_1 i_1 + v_2 i_2. \tag{2.20}$$

Substituting Eqs. (2.19) into Eq. (2.20) gives

$$p_{in} = L_1 i_1 \frac{d}{dt} i_1 \pm M \left(i_1 \frac{d}{dt} i_1 + i_2 \frac{d}{dt} i_1 \right) + L_2 i_2 \frac{d}{dt} i_2. \tag{2.21}$$

Noting that

$$\frac{d}{dt} (i_1 i_2) = i_1 \frac{d}{dt} i_2 + i_2 \frac{d}{dt} i_1, \tag{2.22}$$

Eq. (2.21) becomes

$$p_{in} = L_1 i_1 \frac{d}{dt} i_1 \pm M \frac{d}{dt} (i_1 i_2) + L_2 i_2 \frac{d}{dt} i_2. \tag{2.23}$$

Thus, the total energy delivered to the network between $t = t_0$ and $t = t$ is

$$U_L = L_1 \int_{t_0}^{t} i_1 \frac{d}{dt} i_1 \, dt \pm M \int_{t_0}^{t} \frac{d}{dt} (i_1 i_2) \, dt + L_2 \int_{t_0}^{t} i_2 \frac{d}{dt} i_2 \, dt. \tag{2.24}$$

Evaluating this expression and assuming no currents at t_0 yields

$$U_L = \tfrac{1}{2} L_1 i_1^2(t) \pm M i_1(t) i_2(t) + \tfrac{1}{2} L_2 i_2^2(t). \tag{2.25}$$

The presence of M either increases or decreases the amount of energy stored in the magnetic field of two currents carrying inductances, depending on whether the coils are arranged so that their fluxes are in the same or in opposite directions. Since negative energy cannot be stored (that is, we cannot draw energy from where there is none) it can easily be shown that

$$M \leqq \sqrt{L_1 L_2}. \tag{2.26}$$

For suppose that we consider Eq. (2.25) as a quadratic equation in i_1. Then, since $U_L \geqq 0$, the plot of U_L as a function of i_1 does not cross the i_1 axis. Thus the roots of $U_L = 0$ must be complex or equal. Hence the discriminant must be less than or equal to zero:

$$(\pm M i_2)^2 - 4(\tfrac{1}{2} L_1)(\tfrac{1}{2} L_2) i_2^2 \leqq 0.$$

This implies $M^2 \leqq L_1 L_2$, from which Eq. (2.26) follows.

2.6. Actual Circuit Elements. We have considered three circuit parameters, resistance, capacitance, and inductance. The corresponding physical devices are resistors, capacitors, and inductors. Ideally, a resistor is a two-terminal element which can be described by a single number—its resistance. Similarly, capacitors and inductors should be described by their capacitance and inductance, respectively. With actual elements, this is not the case. Because capacitance is associated with energy storage in an electric field, inductance with a magnetic field, and resistance with energy loss, resistors also have capacitance and inductance; capacitors have resistance and inductance; and inductors have resistance and capacitance. Now, in circuit analysis we are never analyzing a real circuit—we are analyzing a mathematical model of the circuit—and our results will agree with the behavior of the circuit only to the degree to which the model represents the circuit. It is also true that the more accurate the model the more labor is required in its analysis. We therefore make the model no more accurate than necessary. In general, this means that actual resistors are represented only by resistance, and actual capacitors are represented only by capacitance. The losses of real inductors can rarely be ignored, however, and so inductors are usually represented by inductance and resistance, generally in series. When dealing with sources whose current or voltage difference varies rapidly we may have to consider the "stray" capacitance of resistors and coils, and the inductance of short pieces of wire. Only experience can indicate what parameters need be considered. In all problems in this text, the pertinent parameters will be explicitly designated.

2.7. Equilibrium Equations for Circuits with Energy Storage. Kirchhoff's laws apply, of course, to any electric circuit. These laws, in conjunction with the current-voltage relationships just derived, enable us to write the equilibrium equations for all circuits. The writing of these equations will be illustrated by means of several examples.

Example 2.1. Write the equilibrium equation for the current which will flow in the circuit of Fig. 2.14 when a voltage $e(t)$ is applied by closing the switch.

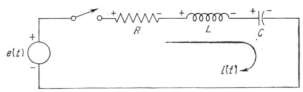

FIG. 2.14. Circuit for Example 2.1.

Solution. Since the same current flows in all parts of the circuit, we may write Kirchhoff's voltage law as

$$e(t) = Ri + L\frac{di}{dt} + \frac{1}{C}\int_0^t i\,dt + v_{c0}$$

where v_{c0} is the voltage on the capacitor when the switch is closed.†

† The footnote on page 44 is applicable here as well as to succeeding examples. It will not assume practical importance, however, until problems of the type discussed in Chap. 10 are considered.

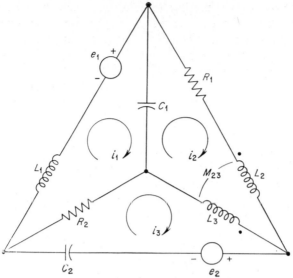

FIG. 2.15. Circuit for Example 2.2.

Example 2.2.   Write the equilibrium equations for the circuit of Fig. 2.15.
Solution.   On the loop basis we have

Loop 1

$$e_1 = \frac{1}{C_1} \int_0^t (i_1 - i_2)\, dt + v_{10} + R_2(i_1 - i_3) + L_1 \frac{d}{dt} i_1$$

Loop 2

$$0 = i_2 R_1 + L_2 \frac{d}{dt} i_2 + M_{23} \frac{d}{dt} (i_2 - i_3) + L_3 \frac{d}{dt} (i_2 - i_3)$$
$$+ M_{32} \frac{d}{dt} i_2 + \frac{1}{C_1} \int_0^t (i_1 - i_2)\, dt + v_{10}$$

Loop 3

$$-e_3 = \frac{1}{C_2} \int_0^t i_3\, dt + v_{30} + R_2(i_3 - i_1) + L_3 \frac{d}{dt} (i_3 - i_2) - M_{32} \frac{d}{dt} i_2.$$

(Observe carefully how the mutual inductance enters these equations.)

Example 2.3.   Write the equilibrium equation on the voltage at node 1 in the circuit of Fig. 2.16.

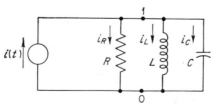

FIG. 2.16. Circuit for Example 2.3.

Solution.   We have immediately

$$i(t) = i_R + i_L + i_C.$$

Using Ohm's law and Eqs. (2.14) and (2.4) we obtain

$$i(t) = \frac{1}{R} v_1 + \frac{1}{L} \int_0^t v_1 \, dt + i_0 + C \frac{d}{dt} v_1.$$

In the foregoing examples we have succeeded in writing systems of integrodifferential equations for electric circuits. The equations we have written have been perfectly general with no restrictions on the waveforms of the voltage or current sources. The general solution of such systems of equations is rather laborious. Fortunately, however, the general solution is not the one usually required. In most cases the current and voltage sources have alternating waveforms and, in particular, usually have sinusoidal waveforms or can be decomposed into sinusoids.

In the next two chapters methods of solving the equilibrium equations will be discussed, and a powerful simplifying concept, *complex impedance*, will be introduced.

2.8. Initial Conditions. If we examine the equilibrium equations written for the previous examples we see that some of the *initial conditions* do not appear explicitly in these equations. For example, in Example 2.2 the currents which exist in the inductors when we connect our voltage sources (and these currents need not be zero) do not appear, and in Example 2.3 the voltage existing across the capacitor when the current is applied is not given. The solutions we obtain cannot be independent of these conditions, for, if they were, the currents and voltages would have to change instantly from their initial values to those given by the solutions. This cannot occur, because to change instantly the current through an isolated inductor requires an infinite voltage,† and to change instantly the voltage across a capacitor requires an infinite current. [These facts follow from Eqs. (2.14) and (2.4).]

The way the problem resolves itself is this. The solutions of the equilibrium equations are found to contain arbitrary constants. That is, some of the terms in the solution contain coefficients which may be set arbitrarily, without destroying the fact that the solution satisfies the equilibrium equations. It develops that there are as many arbitrary constants as there are independent initial conditions. Thus we may adjust the arbitrary constants until we match the solutions to the initial conditions.

It usually proves most convenient to have the initial conditions specified as the initial value, and various initial derivatives, of the solution. However, they are not usually given in that form. Rather, we usually know the initial currents in the inductors and initial voltages across the capacitors. From these we must obtain the initial values and

---

† This statement holds for isolated inductors and does not necessarily apply when mutual inductance is present.

derivatives. In the next chapter we shall see examples wherein this is done.

One of the problems associated with initial conditions is the determination of how many independent ones exist. Knowing this would enable us to tell in advance how many arbitrary constants will appear in our solution and would serve as a check on our work. It also enables us to know if we have specified all the initial conditions. Finding the number of *independent* initial conditions is not merely a matter of adding the number of inductors and capacitors together. For example, if two inductors are connected in series, the current in one is always equal to that in the other, and so they are not independent. The same is true for the voltage across capacitors connected in parallel. These, though, are obvious cases. What is not so obvious are the situations shown in Fig. 2.17. In Fig. 2.17a we note that $i_3 = i_1 + i_2$, and so we can only specify independently two initial currents. Similarly, in Fig. 2.17b, $v_3 = v_1 - v_2$, and so only two initial voltages may be independently specified.

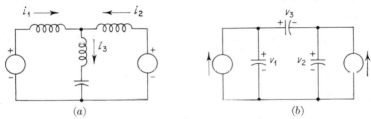

(a)   (b)

FIG. 2.17. Illustrating dependence of initial conditions.

It can be shown that, in order not to be confused by situations like the foregoing, we may use the following procedure† to determine the number of initial conditions.

1. *Number of independent initial currents.* Traverse the meshes, one at a time. If there is an inductor in the first mesh, give that mesh a weight of 1. (If there is no inductor give it a weight of zero.) Mark the inductor as having been counted (count only one inductor if there are several). Traverse the next mesh, giving the mesh a weight 1 if it contains an inductor not already counted, and a weight zero otherwise. Repeat until all meshes are covered. The total weight of the meshes is the number of independent initial currents.

2. *Number of independent initial voltages.* Consider the (independent) nodes, one at a time. Even trivial nodes, having only two branches

† For a detailed discussion, see E. A. Guillemin, "Communication Circuits," vol. 1, John Wiley & Sons, Inc., New York, 1931, pp. 185ff; also, J. Otterman, On the Order of the Differential Equation Describing an Electrical Network, *Proc. IRE*, vol. 45, pp. 1024–1025 (letter), July, 1957.

connected to them, must be considered. If a capacitor is connected to the node, give the node a weight 1, but give it weight zero if no capacitor is connected. Mark the capacitor as having been counted. Consider the next node, giving the node weight 1 if it has connected to it a capacitor not already counted, and zero otherwise. Continue until all nodes are considered. The total weight of the nodes is then the number of initial voltages which may be specified independently.

In the foregoing procedure we should be careful, before starting, to eliminate the trivial class of cases: two inductors in series which are essentially one inductor, and two capacitors in parallel which are essentially the same capacitor. Before applying the rules, also, sources should be eliminated to make apparent these trivial cases.

2.9. Duality. It may already have been observed that the principle of duality discussed in Sec. 1.11 may be further extended to circuits involving inductance and capacitance. If we note that the following pair of quantities, *inductance* and *capacitance*, are duals, it is seen, for example, that the graphs of the circuits used in Examples 2.1 and 2.3 (Figs. 2.14 and 2.16) are duals. The notion of duality will be further extended in Sec. 3.1.

In the next chapter we shall study the solution of the equilibrium equations and show how the initial conditions are applied to the evaluation of the arbitrary constants which appear in the equations.

EXERCISES

2.1. Write the mesh equations for the circuit shown in Fig. 2.18 in integrodifferential form.

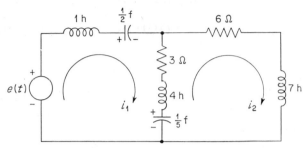

FIG. 2.18. Exercise 2.1.

2.2. Write the current-voltage relation for the circuit shown in Fig. 2.19.

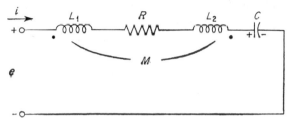

FIG. 2.19. Exercise 2.2.

2.3. Write the equilibrium equations for the circuit of Fig. 2.20 in integrodifferential form.

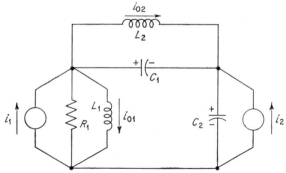

FIG. 2.20. Exercise 2.3.

2.4. How many initial currents may be independently specified for the circuit of Exercise 2.1?   How many initial voltages?

2.5. How many initial currents may be independently specified for the circuit of Exercise 2.2?   How many initial voltages?

CHAPTER 3

SOLUTION OF THE EQUILIBRIUM EQUATIONS

We have seen in the preceding chapter how to set up the equilibrium equations for circuits containing energy storage elements—inductors and capacitors. In the present chapter we shall investigate methods of solving these equations with particular emphasis on the physical significance of the operations involved and results deduced. Toward this end a detailed analysis of single-loop circuits will be made, and the procedures for extending this analysis to multiloop circuits will be indicated.

3.1. The Equilibrium Equation for a Single-loop RL Circuit. As a first illustration, consider the circuit of Fig. 3.1. Here the problem is to determine the current in an RL circuit when a fixed voltage E is suddenly applied. The odd switching arrangement is used in order that a closed loop always be provided for the current. Also, were the path $1b$ not provided, closing the switch would change the graph of the network. Thus we would be dealing not only with a time-varying source but also with a time-varying network.

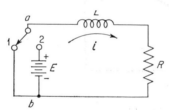

FIG. 3.1. Series RL circuit with a suddenly applied voltage.

Assuming that the switch is thrown instantly from 1 to 2 at time t_0, the equilibrium equation for the loop is

$$L\frac{di}{dt} + Ri = E, \qquad t > t_0. \tag{3.1}$$

The above equation does not indicate the entire situation. Suppose, for example, that the voltage source had been connected for a period before we started to analyze the circuit. Then, at time t_0, some residual current would still flow, yet the equilibrium equation (3.1) would still be the same. Thus to specify uniquely the circuit to be analyzed, we must give, as an additional constraint, the initial current $i_0 \equiv i(t_0)$ in the coil.

Equation (3.1) is a *linear, first-order, nonhomogeneous* differential equation with *constant coefficients*. It is linear, since if i_1 and i_2 are any two currents,

$$\left[L\frac{d}{dt} + R\right](i_1 + i_2) = \left[L\frac{d}{dt} + R\right]i_1 + \left[L\frac{d}{dt} + R\right]i_2 \tag{3.2.1}$$

58

and

$$\left[L\frac{d}{dt} + R\right](\alpha i_1) = \alpha\left[L\frac{d}{dt} + R\right]i_1 \qquad (3.2.2)$$

where α is a constant. In other words, if the differential operator†
$L\frac{d}{dt} + R$ is applied to any linear combination of currents, the result
would be identical if the differential operator were applied to each current
separately and *then* the linear combination taken. For example,

$$a\frac{di}{dt} + bi^2 = C$$

is *not* a linear equation since, in particular,

$$a\frac{d}{dt}(i_1 + i_2) + b(i_1 + i_2)^2 \neq \left[a\frac{d}{dt}i_1 + bi_1{}^2\right] + \left[a\frac{d}{dt}i_2 + bi_2{}^2\right].$$

Equation (3.1) is called *first-order* since the highest derivative of i that
appears is the first. Similarly,

$$a\frac{d^2i}{dt^2} + b\frac{di}{dt} + ci = D$$

is a *second order* equation. Equation (3.1) is called *nonhomogeneous*
since, when all terms involving i are shifted to the left, the right-hand
side is not identically zero. Thus

$$L\frac{di}{dt} + Ri = 0$$

is a *homogeneous* equation. Finally, the description "constant coefficients" refers to the fact that the coefficients of i and its derivatives,
here L and R, are constants and not functions of t. For example,

$$L\frac{di}{dt} + Ri = \sin t$$

---

† If $f(t)$ is a function of t and $f'(t)$ its derivative, we can think of $f'(t)$ as being
obtained from $f(t)$ by *operating* on $f(t)$ with d/dt, that is,

$$f'(t) = \frac{d}{dt}f(t).$$

Thus we call d/dt an *operator*, in particular, a *differential operator*. In many applications it is convenient to replace d/dt by the symbol p. Thus the above equation may
be symbolically written as

$$f'(t) = pf(t)$$

and Eq. (3.1) as

$$Lpi + Ri \equiv (Lp + R)i = E.$$

It is to be emphasized that p as used in the above equation is an *operator* and *not* a
constant or a function. Hence suitable care must be used in manipulating such
expressions.

is still a constant-coefficient equation, while

$$t \frac{di}{dt} + \epsilon^t i = 0$$

is not.

Let us now return to the problem of finding a value of current $i(t)$ such that

$$(Lp + R)i(t) = E \tag{3.1a}$$

where p has been written for d/dt. As a preliminary step, it is simpler to consider the homogeneous equation

$$(Lp + R)i(t) = 0. \tag{3.3}$$

Once we have solved this problem it will not be a difficult matter to obtain the solution of Eq. (3.1). One immediately sees that, if $i(t)$ is identically zero, Eq. (3.3) will be satisfied. If at time $t = t_0$ no current is flowing in the coil of Fig. 3.1, then $i(t) \equiv 0$ is indeed the solution we are seeking. However, suppose that $i_0 \neq 0$. This would be the case, for example, if E were connected before $t = t_0$ and then removed (as in Fig. 3.1 with the switch thrown from 2 to 1 before $t = t_0$, and then back to 2 at $t = t_0$). Thus while $i(t) \equiv 0$ satisfied the differential equation of Eq. (3.3), it does not satisfy the requirement that $i(t_0) = i_0$.

Let us therefore attempt to find a solution of Eq. (3.3) which is not identically zero. We first rewrite Eq. (3.3) as

$$L \frac{d}{dt} i_c + R i_c = 0 \tag{3.3a}$$

using i_c in place of i to emphasize the fact that we are considering the homogeneous case ($E = 0$) rather than the complete solution. In order to integrate Eq. (3.3a) we rearrange it in the form

$$\frac{di_c}{i_c} = -\frac{R}{L} \, dt. \tag{3.3b}$$

Thus we have *separated* the variables. Upon integrating both sides of the above equation we obtain

$$\log i_c = -\frac{R}{L} t + C \tag{3.4}$$

where C is a constant of integration, and solving explicitly for i_c leads to

$$i_c = K\epsilon^{-(R/L)t} \tag{3.5}$$

where $C = \log K$. No matter what the value of K, the function $K\epsilon^{-(R/L)t}$ satisfies Eq. (3.3).

Now in order to have $i_c(t_0)$ equal i_0 we must have

$$i_c(t_0) = i_0 = K\epsilon^{-(R/L)t_0}$$

or

$$K = i_0\epsilon^{+(R/L)t_0}. \tag{3.6}$$

Hence from Eq. (3.5)

$$i_c = i_0\epsilon^{-(R/L)(t-t_0)}. \tag{3.7}$$

This satisfies the differential equation of Eq. (3.3) and assumes the value i_0 at $t = t_0$. Note that if i_0 happened to be zero then $i_c(t) \equiv 0$, which confirms our earlier analysis. This, then, completes the solution of the homogeneous equation (3.3) with the initial condition $i(t_0) = 0$. However, it is the solution of the nonhomogeneous equation (3.1) in which we are interested.

The solution $i_c = K\epsilon^{-(R/L)t}$ (with K arbitrary) just obtained is termed the *complementary* solution of the nonhomogeneous equation (3.1) (thus the suggestive subscript c on i). We shall also refer to it as the *natural behavior* of the network because it indicates how the current behaves "naturally" in the absence of external sources. The source of energy for the current is the initial energy, $\frac{1}{2}Li_0^2$, stored in the inductor.

Let us now return to the original equation

$$(Lp + R)i_p = E \tag{3.1b}$$

where we are using i_p to distinguish it from i_c. A little thought shows that a constant value of i_p, say I_p, is a solution since

$$(Lp + R)I_p = LpI_p + RI_p = 0 + RI_p = E \tag{3.8}$$

and explicitly

$$I_p = \frac{E}{R}. \tag{3.8a}$$

We call I_p a *particular* solution of Eq. (3.1b) since it depends upon the particular form of the source (hence the suggestive subscript p). It is also called the *forced behavior* or *forced response* of the circuit because the source voltage is the *forcing function* which gives rise to I_p.

As a consequence of the linearity of Eq. (3.1),

$$(Lp + R)(i_c + i_p) = (Lp + R)i_c + (Lp + R)i_p = 0 + E \tag{3.9}$$

since $(Lp + R)i_c \equiv 0$ by Eq. (3.3a) and $(Lp + R)i_p = E$ by Eq. (3.1b). Thus if i_p is a particular solution of Eq. (3.1) we may add it to the complementary solution and obtain a new solution of Eq. (3.1) called the *general* solution. The general solution of Eq. (3.1) is

$$i(t) = K\epsilon^{-(R/L)(t-t_0)} + \frac{E}{R}, \qquad t > t_0. \tag{3.10}$$

The current $i(t)$ is called the *response* of the circuit to the forcing function.

Observe that K in Eq. (3.10) is arbitrary and must be obtained from the initial conditions.† Let us suppose, for simplicity, that the switch of Fig. 3.1 is thrown from 1 to 2 at time $t = t_0$ and that i_0 is the initial current. Then, at $t = t_0$,

$$i(t_0) = i_0 = K\epsilon^0 + \frac{E}{R} \tag{3.11}$$

and

$$K = i_0 - \frac{E}{R}. \tag{3.11a}$$

Thus the solution of the differential equation (3.1) with the initial condition $i(t_0) = i_0$ is given by

$$i(t) = \frac{E}{R} + \left(i_0 - \frac{E}{R} \right) \epsilon^{-(R/L)(t-t_0)}. \tag{3.12}$$

It is informative to study Eq. (3.12) in some detail. We shall assume,

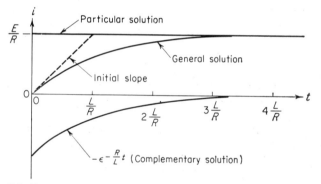

FIG. 3.2. Response of RL circuit to a suddenly applied fixed voltage.

for concreteness, that $i_0 = 0$ and $t_0 = 0$ and hence from Eq. (3.12)

$$i(t) = \frac{E}{R} [1 - \epsilon^{-(R/L)t}]. \tag{3.13}$$

This equation is plotted in Fig. 3.2. The time axis has been *normalized*

† One cannot obtain K from the initial condition using the complementary solution alone and then append the particular solution. This would lead to

$$i(t) = \frac{E}{R} + K\epsilon^{-(R/L)t}, \qquad K = i_0 \epsilon^{(R/L)t_0}$$

which is not the same as Eq. (3.12) and, in fact, $i(t_0) \neq i_0$. Of course, if the over-all equation which we wish to solve *is* a homogeneous equation, then no problem arises since the particular solution is zero. This was the case investigated at the beginning of this section.

by presenting it in units of L/R,† and the current axis has been normalized in units of E/R. The term L/R is called the *time constant* of the circuit. Physical significance may be attached to the time constant by considering the initial slope of $i(t)$. From Eq. (3.13),

$$\frac{di}{dt} = \frac{E}{R}\frac{R}{L}\epsilon^{-(R/L)t} \tag{3.14}$$

and at $t = 0$

$$\left(\frac{di}{dt}\right)_{t=0} = \frac{R}{L}\frac{E}{R}. \tag{3.14a}$$

If the current were to continue at this rate of change its equation would be

$$i = \frac{R}{L}\frac{E}{R}t \tag{3.15}$$

and it would reach its final value of E/R at

$$t = \frac{L}{R}, \tag{3.16}$$

that is, in a time of one time constant, as is seen by letting $t = L/R$ in Eq. (3.15) and normalizing by dividing by E/R. It actually takes a time equal to three time constants to reach 95 per cent of its final value.‡

An alternative approach to the solution of Eq. (3.1), based on hindsight, may now be developed. The reason for introducing this new technique is that it also works for higher-order equations, while our original method cannot be so extended. This new method assumes that the solution of the differential equation may be written in the form $i = I_0 \epsilon^{st}$, where I_0 and s are numbers, perhaps complex. Equation (3.1) then becomes

$$L\left(\frac{d}{dt}I_0\epsilon^{st}\right) + R(I_0\epsilon^{st}) = E \tag{3.17}$$

or

$$LI_0 s\epsilon^{st} + RI_0\epsilon^{st} = E$$

which, on solving for i, is

$$i = I_0\epsilon^{st} = \frac{E}{Ls + R}. \tag{3.18}$$

---

† The unit of inductance is the henry. A one-henry inductance has a potential difference of one volt when the current changes at the rate of one ampere per second. Thus, a henry may be specified as a volt/(amp/sec) or ohm-second. Hence the unit of L/R is the second.

‡ Theoretically the current *never* reaches its final value. However, there always exist small random fluctuations of current corresponding to the Brownian motion of the electrons in the conductors. This is called *noise*. Eventually the difference between the actual and final values of the current is masked by the noise.

We shall first determine a particular solution. Since the right-hand side of Eq. (3.18) is a constant, the term $I_0\epsilon^{st}$ must also be constant. Thus if $I_0\epsilon^{st}$ is to be a solution it follows that $s = 0$ and

$$I_p = I_0 = \frac{E}{R} \tag{3.19}$$

is a particular solution.†

The complementary solution is found by setting

$$(Ls + R)I_c\epsilon^{st} = 0 \tag{3.20}$$

where I_c is a constant. Since ϵ^{st} is never zero, we must have either $Ls + R$ or I_c equal to zero if $I_c\epsilon^{st}$ is to be a solution of Eq. (3.3a). But $I_c = 0$ implies that the complementary solution is identically zero. Thus to obtain a solution which is not identically zero it follows that

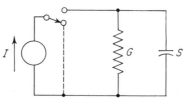

FIG. 3.3. Single-node GS circuit.

$$Ls + R = 0 \tag{3.21}$$

or

$$s = -\frac{R}{L}. \tag{3.22}$$

Thus $I_c\epsilon^{-(R/L)t}$ is the complementary solution. The constant I_c may be evaluated as before by utilizing the initial value of the current.

The value of s, $s = 0$, is characteristic of the forcing function E and is called the *forcing frequency*. That is, E may be written $E\epsilon^{st}$, where $s = 0$. The value $s = -R/L$ is characteristic of the circuit and is called the *natural frequency* (that is, the frequency associated with the natural behavior).

An examination of Eq. (3.18) seems to indicate that it is a generalization of Ohm's law, and indeed it is. The generalized resistance $Ls + R$ is called the *impedance* or *impedance function* and is abbreviated $Z(s)$. Current can flow without a forcing function only if the impedance is zero; the frequency at which the impedance function $Z(s)$ is zero is the *natural frequency* and is also called a *zero* of the impedance function, or a *root* of the equation $Z(s) = 0$.

The dual of the single-loop RL circuit treated here is the single-node GS circuit suddenly connected to a current source, as shown in Fig. 3.3. Here we do not need an extra contact on the switch to preserve the circuit geometry. For aesthetic reasons, though, we may wish to arrange the dotted connection so that the current source is not feeding an open circuit. It is suggested that the reader solve this problem, using the

† This argument will not work for an *arbitrary* forcing function $E(t)$. However, the second part of the method, that of finding the complementary solution, is perfectly general for all linear equations with constant coefficients.

method of assuming a solution of the form $V_0\epsilon^{st}$ outlined above. In this case it will be noted that the natural behavior (voltage without any corresponding forcing-current term) can occur only for those values of s which make the ratio of current to voltage (reciprocal of impedance, or *admittance*) equal to zero.

Many new terms and definitions have been introduced in this section. In order to emphasize their significance and illustrate their application to more complicated solutions the next several sections will use them in examples of increasing complexity.

3.2. The Equilibrium Equation for a Single-loop RC Circuit. As a second example, we consider the response (current) of the RC circuit shown in Fig. 3.4.   We assume that the capacitor has an initial voltage v_{c0} and that the switch is thrown at $t = 0$.   The response of the circuit for $t > 0$ will be considered. (Clearly for $t < 0$ the current is zero.)   The equilibrium equation for the circuit under consideration is

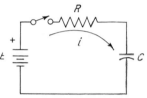

$$Ri + \frac{1}{C}\int_0^t i\,dt + v_{c0} = E, \qquad t > 0. \quad (3.23)$$

FIG. 3.4. Single-loop RC circuit with sudden voltage applied.

This equation is not a differential equation since the integral of the unknown function appears.   Such equations are called *integrodifferential* equations.   However, it is easy to reduce Eq. (3.23) to a differential equation by differentiating it with respect to t.   We thus obtain

$$R\frac{di}{dt} + \frac{1}{C}i = 0, \qquad t > 0. \quad (3.24)$$

Since this is a homogeneous equation the particular solution is zero. The complementary solution (natural behavior) may be obtained as before by separating the variables,

$$-RC\frac{di}{i} = dt. \quad (3.25)$$

Integrating with respect to t yields

$$-RC \log i = t + k$$

where k is a constant of integration.   Thus

$$i(t) = K\epsilon^{-t/RC} \quad (3.26)$$

where $k = -RC \log K$.

To determine the arbitrary constant K we use the fact that the initial voltage across the capacitor is v_{c0}.   Thus the voltage across the resistor at the instant the switch is thrown is $E - v_{c0}$. The initial current is, therefore,

$$i(0) = \frac{E - v_{c0}}{R}. \tag{3.27}$$

From Eq. (3.26),

$$K\epsilon^{-0/RC} = \frac{E - v_{c0}}{R} \tag{3.28}$$

and

$$K = \frac{E - v_{c0}}{R}. \tag{3.28a}$$

Thus the current $i(t)$ which satisfies the differential equation and the initial conditions is

$$i(t) = \frac{E - v_{c0}}{R} \epsilon^{-t/RC}. \tag{3.29}$$

The voltage across the capacitor is given by

$$v_c = \frac{1}{C} \int_0^t i(t) \, dt + v_{c0} = \frac{E - v_{c0}}{RC} \int_0^t \epsilon^{-t/RC} \, dt + v_{c0}$$
$$= v_{c0} + (E - v_{c0})(1 - \epsilon^{-t/RC}). \tag{3.30}$$

The variations of i and v_c with time are plotted in Fig. 3.5. The time scale is again normalized in terms of the time constant RC. This time constant RC is analogous to the L/R term in the analysis of the RL circuit. The variation of capacitor voltage with time is easily remembered if it is noted that the voltage proceeds exponentially from its initial to its final value with time constant RC. The initial slope of i is $-(E - v_{c0})/R^2C$ and that of v_c is $(E - v_{c0})/RC$. Lines with these slopes intersect the t axis and the line $v_c = E$, respectively, at a value of t equal to one time constant.

The alternative method of solution, namely, that of assuming a solution of the form $i(t) = I_0\epsilon^{st}$, may be applied here. Substituting $i = I_0\epsilon^{st}$ into Eq. (3.24) yields

$$RsI_0\epsilon^{st} + \frac{1}{C} I_0\epsilon^{st} = 0 \tag{3.31}$$

or

$$\left(Rs + \frac{1}{C}\right) I_0\epsilon^{st} = 0. \tag{3.32}$$

Since ϵ^{st} is never zero, we may cancel it to obtain

$$\left(Rs + \frac{1}{C}\right) I_0 = 0. \tag{3.33}$$

Now $I_0 = 0$ would imply $i \equiv 0$. Since this will not, in general, then

satisfy the initial condition, we must rule out this trivial case.   The
only other possibility is that

$$Rs + \frac{1}{C} = 0 \qquad\qquad (3.34)$$

or

$$s = -\frac{1}{RC}.$$

Thus

$$i(t) = I_0\epsilon^{-t/RC}, \qquad t > 0 \qquad\qquad (3.35)$$

is the complementary solution.   The natural frequency of the network is
$-1/RC$.   Since the particular solution is zero, Eq. (3.35) also represents
the general solution.   The constant
I_0 of Eq. (3.35) may be evaluated as
was done earlier in this section.

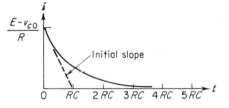

Let us see if we can interpret our
results in terms of the *impedance
function* described in the previous
section.   To do this a preliminary
result must be developed.   We have
already noted that differentiating
$I_0\epsilon^{st}$ lead to $sI_0\epsilon^{st}$.   Some of the manipulations carried out above seem
to indicate that integrating $I_0\epsilon^{st}$ is
equivalent to writing $I_0\epsilon^{st}/s$.   This
is not so, for

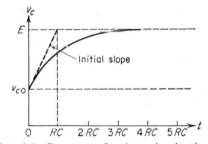

$$\frac{1}{C}\int_0^t I_0\epsilon^{st}\,dt = \frac{I_0\epsilon^{st}}{Cs} - \frac{I_0}{Cs}. \qquad (3.36)$$

However, the term I_0/Cs is related
to the initial voltage on the capac-

FIG. 3.5. Current and voltage in circuit
of Fig. 3.4.

itor, and, as we have seen, the initial voltage is used only in establishing
the values of the arbitrary constants in the solution and not the *nature*
of the solution.   Let us therefore neglect I_0/Cs and also v_{c0}.   If this is
done, Eq. (3.23) becomes

$$RI_0\epsilon^{st} + \frac{1}{Cs}\epsilon^{st} = E \qquad\qquad (3.37)$$

or

$$\left(R + \frac{1}{Cs}\right)I_0\epsilon^{st} = E. \qquad\qquad (3.37a)$$

Thus

$$i = I_0\epsilon^{st} = \frac{E}{R + 1/Cs}. \qquad\qquad (3.38)$$

Now $R + 1/Cs$ has the dimensions of ohms and is called the impedance or impedance function $Z(s)$. Since the right-hand side of Eq. (3.38) is independent of t, $I_0\epsilon^{st}$ must be independent of t, which requires $s = 0$. This in turn implies $I_0 = 0$ since $Z(s) = R + 1/Cs$ evaluated at $s = 0$ is infinite. Thus, the particular solution of Eq. (3.23) is zero. We call $s = 0$ a *pole* of the impedance function. The natural behavior of the integrodifferential equation may be found by setting $E = 0$ to obtain

$$\left(R + \frac{1}{Cs}\right) I_c\epsilon^{st} = 0$$

which leads to the result $s = -1/RC$, and $i_c = I_c\epsilon^{-t/RC}$.

The formal method of solution whereby integrals of i are replaced by $I_0\epsilon^{st}/s$ and initial conditions are neglected always is consistent for linear integrodifferential equations with constant coefficients. It is more than a mnemonic scheme. In Chap. 10 we shall give a mathematical justification of this technique using the Laplace transform.

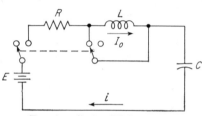

Fig. 3.6. Series *RLC* circuit.

3.3. The Equilibrium Equation for a Single-loop *RLC* Circuit. A more elaborate circuit than those already analyzed, and one whose solution involves some new mathematical ideas, is the series *RLC* circuit shown in Fig. 3.6. (The extra switch is shown so that any conceptual difficulties with the initial current through the inductance do not arise.)

The equilibrium equation for this circuit may be written as

$$L \frac{di}{dt} + Ri + \frac{1}{C} \int_0^t i\, dt + v_{c0} = E, \qquad t > 0 \qquad (3.39)$$

where v_{c0} is the initial voltage across the capacitor. Differentiating Eq. (3.39) with respect to time leads to

$$L \frac{d^2i}{dt^2} + R \frac{di}{dt} + \frac{1}{C} i = 0, \qquad t > 0 \qquad (3.40)$$

which is a linear, second-order, homogeneous differential equation with constant coefficients. Since it is homogeneous, the particular solution is zero, that is,

$$i_p = 0. \qquad (3.41)$$

The determination of the complementary solution is less straightforward; there is no simple method of separating variables. Let us then directly make use of the method of assuming an exponential solution $I_0\epsilon^{st}$, using the concept of impedance introduced in the previous sections. It was seen in the discussion of the RC circuit that we may work directly with the integrodifferential equation of Eq. (3.39), obviating the necessity of reducing it to the differential equation of Eq. (3.40).   Equation (3.39) then becomes

$$LsI_0\epsilon^{st} + RI_0\epsilon^{st} + \frac{1}{Cs} I_0\epsilon^{st} = E \qquad (3.42)$$

or

$$\left(Ls + R + \frac{1}{Cs}\right) I_0\epsilon^{st} = E. \qquad (3.43)$$

We note in passing that at the forcing frequency ($s = 0$)† the impedance

$$Z(s) = Ls + R + \frac{1}{Cs} \qquad (3.44)$$

is infinite [$s = 0$ is a pole of $Z(s)$], so that the forced part of the response (the particular solution) is zero.   This confirms our earlier result [Eq. (3.41)].

To find the natural behavior, we set the right-hand side of Eq. (3.43) equal to zero,

$$\left(Ls + R + \frac{1}{Cs}\right) I_0\epsilon^{st} = 0. \qquad (3.45)$$

Since ϵ^{st} is never zero we may divide by it to obtain

$$\left(Ls + R + \frac{1}{Cs}\right) I_0 = 0 \qquad (3.46)$$

and if the complementary solution is not to be identically zero it follows that

$$Ls + R + \frac{1}{Cs} = 0. \qquad (3.47)$$

That is, the natural frequency must be a zero of the impedance $Z(s)$.

Equation (3.47) may be written

$$Ls^2 + Rs + \frac{1}{C} = 0. \qquad (3.48)$$

This is a quadratic *algebraic* equation on s.   It therefore has *two* roots which are given explicitly by

$$s_{1,2} = -\frac{R}{2L} \pm \sqrt{\frac{R^2}{4L^2} - \frac{1}{LC}}. \qquad (3.49)$$

† For E may be written $E\epsilon^{st}$, where $s = 0$.

Clearly s_1 and s_2 may be real and unequal, real and equal, or a pair of complex conjugates. These cases will be discussed below. First, though, we consider the significance of having *two* values of s. Which should we use in our complementary solution? The answer is that we use both. We sought a value of s which would satisfy Eq. (3.48) and found two. Either of these values will yield a solution of the equilibrium equation. Thus we have the two solutions

$$i_{c1} = A\epsilon^{s_1 t} \tag{3.50}$$

and

$$i_{c2} = B\epsilon^{s_2 t} \tag{3.51}$$

where A and B are arbitrary constants. Now if two functions are solutions of a linear homogeneous differential equation their sum is also a solution. This follows from the definition of linearity. Thus

$$i = A\epsilon^{s_1 t} + B\epsilon^{s_2 t} \tag{3.52}$$

is the complementary solution of Eq. (3.39). [One may verify by a direct calculation that Eq. (3.52) satisfies Eq. (3.40) when s_1 and s_2 are given by Eq. (3.49).] Since the particular solution is zero, Eq. (3.52) also represents the general solution.

We now turn to the investigation of the three cases for the pair of roots s_1 and s_2 (that is, real and unequal, real and equal, a pair of complex conjugates).

I. *Roots Real and Unequal.* The solution in this case is given by Eq. (3.52). The values of A and B are determined from the initial conditions. (The initial conditions are the initial charge on, or voltage v_{c0} across, the capacitor, and the initial current i_0 through the inductor.) We illustrate by means of an example.

Example 3.1. Determine the current which flows in the circuit of Fig. 3.6 for $t > 0$. The initial voltage across the capacitor and the current through the inductor are zero. Assume that $L = 1$ henry, $C = 1$ farad, $R = 3\ \Omega$, $E = 4$ volts. Also find the voltage across the capacitor for $t > 0$.

Solution. From Eq. (3.49) the zeros of $Z(s)$ are

$$s_{1,2} = -\frac{3}{2} \pm \sqrt{\frac{9}{4} - \frac{1}{1}} = \frac{-3 \pm \sqrt{5}}{2}$$

and

$$s_1 = -0.382, \qquad s_2 = -2.618.$$

Thus

$$i(t) = A\epsilon^{-0.382t} + B\epsilon^{-2.618t}.$$

To evaluate the coefficients A and B we write $i(0) = 0$ and hence

$$0 = A + B. \tag{a}$$

One more equation is necessary to determine A and B. A suitable equation would be obtained if we knew the initial rate of change of the current. This can be found by writing the voltage equation around the loop at $t = 0+\dagger$ (remembering that $i(0) = 0$ and hence $Ri = 0$):

$$E = L\left(\frac{di}{dt}\right)_{t=0+} + v_{c0}.$$

Hence

$$\left(\frac{di}{dt}\right)_{t=0+} = \frac{E - v_{c0}}{L} = \frac{4 - 0}{1} = 4.$$

But

$$\frac{di}{dt} = -0.382A\epsilon^{-0.382t} - 2.618B\epsilon^{-2.618t}$$

and

$$\left(\frac{di}{dt}\right)_{t=0+} = -0.382A - 2.618B.$$

Thus

$$4 = -0.382A - 2.618B. \tag{b}$$

Solving Eqs. (a) and (b) for A and B yields

$$A = 1.788, \qquad B = -1.788$$

and hence

$$i(t) = 1.788\epsilon^{-0.382t} - 1.788\epsilon^{-2.618t}, \qquad t > 0.$$

This equation is plotted in Fig. 3.7a.

The voltage v_c across the capacitor is given by

$$v_c = v_{c0} + \frac{1}{C}\int_0^t i\, dt = 0 + \int_0^t (1.788\epsilon^{-0.382t} - 1.788\epsilon^{-2.618t})\, dt$$
$$= 4.683(1 - \epsilon^{-0.382t}) - 0.683(1 - \epsilon^{-2.618t}), \qquad t > 0.$$

This is plotted in Fig. 3.7b.

One can also evaluate the constants A and B in the general case.   Thus if s_1 and s_2 are two distinct roots of Eq. (3.48),

$$i = A\epsilon^{s_1 t} + B\epsilon^{s_2 t}$$

is the general solution.   As in the numerical example, the initial conditions require that A and B satisfy the two linear algebraic equations

$$A + B = i(0)$$
$$s_1 A + s_2 B = \frac{E - v_{c0}}{L}. \tag{3.53}$$

Solving these equations simultaneously yields

$$A = \frac{i(0)s_2 - (E - v_{c0})/L}{s_2 - s_1}, \qquad B = \frac{(E - v_{c0})/L - i(0)s_1}{s_2 - s_1} \tag{3.54}$$

$\dagger$ The symbols $0-$ and $0+$ are used to resolve ambiguities in cases where there is a discontinuity at $t = 0$.   The symbol $0-$ refers to the time immediately preceding the discontinuity; $0+$ is the time immediately following the discontinuity.   Mathematically, $0- = \lim_{\substack{t\to 0 \\ t<0}} t$, $0+ = \lim_{\substack{t\to 0 \\ t>0}} t$.

and hence the general solution is

$$i(t) = \frac{i(0)s_2 - (E - v_{c0})/L}{s_2 - s_1} \epsilon^{s_1 t} + \frac{(E - v_{c0})/L - i(0)s_1}{s_2 - s_1} \epsilon^{s_2 t}. \quad (3.55)$$

In practice it is easier to recall the general form of Eq. (3.52) and to

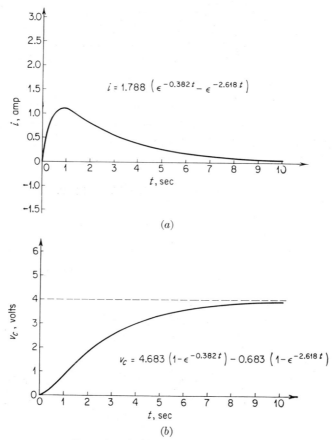

FIG. 3.7. Waveforms in Example 3.1.

evaluate the coefficients A and B in each numerical example rather than to try to memorize Eqs. (3.53) to (3.55).

II. *Roots Real and Equal.* Let $\bar{s}$ be the common value of the two roots. Then from Eq. (3.52) it appears that

$$i = A\epsilon^{\bar{s}t} + B\epsilon^{\bar{s}t} = C\epsilon^{\bar{s}t}$$

(where $C = A + B$) is the general solution. But we have only *one* arbitrary constant C whereas there are *two* independent initial conditions to be satisfied (the initial current in the coil and the initial voltage across the capacitor which determines the initial rate change of current in the circuit). Thus we must find another function distinct from $\epsilon^{\bar{s}t}$ which satisfies the equilibrium equation (3.40).

In order to determine this second solution we return to Eq. (3.55) which we may write as

$$- \frac{E - v_{c0}}{L} \left[\frac{\epsilon^{s_1 t}}{s_2 - s_1} - \frac{\epsilon^{s_2 t}}{s_2 - s_1} \right] + i(0) \left[\frac{s_2 \epsilon^{s_1 t}}{s_2 - s_1} - \frac{s_1 \epsilon^{s_2 t}}{s_2 - s_1} \right]. \quad (3.56)$$

Now if we let $s_1 = s_2$ the terms in brackets become zero over zero; that is

$$\lim_{s_2 \to s_1} \left[\frac{\epsilon^{s_1 t} - \epsilon^{s_2 t}}{s_2 - s_1} \right] = \frac{0}{0}, \qquad \lim_{s_2 \to s_1} \left[\frac{s_2 \epsilon^{s_1 t} - s_1 \epsilon^{s_2 t}}{s_2 - s_1} \right] = \frac{0}{0}.$$

These are indeterminate forms which may be evaluated by L'Hospital's rule.† We shall consider only the first of these forms, as the evaluation of the other leads to essentially the same result. Thus

$$\lim_{s_2 \to s_1} \frac{\epsilon^{s_1 t} - \epsilon^{s_2 t}}{s_2 - s_1} = \lim_{s_2 \to s_1} \frac{\dfrac{d}{ds_2} (\epsilon^{s_1 t} - \epsilon^{s_2 t})}{\dfrac{d}{ds_2} (s_2 - s_1)}$$

$$= \lim_{s_2 \to s_1} \frac{-t\epsilon^{s_2 t}}{1} = -t\epsilon^{s_1 t}. \quad (3.57)$$

Hence if $\bar{s}$ is the value of the double root we see that $\epsilon^{\bar{s}t}$ and $t\epsilon^{\bar{s}t}$ are both solutions of the equilibrium equation, and hence

$$i(t) = A\epsilon^{\bar{s}t} + Bt\epsilon^{\bar{s}t} \quad (3.58)$$

is the general solution. [One may verify that Eq. (3.58) satisfies Eq. (3.40), by direct calculation.] We illustrate this situation with an example.

Example 3.2. Determine the current which flows in the circuit of Fig. 3.6 for $t > 0$ where

$R = 2\ \Omega$
$L = 1$ henry
$C = 1$ farad
$i_0 = 0$
$v_{c0} = 0$
$E = 4$ volts.

Also compute the voltage across the capacitor for $t > 0$.

† See, for example, M. G. Salvadori and K. S. Miller, "The Mathematical Solution of Engineering Problems," rev. print., Columbia University Press, New York, 1953, p. 33. If $\lim_{x \to a} f(x)/g(x) = 0/0$, then L'Hospital's rule states that $\lim_{x \to a} f(x)/g(x) = f'(a)/g'(a)$, provided $g'(a) \neq 0$.

Solution.   We first obtain the natural frequency from Eq. (3.49),

$$\tilde{s} = -\tfrac{2}{2} \pm \sqrt{\tfrac{4}{4} - \tfrac{4}{1}} = -1.$$

Thus

$$i(t) = A\epsilon^{-t} + Bt\epsilon^{-t}$$

is the general solution.   Since $i_0 = 0$, we have

$$i(0) = i_0 = 0 = A.$$

The constant A is therefore zero.   To determine B we proceed as in Example 3.1 to find that

$$\left(\frac{di}{dt}\right)_{t=0+} = \frac{E - v_{c0}}{L} = 4. \qquad (a)$$

But

$$\frac{di}{dt} = B\epsilon^{-t} - Bt\epsilon^{-t}$$

and

$$\left(\frac{di}{dt}\right)_{t=0+} = B. \qquad (b)$$

Hence Eqs. (a) and (b) imply $B = 4$, and

$$i(t) = 4t\epsilon^{-t}$$

is the general solution of the equilibrium equation.   This equation is plotted in Fig. 3.8a.

The voltage across the capacitor is given by

$$v_c = v_{c0} + \frac{1}{C}\int_0^t i\,dt = 0 + \int_0^t 4t\epsilon^{-t}\,dt = 4 - 4(1 + t)\epsilon^{-t}.$$

This is plotted in Fig. 3.8b.

III. *Roots Complex Conjugates.*   The solution in this case is again given by Eq. (3.52) as

$$i(t) = A\epsilon^{s_1 t} + B\epsilon^{s_2 t}.$$

However we may more easily appreciate the behavior of this solution if we rearrange the terms slightly.   Let†

$$s_1 = -\alpha + j\beta, \qquad s_2 = -\alpha - j\beta \qquad (3.59)$$

where

$$\alpha = \frac{R}{2L}, \qquad \beta = \sqrt{\frac{1}{LC} - \frac{R^2}{4L^2}}. \qquad (3.60)$$

Then

$$i = A\epsilon^{-\alpha t + j\beta t} + B\epsilon^{-\alpha t - j\beta t} = \epsilon^{-\alpha t}(A\epsilon^{j\beta t} + B\epsilon^{-j\beta t}). \qquad (3.61)$$

This may be further modified by making use of the relation (to be derived in Sec. 3.5)

$$\epsilon^{j\theta} = \cos\theta + j\sin\theta. \qquad (3.62)$$

† The symbol j is used to represent $\sqrt{-1}$.   This is done in electric-circuit analysis since the usual symbol i is reserved for current.   We call s_2 the *conjugate* of s_1 and frequently write s_1^* ($=s_2$) to denote this conjugate.   For a more detailed discussion of complex numbers see Secs. 3.5 and 4.5.

Thus

$$i(t) = \epsilon^{-\alpha t}[A \cos \beta t + jA \sin \beta t + B \cos \beta t - jB \sin \beta t]$$
$$= \epsilon^{-\alpha t}[(A + B) \cos \beta t + j(A - B) \sin \beta t]. \qquad (3.63)$$

Note that the current must be real, for imaginary currents have no meaning. Therefore, $A + B$ and $j(A - B)$ must be real numbers, say

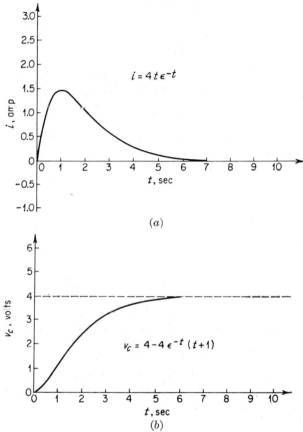

$$i = 4t\epsilon^{-t}$$

(a)

$$v_c = 4 - 4\epsilon^{-t}(t+1)$$

(b)

FIG. 3.8. Waveforms in Example 3.2.

D and F, respectively. Thus we may write Eq. (3.63) in the form

$$i(t) = \epsilon^{-\alpha t}(D \cos \beta t + F \sin \beta t) \qquad (3.64)$$

where D and F are now our two arbitrary constants.

Equation (3.64) thus represents the general solution of the equilibrium equations. [One may verify that Eq. (3.64) satisfies Eq. (3.40), by a direct calculation.] It is also possible to write Eq. (3.64) in the *phase-angle form*

$$i(t) = H\epsilon^{-\alpha t} \cos (\beta t + \theta). \qquad (3.65)$$

To find the relation between the arbitrary constants H and θ of Eq. (3.65) and D and F of Eq. (3.64) we write

$$H \cos (\beta t + \theta) = H[\cos \beta t \cos \theta - \sin \beta t \sin \theta]$$

by using the trigonometric identity for the cosine of the sum of two angles.   Equating this to $D \cos \beta t + F \sin \beta t$ implies

$$H \cos \theta = D \tag{3.66a}$$

and

$$-H \sin \theta = F. \tag{3.66b}$$

Equation (3.65) clearly shows that the response in this case (the so-called *oscillatory* case) is a sinusoidal wave multiplied by an exponential. An example follows to illustrate the method of solution.

Example 3.3.   Find the current in the circuit of Fig. 3.6 for $t > 0$.   Also find the voltage across the capacitor.   Assume

$R = 1 \ \Omega$
$L = 1$ henry
$C = 1$ farad
$i_0 = 0$
$v_{c0} = 0$
$E = 4$ volts

Solution.   From Eq. (3.49) we find

$$s_{1,2} = -\tfrac{1}{2} \pm \sqrt{\tfrac{1}{4} - \tfrac{1}{1}} = -0.500 \pm j0.866$$

whence

$$i(t) = H\epsilon^{-0.500t} \cos (0.866t + \theta). \tag{a}$$

The constants H and θ are again determined by the initial conditions.   We have

$$i_0 = i(0) = 0 = H \cos \theta.$$

Thus $H = 0$ or $\cos \theta = 0$.   Now $H = 0$ would result in a complementary solution identically zero, and we could not hope to satisfy the second initial condition.   Thus we must have $\cos \theta = 0$ or $\theta = \pi/2$.

As in the previous examples,

$$\left(\frac{di}{dt}\right)_{t=0+} = \frac{E - v_{c0}}{L} = 4.$$

But from Eq. (a)

$$\frac{di}{dt} = -0.866H\epsilon^{-0.500t} \sin (0.866t + \theta) - 0.500H\epsilon^{-0.500t} \cos (0.866t + \theta)$$

and

$$\left(\frac{di}{dt}\right)_{t=0+} = -0.866H \sin \theta - 0.500H \cos \theta$$

$$= -0.866H \sin \frac{\pi}{2} = -0.866H$$

since $H \cos \theta = 0$.

Hence H can be determined from the equation

$$4 = -0.866H$$

as

$$H = -4.62.$$

Therefore

$$i(t) = -4.62\epsilon^{-0.500t} \cos\left(0.866t + \frac{\pi}{2}\right)$$

is the general solution of the equilibrium equation.   The above equation is plotted in Fig. 3.9a.

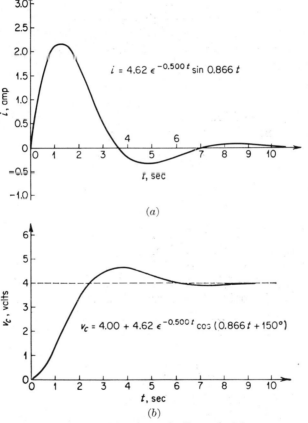

$$i = 4.62\,\epsilon^{-0.500\,t} \sin 0.866\,t$$

(a)

$$v_c = 4.00 + 4.62\,\epsilon^{-0.500\,t} \cos(0.866\,t + 150°)$$

(b)

FIG. 3.9. Waveforms in Example 3.3.

The voltage across the capacitor is

$$v_c = v_{c0} + \int_0^t i\,dt = 0 + \int_0^t \left[-4.62\epsilon^{-0.500t} \cos\left(0.866t + \frac{\pi}{2}\right) \right] dt$$

$$= 4 + 4.62\epsilon^{-0.500t} \cos\left(0.866t + \frac{5\pi}{6}\right)$$

and this result is plotted in Fig. 3.9b.

Summary.   Because the results of this section are scattered through many pages it is helpful to collect them in one place.

The response of an RLC circuit to a suddenly applied constant voltage may have one of three forms, depending on the nature of the roots of $Z(s) = 0$, that is, on the value of $R^2/4L^2 - 1/LC$.

Case 1. $R^2/4L^2 - 1/LC > 0$.   The impedance function has two real and unequal roots which are negative.   The current is given by

$$i(t) = A\epsilon^{s_1 t} + B\epsilon^{s_2 t} \tag{3.52}$$

where

$$s_{1,2} = -\frac{R}{2L} \pm \sqrt{\frac{R^2}{4L^2} - \frac{1}{LC}} \tag{3.49}$$

and the coefficients A and B are determined by the initial conditions (current through the inductance and voltage across the capacitor).

This is called the *overdamped* case, because the current, after initially increasing, decreases to zero without going negative.

Case 2. $R^2/4L^2 - 1/LC = 0$.   The impedance function has two equal roots which are negative.   The current is given by

$$i(t) = A\epsilon^{\bar{s}t} + Bt\epsilon^{\bar{s}t} \tag{3.58}$$

where

$$\bar{s} = -\frac{R}{2L}.$$

The coefficients A and B are determined from the initial conditions.

This is called the *critically* damped (or sometimes *deadbeat*) case, because it separates Cases 1 and 3.

Case 3. $R^2/4L^2 - 1/LC < 0$.   The impedance function has two complex conjugate roots.   The current is usually expressed in the form

$$i(t) = H\epsilon^{-\alpha t} \cos{(\beta t + \theta)} \tag{3.65}$$

where

$$\alpha = \frac{R}{2L}, \qquad \beta = \sqrt{\frac{1}{LC} - \frac{R^2}{4L^2}}. \tag{3.60}$$

The values of H and θ are determined from the initial conditions.

This is called the *underdamped* or *oscillatory* case, because the current, after reaching its first peak, does not return directly to zero but rather crosses the t axis regularly with ever-diminishing amplitudes (for $\alpha > 0$).

The quantity $1/\sqrt{LC}$ is sometimes called the *undamped frequency*† ω_0, and so we may write

$$\beta^2 = \omega_0{}^2 - \alpha^2.$$

† Strictly speaking, this should be called the undamped *imaginary* frequency $j\omega_0$ because j is always associated with β.   However, earlier usage, before generalized frequencies were considered, led to the name *undamped frequency,* which still prevails.

The term "undamped frequency" results from the fact that, as R approaches zero, β approaches ω_0.

3.4. Transient and Steady-state Response. It has been observed that the response of a network consists of two components, the forced response and the natural behavior. In circuits containing dissipative elements (resistors), the natural behavior always decays to zero. That is, the zeros of the impedance function are complex numbers with negative real parts. Under these circumstances we may consider the natural behavior to be a *transient* component, that is, one which eventually disappears with time. After the natural behavior has decayed away, the response of the circuit consists of the forced component alone. Thus, it is seen that the transient serves to join the initial values of current and voltage with the values given by the forced response. If the initial values were equal to the values of the forced response, there would be no difference to be "bridged."

If the forcing function varies periodically, it is often found (see Chap. 4) that the forced response is also periodic. In this case the forced response is referred to as the *steady-state* solution.†

It will be seen later that not every network has a steady-state component, so that breaking a solution into two components, transient and steady-state, is not always meaningful. This should be carefully recognized, lest one attempt to find steady-state components when there are none.

A useful observation which aids in determining the response of networks excited by forcing functions which are constant concerns the initial and final behavior of inductances and capacitances. Since the current through an inductance and the voltage across a capacitance cannot change instantly, an inductance initially acts as a current source, the value of which is the initial current through the inductance; and a capacitance acts as a voltage source, the initial value of which is the voltage across the capacitance. On the other hand, when the responses settle to their final values, there is no voltage drop across an inductance (since $di/dt = 0$), and so it acts as a short circuit; the current through a capacitance is zero ($dv/dt = 0$), and so it acts as an open circuit. This latter rule is particularly helpful in determining final values of response.

3.5. Sinusoidal Forcing Functions. We have already considered forcing functions which are constants. Now we shall devote our attention to another class of functions which are very important in electrical engineering. These are the sinusoidal forcing functions. By sinusoidal functions we mean those which have the form of sine waves. Thus a cosine function as well as a function of the form $A \sin (\omega t + \theta)$, where A, ω, and θ are constants, is also considered to be a sinusoidal function.

† Sometimes the *final value* of the forced component for a constant forcing function is also called the steady-state solution.

Before considering circuits to which sinusoidal functions are applied, it will be convenient to point out a very important relationship between sinusoidal functions and exponential functions known as *Euler's formula*. This result and its corollaries will also be frequently used in the next chapter.

We recall from the calculus that a function $f(t)$ may be expanded in a power series by Maclaurin's formula,

$$f(t) = f(0) + f'(0)t + f''(0)\frac{t^2}{2!} + f'''(0)\frac{t^3}{3!} + \cdots \qquad (3.67)$$

provided that $f(t)$ has derivatives of all orders.   For example,

$$\epsilon^t = 1 + t + \frac{t^2}{2!} + \frac{t^3}{3!} + \cdots \qquad (3.68)$$

$$\cos t = 1 - \frac{t^2}{2!} + \frac{t^4}{4!} - \frac{t^6}{6!} + \cdots \qquad (3.69)$$

$$\sin t = t - \frac{t^3}{3!} + \frac{t^5}{5!} - \frac{t^7}{7!} + \cdots . \qquad (3.70)$$

Now if in the expression for ϵ^t we replace t by $j\theta$ then

$$\epsilon^{j\theta} = 1 + (j\theta) + \frac{(j\theta)^2}{2!} + \frac{(j\theta)^3}{3!} + \cdots . \qquad (3.71)$$

Recalling that

$$j^2 = j^6 = j^{10} = \cdots = -1$$
$$j^3 = j^7 = j^{11} = \cdots = -j$$
$$j^4 = j^8 = j^{12} = \cdots = +1$$
$$j^5 = j^9 = j^{13} = \cdots = +j$$

we may write Eq. (3.71) as

$$\epsilon^{j\theta} = 1 + j\theta - \frac{\theta^2}{2!} - j\frac{\theta^3}{3!} + \frac{\theta^4}{4!} + j\frac{\theta^5}{5!} - \cdots . \qquad (3.72)$$

On collecting real and imaginary parts the above expression becomes

$$\epsilon^{j\theta} = \left(1 - \frac{\theta^2}{2!} + \frac{\theta^4}{4!} - \cdots \right) + j\left(\theta - \frac{\theta^3}{3!} + \frac{\theta^5}{5!} - \cdots \right) \qquad (3.72a)$$

which, on comparison with the expansions for sine and cosine given above, becomes

$$\epsilon^{j\theta} = \cos \theta + j \sin \theta. \qquad (3.73)$$

This is *Euler's formula*.

If we replace θ by $-\theta$ in Eq. (3.73) we obtain

$$\epsilon^{-j\theta} = \cos \theta - j \sin \theta. \qquad (3.74)$$

On adding and subtracting Eqs. (3.73) and (3.74) we obtain

$$\cos \theta = \frac{\epsilon^{j\theta} + \epsilon^{-j\theta}}{2} \tag{3.75}$$

and

$$\sin \theta = \frac{\epsilon^{j\theta} - \epsilon^{-j\theta}}{2j} \tag{3.76}$$

which express the trigonometric functions in terms of the complex exponentials.

We now wish to mention a few facts about complex numbers. A more detailed analysis will be relegated to Chap. 4. Consider a complex number A,

$$A = B + jC$$

where B and C are real numbers. We use the notation Re $[A]$ to designate the *real part* of A, viz.,

$$\text{Re } [A] = B$$

and we use the notation Im $[A]$ to designate the *imaginary part* of A, viz.,

$$\text{Im } [A] = C.$$

For example,

$$\text{Re } [\epsilon^{j\theta}] = \cos \theta$$

and

$$\text{Im } [\epsilon^{j\theta}] = \sin \theta.$$

The operations "take real part of" and "take imaginary part of" are linear operators since

$$\text{Re } [\alpha A_1 + \beta A_2] = \alpha \text{ Re } [A_1] + \beta \text{ Re } [A_2]$$

and

$$\text{Im } [\alpha A_1 + \beta A_2] = \alpha \text{ Im } [A_1] + \beta \text{ Im } [A_2]$$

where A_1 and A_2 are any two complex numbers and α and β are *real* numbers.† Also if $f(t)$ is a complex-valued function of the real variable t, then

$$\frac{d}{dt} \text{ Re } [f(t)] = \text{Re } \left[\frac{d}{dt} f(t) \right].$$

For, let

$$f(t) = g(t) + jh(t)$$

where $g(t)$ and $h(t)$ are real-valued functions of the real variable t. Then

$$\frac{df}{dt} = g' + jh'$$

† It is well to note that the foregoing properties do *not* in general imply that
$$\text{Re } [A_1] \text{ Re } [A_2] = \text{Re } [A_1 A_2].$$

and

$$\text{Re}\left[\frac{df}{dt}\right] = g' = \frac{d}{dt}\,\text{Re}\,[f] = \frac{dg}{dt}.$$

Similarly,

$$\frac{d}{dt}\,\text{Im}\,[f(t)] = \text{Im}\left[\frac{d}{dt}f(t)\right],$$

and of course the appropriate formulas hold for higher derivatives.

Suppose now that we have a linear differential equation with constant coefficients, say

$$\frac{d^2x}{dt^2} + \frac{dx}{dt} + x = \cos\omega t. \tag{3.77}$$

This may be written as

$$\frac{d^2x}{dt^2} + \frac{dx}{dt} + x = \text{Re}\,[\epsilon^{j\omega t}]. \tag{3.77a}$$

Sometimes it is convenient to write

$$z(t) = x(t) + jy(t),$$

that is, to let $x(t)$ be the real part of some complex function such as $z(t)$. The remarks of the previous paragraph imply that

$$\text{Re}\left[\frac{d^2z}{dt^2} + \frac{dz}{dt} + z\right] = \text{Re}\,[\epsilon^{j\omega t}]. \tag{3.77b}$$

Thus the real part of a solution of Eq. (3.78),

$$\frac{d^2z}{dt^2} + \frac{dz}{dt} + z = \epsilon^{j\omega t} \tag{3.78}$$

is also a solution of Eq. (3.77), for in order that both sides of Eq. (3.78) be equal, their real and imaginary parts must separately be equal.

We have already indicated that the natural behavior of networks represented by linear differential equations is the sum of exponential terms. One might suspect that networks having exponential forcing functions have exponential forced responses. This is, in general, true. The forced response of Eq. (3.78) has the form $I_0\epsilon^{j\omega t}$. Analytically this result stems from the fact that the derivatives of sinusoidal functions are also sinusoidal functions of the same frequency and that the sum of sinusoids of the same frequency is also a sinusoid of that frequency.

Examples will be given in Secs. 3.7 to 3.9 below of applications of this property of sinusoidal forcing functions to the determination of steady-state solutions for various circuits.

3.6. Complex Frequencies and the Complex Plane. We have already referred to the term s in the expression ϵ^{st} as the *frequency*. This is fairly modern usage. Originally, the term ω in the expression $\epsilon^{j\omega t}$ was called the frequency. Unhappily, this ambiguity in definition still exists.   To be precise, ω should be called the imaginary component of generalized frequency, and this is done when s is a complex number, say

$$s = \sigma + j\omega. \tag{3.79}$$

However, when s is a pure imaginary, say $s = j\omega$ (that is, $\sigma = 0$), we call ω (and *not* $j\omega$) the frequency.   This ambiguity is actually not as troublesome as one might suspect, for the usage is always clear from the context.   When there is any possibility of confusion we refer to s as the *complex frequency* and to ω as the *angular frequency*.

The concept of complex frequency is quite useful because it brings out the essential similarity among solutions which are simple exponentials, damped sinusoids, growing sinusoids, and undamped sinusoids.

As will be seen later, there are occasions when it is convenient to indicate complex frequencies in graphical form. This is done on the *complex frequency plane*, or s plane, as shown in Fig. 3.10. The horizontal axis is the *real* axis and the vertical axis is the *imaginary* axis.

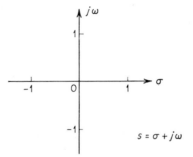

FIG. 3.10.   Complex   frequency plane, or s plane

The time functions corresponding to various points on this plane are shown in Fig. 3.11.   This figure shows that points on the $j\omega$ axis (purely imaginary frequencies) represent sinusoidal time functions, whereas those on the σ axis represent exponential time functions.   Points in the *right-half plane*, for which Re $[s] > 0$, represent increasing exponentials, or exponentially increasing sinusoids, whereas those in the *left-half plane*, for which Re $[s] < 0$, represent decreasing exponentials, or exponentially decreasing sinusoids.   The lower half of the complex plane represents frequencies which are conjugates of those in the upper half, and so, since Re $[\epsilon^s]$ = Re $[\epsilon^{s*}]$,[†] frequencies in the lower half of the complex plane represent the same time functions as the conjugate frequencies in the upper half of the complex plane.

As an indication of the utility of the complex plane in analysis, let us plot on the complex plane the natural frequencies (or poles of the impedance function) of the networks discussed in Examples 3.1 to 3.3 (see Table 3.1).   Note that these networks are the same, except for the values of R.   Also shown are additional values of natural frequencies corresponding to other values of R.

It is seen that for large values of R (overdamped cases) the poles lie on the axis of reals.   As R is decreased, the poles move closer together,

[†] We denote the conjugate of s by s^*.   See p. 103.

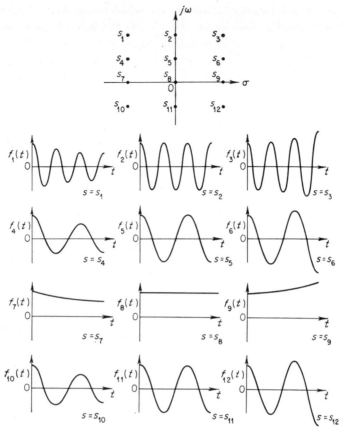

FIG. 3.11. Time functions corresponding to various values of complex frequency

still on the real axis, until the two roots coalesce into a double root on the real axis. This is the critically damped case. For smaller values of R (undamped cases) the roots occur as complex conjugates, corresponding to damped sinusoidal time functions. Finally, for $R = 0$, the poles lie on the real axis, corresponding to undamped sinusoids.

TABLE 3.1

Example	R	L	C	Natural frequencies
3.1	3	1	1	$s_1 = -0.382,\ s_2 = -2.618$
3.2	2	1	1	$s_3 = s_4 = -1$
3.3	1	1	1	$s_{5,6} = -0.500 \pm j0.866$
	1.5	1	1	$s_{7,8} = -0.750 \pm j0.662$
	0.5	1	1	$s_{9,10} = -0.250 \pm j0.969$
	0	1	1	$s_{11,12} = \pm j$

Observe that the roots lie either on the negative real axis or on the semi-circle shown (see Fig. 3.12).   These paths, taken together, are known as the *root locus* for the circuit considered as R is varied.   As might be expected, the root locus lies entirely in the left-hand plane, or on the $j\omega$ axis.   This is because the roots lying in the left-half plane correspond to decreasing functions of time, and hence decreasing energy (the energy

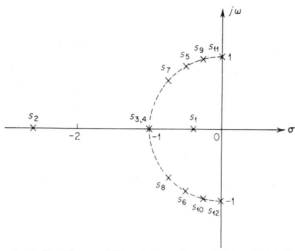

FIG. 3.12. Root locus of Fig. 3.6 as R is varied (see Table 3.1).

being dissipated in R).   Roots in the right-half plane correspond to increasing time functions, and hence increasing energy, and so cannot be natural frequencies of dissipative circuits.

3.7. The Steady-state Response of a Single-loop RLC Circuit.   We shall now show how the principles discussed above may be applied to the determination of the particular solution (or in this case, the steady-state response) of an RLC circuit excited by a sinusoidal voltage source.   This will be done by means of an example.

Example 3.4.   Determine the steady-state current in the circuit of Fig. 3.13 when the applied voltage is given by

$$e = E_0 \cos \omega t.$$

Solution.   The equilibrium equation for this circuit is

$$L \frac{di}{dt} + Ri + \frac{1}{C} \int_0^t i \, dt + v_{c0} = E_0 \cos \omega t. \quad (a)$$

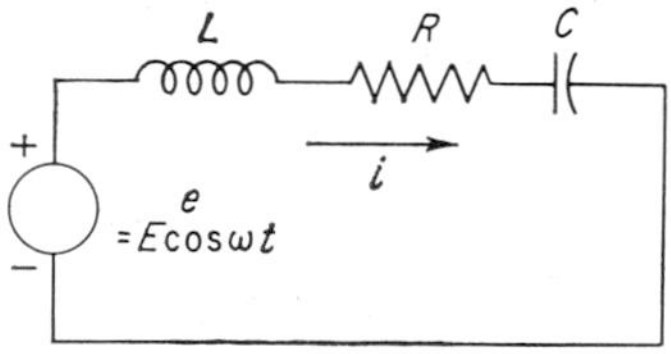

FIG. 3.13. Circuit for Example 3.4.

We now replace $\cos \omega t$ by $\epsilon^{j\omega t}$ to write the above equation as

$$L \frac{di}{dt} + Ri + \frac{1}{C} \int_0^t i \, dt + v_{c0} = E_0 \epsilon^{j\omega t} \qquad (b)$$

recalling that only the real part of the solution will be of interest.   That is, if i is a solution of Eq. (b), Re $[i]$ is the solution of Eq. (a).

We now assume that $i = I_0\epsilon^{j\omega t}$. Equation (b) then becomes (neglecting initial conditions as before)

$$j\omega L I_0 \epsilon^{j\omega t} + R I_0 \epsilon^{j\omega t} + \frac{1}{j\omega C} I_0 \epsilon^{j\omega t} = E_0 \epsilon^{j\omega t}.$$

Since $\epsilon^{j\omega t}$ is never zero, we may divide both sides by $\epsilon^{j\omega t}$ to obtain

$$j\omega L I_0 + R I_0 + \frac{1}{j\omega C} I_0 = E_0$$

or

$$\left(j\omega L + R + \frac{1}{j\omega C} \right) I_0 = E_0.$$

The term $j\omega L + R + 1/j\omega C$ is the impedance $Z(s)$ of the circuit evaluated at $s = j\omega$. Thus

$$I_0 = \frac{E_0}{Z(j\omega)} = \frac{E_0}{j\omega L + R + 1/j\omega C}.$$

This means that

$$\mathrm{Re}\,[i] = \mathrm{Re}\,[I_0 \epsilon^{j\omega t}] = \mathrm{Re}\left[\frac{E_0}{j\omega L + R + 1/j\omega L}\, \epsilon^{j\omega t} \right] \qquad (c)$$

is the steady-state solution of Eq. (a). The technique of manipulating this complex expression will be explained in the next chapter.

It is to be noted that since this is the steady-state response of the circuit, the above expression represents the current only for large values of t, or, alternatively, it is assumed that the switch was closed at $t \ll 0$ (a long time ago).

3.8. General Case of the RLC Circuit.

We shall now make use of the results of the previous section to determine the current which flows in a circuit when a sinusoidal voltage source is suddenly applied.

Example 3.5. In the circuit of Fig. 3.14 the switch is thrown at $t = 0$. The initial voltage on the capacitor is -0.3 volt and $i(0)$ is zero. Let the forcing function be

$$e = 1 \sin 10t = 1 \cos\left(10t - \frac{\pi}{2} \right) = \mathrm{Re}\,[\epsilon^{j(10t - \pi/2)}].$$

Assume that $R = 0.250\ \Omega$, $L = 1$ henry, $C = 1$ farad.

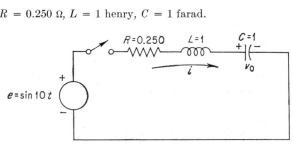

FIG. 3.14. Circuit for Example 3.5.

Solution. The equilibrium equation, Eq. (b) of Example 3.4, thus becomes

$$\frac{di}{dt} + 0.250i + \int_0^t i\,dt - 0.3 = \mathrm{Re}\,[\epsilon^{j(10t - \pi/2)}]$$

The steady-state current (particular solution, or forced response) is given immediately by Eq. (c) of Example 3.4 as

$$i_p = \text{Re } [I] = \text{Re } \left[\frac{1}{0.250 + j10 + 1/j10} \, \epsilon^{j(10t - \pi/2)} \right], \quad t > 0.$$

It can be shown by methods to be developed in the next chapter that

$$i_p = -0.101 \cos (10t + 1.4°), \quad t > 0.$$

The transient component (complementary solution or natural behavior) depends on the roots of the impedance function. Since

$$\frac{R^2}{4L^2} - \frac{1}{LC} < 0,$$

the two roots are imaginary. Thus from Eq. (3.65),

$$i_c = H\epsilon^{-\alpha t} \cos (\beta t + \theta)$$

where

$$\alpha = \frac{R}{2L} = 0.125$$

and

$$\beta = \sqrt{\frac{1}{LC} - \frac{R^2}{4L^2}} = \sqrt{\frac{1}{1 \times 1} - \frac{(0.25)^2}{4}} = 0.992.$$

Hence

$$i_s = H\epsilon^{-0.125t} \cos (0.992t + \theta).$$

The complete response is, therefore,

$$i(t) = H\epsilon^{-0.125t} \cos (0.992t + \theta) - 0.101 \cos (10t + 1.4°).$$

To evaluate the constants H and θ we note that

$$i(0) = 0 = H \cos \theta - 0.101 \cos 1.4°$$
$$= H \cos \theta - 0.101$$

since $\cos 1.4° = 1$ to three significant figures. Hence

$$H \cos \theta = 0.101. \quad (a)$$

We also have

$$\frac{di}{dt} = H[-0.992\epsilon^{-0.125t} \sin (0.992t + \theta) - 0.125\epsilon^{-0.125t} \cos (0.992t + \theta)]$$
$$+ 0.101 \times 10 \sin (10t + 1.4°)$$

and at $t = 0+$,

$$\left(\frac{di}{dt} \right)_{t=0+} = -H(0.992 \sin \theta + 0.125 \cos \theta) + 1.01 \sin 1.4°.$$

But, from the original equilibrium equation,

$$\left(\frac{di}{dt} \right)_{t=0+} = \frac{e(0) - v_{c0}}{L} = \frac{0 + 0.3}{1} = 0.300.$$

Therefore,

$$0.300 = -0.992H \sin \theta - 0.125 \times 0.101 + 1.01 \sin 1.4°$$

since $H \cos \theta = 0.101$. The above equation implies

$$H \sin \theta = -0.290. \qquad (b)$$

Equations (a) and (b) together imply

$$\theta = \arctan \frac{-0.290}{0.101} = -70.8°$$

and

$$H = \frac{0.101}{\cos 70.8} = 0.307.$$

The general solution is then, numerically,

$$i = 0.307\epsilon^{-0.125t} \cos (0.992t - 70.8°) - 0.101 \cos (10t + 1.4°).$$

3.9. The Steady-state Response of a Two-mesh Circuit. A two-mesh circuit provides a more complex example. We shall consider a fairly simple case involving no mutual inductances (Fig. 3.15). The circuit contains two sources, each producing a sinusoid of the same frequency. (Sources of different frequencies may be treated by the method of superposition to be explained in the next chapter.)

Example 3.6. Determine the steady-state current in the center branch of the circuit of Fig. 3.15. Assume $\omega = 1$. The numerical values of the components are given in the figure.

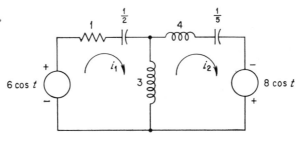

$$\omega = 1$$

FIG. 3.15. Circuit for Example 3.6.

Solution. The mesh equations for this circuit are

$$i_1 + 2 \int_0^t i_1 \, dt + v_{c01} + 3 \frac{d}{dt} i_1 - 3 \frac{d}{dt} i_2 = 6 \cos t$$

$$3 \frac{d}{dt} i_2 - 3 \frac{d}{dt} i_1 + 4 \frac{d}{dt} i_2 + 5 \int_0^t i_2 \, dt + v_{c02} = 8 \cos t.$$

The initial voltages on the capacitors in loops 1 and 2 are v_{c01} and v_{c02}, respectively.

Writing the forcing functions in exponential form and assuming that the solutions are of the form $I\epsilon^{j\omega t}$ (with $\omega = 1$) we obtain

$$I_1 \epsilon^{jt} + \frac{2}{j} I_1 \epsilon^{jt} + 3jI_1 \epsilon^{jt} - 3jI_2 \epsilon^{jt} = 6\epsilon^{jt}$$

$$3jI_2 \epsilon^{jt} - 3jI_1 \epsilon^{jt} + 4jI_2 \epsilon^{jt} + \frac{5}{j} I_2 \epsilon^{jt} = 8\epsilon^{jt}.$$

Canceling ϵ^{jt} and collecting terms yield

$$I_1 \left(1 + 3j + \frac{2}{j} \right) - I_2(j3) = 6$$

$$-I_1 (j3) + I_2 \left(7j + \frac{5}{j} \right) = 8.$$

We have now reduced the solution of the original differential equation to the solution of a pair of simultaneous algebraic equations having complex coefficients. Using the methods discussed in the next chapter, it may be shown that

$$I_1 = 1.36 + j4.75$$
$$I_2 = -1.38 + j0.678.$$

Recalling that only the real parts of I_1 and I_2 are of interest, we see that

$$i_1 = \text{Re}\,[I_1\epsilon^{jt}] = \text{Re}\,[(1.36 + j4.75)\epsilon^{jt}] = 4.95 \cos (t + 74.05°)$$
$$i_2 = \text{Re}\,[I_2\epsilon^{jt}] = \text{Re}\,[(-1.38 + j0.678)\epsilon^{jt}] = 1.54 \cos (t + 153.83°).$$

The current in the center branch is thus

$$i = i_1 - i_2$$
$$= 4.95 \cos (t + 74.05°) - 1.54 \cos (t + 153.83°)$$
$$= 4.91 \cos (t + 56.05°).$$

In this example, involving two loops, the impedance does not seem to appear. Actually, there are several impedances, the definitions and significance of which will appear in the next chapter. With the help of these impedances it is also a simple matter to determine the transient response. The techniques illustrated above may be applied to networks containing many loops.

EXERCISES

3.1. The circuit illustrated in Fig. 3.16 is initially at rest. How long after switch S_1 is closed does i reach 500 ma (S_2 remains open)? [HINT: Apply Thévenin's theorem.]

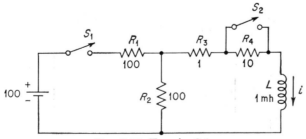

FIG. 3.16. Exercise 3.1.

3.2. After S_1 has been closed for 0.1 sec, S_2 is closed. How long will it take for i to reach 950 ma? What are the values of current in R_1 and R_2 at the instant i reaches 950 ma?

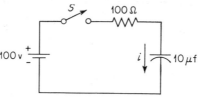

Fig. 3.17. Exercise 3.3.

3.3. In the circuit in Fig. 3.17 the capacitor is initially uncharged.
(*a*) What is the value of the current exactly 0.001 sec after the switch is closed?
(*b*) What is the charge on the capacitor at this time?
(*c*) What is the rate of change of current at this time?
(*d*) What is the initial rate of change of current?

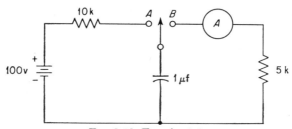

Fig. 3.18. Exercise 3.4.

3.4. The switch in the circuit of Fig. 3.18 is held alternately in positions A and B for 0.01 sec in each position (requiring 0.02 sec for a complete cycle). The meter reads the average current through it. Determine the final meter reading.
3.5. Determine the voltage across the circuit of Fig. 3.3 as a function of time if the switch is operated at $t = 0$.
3.6. For the circuit shown in Fig. 3.19 find $i(t)$ and $v_c(t)$ if the switch moves from A to B at $t = 0$. What is the natural frequency?

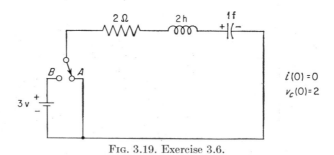

Fig. 3.19. Exercise 3.6.

3.7. Find the voltage across the capacitor for $t > 0$ in the circuit of Fig. 3.20.   The current is applied at $t = 0$.   Sketch the result.

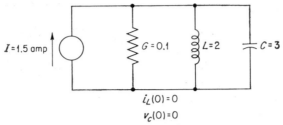

$$i_L(0) = 0$$
$$v_c(0) = 0$$

FIG. 3.20. Exercise 3.7.

3.8. In Fig. 3.21 the switch is thrown from A to B at $t = 0$ and from B to C at $t = 5$ sec.   Determine the current which flows as a function of time.   Sketch the current.

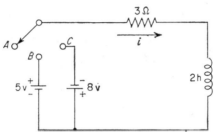

FIG. 3.21. Exercise 3.8.

3.9. Show that the natural response of a critically damped RLC circuit is

$$i = A_1 \epsilon^{-pt} + A_2 t \epsilon^{-pt}$$

where $p = R/2L$. [HINT: Consider an overdamped circuit and let p_1 approach p_2.]

3.10. The switch in Fig. 3.22 is moved instantly from A to B at $t = 0$.

(*a*) Find the smallest permissible value of C so that the maximum voltage across the inductor does not exceed 1000 volts.   (As an approximation, neglect R.)

(*b*) Using the value of C found by the approximation above, find the actual maximum voltage across the inductor.

3.11. Repeat Exercise 3.10 with a resistor in place of C.

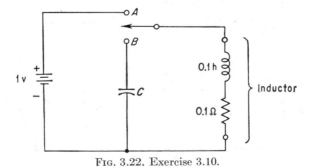

FIG. 3.22. Exercise 3.10.

3.12. Show that after the switch illustrated in Fig. 3.23 is closed the energy dissipated in R is $\frac{1}{2}CV^2$, where V is the initial voltage on the capacitor.

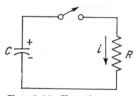
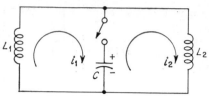

FIG. 3.23. Exercise 3.12.   FIG. 3.24. Exercise 3.13.

3.13. The capacitor in Fig. 3.24 is initially charged to V volts. The switch is closed at $t = 0$. Determine the maximum values of i_1 and i_2. [HINT: Consider L_1 and L_2 in parallel.]

3.14. Consider the differential equation

$$\frac{d^3x}{dt^3} + a\frac{d^2x}{dt^2} + b\frac{dx}{dt} + cx = 0 \qquad (*)$$

or $(p^3 + ap^2 + bp + c)x = 0$ and assume that the three roots of the algebraic equation

$$m^3 + am^2 + bm + c = 0$$

are equal, say,

$$m_1 = m_2 = m_3.$$

Show that $\epsilon^{m_1 t}$, $t\epsilon^{m_1 t}$, $t^2\epsilon^{m_1 t}$ are independent solutions of the differential equation (*).

3.15. Show that evaluation of the second bracketed term in Eq. (3.56) does not change the form of Eq. (3.58).

3.16. Find, as a function of R, the value of current at $t = 3$ sec in the RLC circuit illustrated in Fig. 3.25.

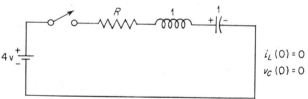

$$i_L(0) = 0$$
$$v_C(0) = 0$$

FIG. 3.25. Exercise 3.16.

3.17. In the circuit shown in Fig. 3.26 the switch S_1 is closed at $t = 0$ sec and S_2 is opened at $t = 10$ sec. Compute the current i as a function of time. Sketch the variation of i with time.

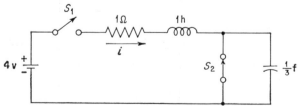

FIG. 3.26. Exercise 3.17.

3.18. If A and B are complex numbers, show that

(a) Re $[A]$ Re $[B]$ − Im $[A]$ Im $[B]$ = Re $[AB]$.

(b) Re $[A]$ Im $[B]$ + Im $[A]$ Re $[B]$ = Im $[AB]$.

3.19. If A is a complex number, is Re $[A^2]$ = (Re $[A]$)² a true equation? If it is not, express Re $[A^2]$ in terms of Re $[A]$ and Im $[A]$.

3.20. The hyperbolic sine and hyperbolic cosine are functions that frequently occur in the study of filters and transmission lines. The hyperbolic sine of x is written sinh x and is defined by the equation

$$\sinh x = \frac{\epsilon^x - \epsilon^{-x}}{2}.$$

The hyperbolic cosine of x is written cosh x and is defined by the equation

$$\cosh x = \frac{\epsilon^x + \epsilon^{-x}}{2}.$$

Prove that

(a) $\cosh^2 x - \sinh^2 x = 1$.

(b) $\cosh(x + y) = \cosh x \cosh y + \sinh x \sinh y$.

(c) $\sinh(x + y) = \sinh x \cosh y + \sinh y \cosh x$.

3.21. Show that the relation between hyperbolic and circular functions is given by

(a) $\sin x = -j \sinh jx$ (b) $\cos x = \cosh jx$

(c) $\sin jx = j \sinh x$ (d) $\cos jx = \cosh x$

3.22. Plot on the complex plane the zeros of the impedance functions appropriate to Exercises 3.5, 3.8, and 3.17.

3.23. Plot on the complex plane the zeros of the admittance function of Exercise 3.7.

3.24. Plot on the complex plane the root locus of the circuit of Exercise 3.16 as R is varied.

CHAPTER 4

COMPLEX IMPEDANCE AND THE USE OF PHASORS

In the previous chapter it was demonstrated that sinusoidal forcing functions produce responses which are, in the steady state, sinusoidal. The sinusoidal currents were shown to be related to the sinusoidal voltages by a form of Ohm's law, wherein complex impedance took the place of resistance. In this chapter, after some preliminary remarks on the general theory of alternating currents, we shall explore this result further by developing methods for the manipulation of complex impedances. We shall also investigate useful graphical interpretations of complex voltages and currents and show how these techniques may be applied to the computation of power in simple circuits.

4.1. Alternating Voltages and Currents. Although we shall be concerned for the next few chapters only with sinusoidal voltages and currents, many of the definitions applicable to sinusoidal waveforms are also applied to nonsinusoidal waves. Therefore we shall give these definitions in a broader setting.

An alternating voltage† is defined as one whose polarity reverses at regularly occurring intervals. An alternating current is defined similarly. To quote the AIEE Standards, "Unless distinctly otherwise specified, the term alternating current refers to a periodically varying current with successive half waves of the same shape and area."

Examples of various alternating waveforms are shown in Fig. 4.1. Alternating voltages are generally produced by rotating machines or by electronic devices known as *oscillators* or *waveform generators.*‡

It is often assumed that the importance of sinusoidal waveforms stems from the fact that an elementary alternator of the type shown in Fig. 4.2 naturally produces a waveform which is sinusoidal. This is not the reason. The true justification for the importance of sine waves results from the fact that sinusoidal forcing functions produce sinusoidal responses in electric networks. This follows from the fact that the derivatives and integrals of sinusoidal waves are also sinusoidal

† The abbreviation a-c stands for *alternating current*. The terms "a-c voltage" and "a-c current," although incorrect and redundant, are in common use.

‡ Oscillators generally produce sinusoidal waveforms. Waveform generators usually produce waveforms other than sinusoids.

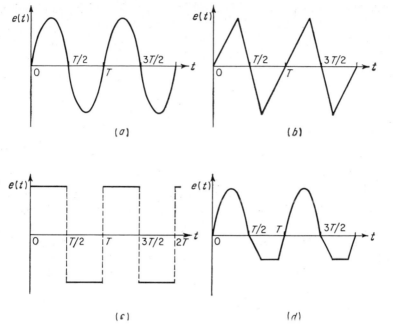

Fig. 4.1. Alternating waveforms.   (a) Sine wave; (b) triangular wave; (c) square wave; (d) arbitrary wave.   (Observe that this wave does not satisfy the usual definition of an alternating wave.)

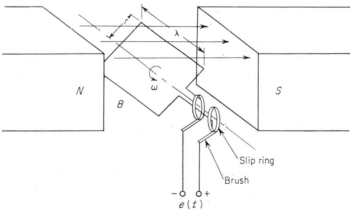

Fig. 4.2. Elementary alternator.

waves, as are the sums of sinusoidal waves.   Thus, at any point in an electric network the steady-state currents and voltages are sinusoidal, which permits a much easier analysis than would otherwise be the case. Actually, it is a significant problem in alternator design to assure that the output voltage be truly sinusoidal.

Several other terms are also used in connection with a-c circuits. A *cycle* is a complete set of positive and negative values of an alternating current or voltage. It is the set of values which starts at some time, say t_0, and continues until the variation begins to repeat itself at time $t_0 + T$. Thus T is the length or *period* of the cycle. For an alternating wave,

$$e(t) = e(t + T) \tag{4.1}$$

and, from the definition of period, it is easily seen that

$$e(t) = e(t + nT) \tag{4.1a}$$

where n is an integer (see Sec. 9.1 for a more detailed discussion of periodic functions, including a proof of this fact). Each of the waves in Fig. 4.1 has two cycles shown. Because of the periodic nature of alternating waves and the fact that they are generally trigonometric functions of time, angular measure is frequently used in describing them. One cycle is said to occupy 360° or 2π radians.

The *frequency* f of a wave is the number of cycles occurring per unit time (cycles/sec). Clearly,

$$f = \frac{1}{T}. \tag{4.2}$$

The *angular frequency* ω is defined as the number of radians/sec. Therefore

$$\omega = 2\pi f. \tag{4.3}$$

It is apparent that these definitions conflict somewhat with those given in Sec. 3.6. This is unfortunate and is a source of much confusion to the beginner. One must rely on the context in which the word frequency is used in order to determine which meaning is implied.

The *waveform* of an alternating current or voltage is the shape of the plot of the instantaneous value of current or voltage vs. time as abscissa.

The *phase* of a point on a wave designates that point relative to some other point on the wave chosen as a reference. This term is usually restricted to designate the portion of the period elapsed between the time at which the wave passed through zero and the origin of time, $t = 0$. Phase is usually expressed in angular measure. The wave of Eq. (4.4),

$$e(t) = E_m \cos (\omega t + \theta_0), \tag{4.4}$$

for example, passes through zero at time t so that $\omega t = -(90° + \theta_0)$. At $t = 0$, $\omega t = 0$ so that the phase (that is, the difference between these two numbers) is $-(90° + \theta_0°)$, or $-(\pi/2 + \theta_0)$ if the angle is measured in radians. A more useful concept than phase is the *phase difference* between two waves. This is the portion of a period which elapses between

the times each wave passes through zero.   If, for example, the two waves
are represented by

$$e_1(t) = E_{1m} \sin (\omega t + \theta_1) \tag{4.5a}$$

and

$$e_2(t) = E_{2m} \sin (\omega t + \theta_2) \tag{4.5b}$$

then $e_1(t)$ passes through zero at $\omega t = -\theta_1$ and $e_2(t)$ passes through zero at
$\omega t = -\theta_2$.   Thus the phase difference between $e_1(t)$ and $e_2(t)$ is $-\theta_1 + \theta_2$.
Phase difference is meaningful only for waves having the same frequency.
Also, good usage requires that the two waves have the same shape, or
better yet, both be sine waves.   However, this usage is not universally
accepted.   Because of this unfortunate lack of standardization in specifying the conditions under which phase difference is meaningful, it is
frequently found that phasemeters (that is, instruments for measuring
phase) yield meaningless readings.

In writing literal expressions for alternating currents and voltages,
lower-case letters will be reserved for instantaneous values and capital
letters for maximum or effective values (see
Sec. 4.2).   Also, time as the independent
variable is not always explicitly written.
Thus we sometimes write

$$e(t) = e = E_m \sin \omega t. \tag{4.6}$$

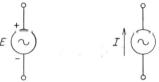

FIG. 4.3. Symbols for sinusoidal
voltage and current sources.

Sources of alternating voltage or current
are usually designated on circuit diagrams
by the symbols shown in Fig. 4.3.   It is
pertinent to review here the material of Secs. 1.4 and 2.2 on reference
polarities in order that one not be confounded by the question: How may
terminals be marked $+$ and $-$ when the polarity changes periodically?

4.2. Effective and Average Values of an Alternating Wave.   Instantaneous values of alternating waves are difficult to manipulate analytically.   Also, instruments which measure instantaneous values (oscil-
loscopes) are expensive, and their readings are often difficult to interpret.
What is desirable is a measure of an alternating wave which is a single
meaningful number.   The *peak value* of the wave is such a number, if
the waveform is known; it is of less utility for arbitrary waveforms.
A more suitable quantity is one based on the energy transferred by an
alternating current or voltage.   This we shall call the *effective value*
of current or voltage.

We have already shown (Sec. 1.3) that the rate at which energy is
dissipated in a resistor is

$$p = i^2 R \tag{4.7}$$

(the lower-case letters indicate that the current and hence the power vary with time). During a complete cycle, the average rate at which energy is dissipated is

$$P_{av} = \frac{1}{T} \int_0^T i^2 R \, dt = \frac{R}{T} \int_0^T i^2 \, dt. \qquad (4.8)$$

Clearly the average rate for any integral number of cycles is the same, and hence Eq. (4.8) also gives the average rate over a very long time.

We define the *effective value* of current I_{eff} as that current which when flowing continuously produces the same average power dissipation in the resistor. That is,

$$P_{av} = I_{eff}{}^2 R. \qquad (4.9)$$

Comparing Eqs. (4.8) and (4.9) we see that

$$I_{eff} = \sqrt{\frac{1}{T} \int_0^T i^2 \, dt}. \qquad (4.10)$$

The effective value of current is thus the *root-mean-square* (rms) current; that is, it is the square root of the mean (average) value of the square of the current. Frequently, therefore, we use the subscript rms rather than *eff* to designate the effective value of a wave.

Actually the rms value of current is subject to a more general definition. Suppose that $i(t)$ is a current (not necessarily periodic) extending from $-\infty$ to $+\infty$. Then we *define* the rms value as

$$I_{rms} = \lim_{T \to \infty} \sqrt{\frac{1}{T} \int_{-T/2}^{T/2} i^2(t) \, dt} \qquad (4.10a)$$

if it exists. If $i(t)$ happens to be periodic, Eq. (4.10a) reduces to Eq. (4.10). This more general definition is particularly useful in considering "noise currents" and sums of sinusoidal currents of different frequencies.

A similar derivation shows that the effective value of an alternating voltage is the root-mean-square value of the voltage.

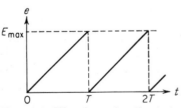

FIG. 4.4. Waveform for Example 4.1.

Example 4.1. Determine the effective value of the voltage wave shown in Fig. 4.4. (This waveform is known as a saw-tooth wave. The saw-tooth waveform shown here is one of many important waveforms which do not have negative portions.)

Solution. We may express a single cycle of this wave analytically as follows:

$$e(t) = E_{max} \frac{t}{T}, \qquad 0 \leq t < T.$$

Then

$$E_{eff} = E_{rms} = \sqrt{\frac{1}{T} \int_0^T E_{max}{}^2 \frac{t^2}{T^2} \, dt} = E_{max} \sqrt{\frac{1}{T} \frac{t^3}{3T^2} \Big|_0^T} = \frac{E_{max}}{\sqrt{3}}.$$

Example 4.2.   Find the effective value of a sine wave of current.

Solution.   A sine wave of period T may be expressed as $I_{max} \sin 2\pi \dfrac{t}{T}$.   Thus

$$I_{rms} = \sqrt{\frac{1}{T} \int_0^T \left(I_{max} \sin \frac{2\pi t}{T} \right)^2 dt} = I_{max} \sqrt{\frac{1}{T} \int_0^T \left(\frac{1}{2} - \frac{1}{2} \cos \frac{4\pi t}{T} \right) dt}$$

$$= \frac{I_{max}}{\sqrt{2}} = 0.707 I_{max}.$$

This relationship between the effective and maximum value of a sine wave appears frequently in a-c circuit analysis.

Example 4.3.   Consider a wave having the following form:

$$e(t) = E_0 + E_1 \sin \frac{2\pi t}{T} + E_2 \sin \frac{4\pi t}{T}.$$

Find the effective value of each of the component waves and also the effective value of the total wave.

Solution.   The effective value of the E_0 term (the d-c component) is E_0.   From Example 4.2 the effective values of the E_1 and E_2 terms are $0.707E_1$ and $0.707E_2$, respectively.

The effective value of the total wave is

$$E_{rms} = \sqrt{\frac{1}{T} \int_0^T \left(E_0 + E_1 \sin \frac{2\pi t}{T} + E_2 \sin \frac{4\pi t}{T} \right)^2 dt}$$

$$= \sqrt{\frac{1}{T} \int_0^T \left[\left(E_0{}^2 + E_1{}^2 \sin^2 \frac{2\pi t}{T} + E_2{}^2 \sin^2 \frac{4\pi t}{T} \right) + 2 \left(E_0 E_1 \sin \frac{2\pi t}{T} \right. \right.}$$
$$\overline{\left. \left. + E_0 E_2 \sin \frac{4\pi t}{T} + E_1 E_2 \sin \frac{2\pi t}{T} \sin \frac{4\pi t}{T} \right) \right] dt}.$$

Carrying out the indicated integrations, we find that

$$E_{rms} = \sqrt{E_0{}^2 + \tfrac{1}{2} E_1{}^2 + \tfrac{1}{2} E_2{}^2}.$$

But this is merely

$$E_{rms} = \sqrt{E_0{}^2 + E_{1\text{-rms}}{}^2 + E_{2\text{-rms}}{}^2}.$$

The foregoing example demonstrates that the rms value of a wave made up of several components each having a different frequency is the square root of the sum of the effective values of the components squared. Alternatively stated, the square of the effective value of the sum of components is the sum of the squares of the effective values of the components.

This conclusion is general and applies even when the frequencies of the components are not integral ratios.   It does not apply if the components are of the same frequency, because then they are not truly separate components.   The conclusion may also be developed using the *orthogonality* property of sinusoids.   This point of view will be expounded in Chap. 9.

That the result will also be true even if the frequencies of the components are *not* integrally related is seen if the definition of Eq. (4.10a) is employed.   For example, consider

$$i(t) = i_1(t) + i_2(t) \tag{4.11}$$

where

$$i_1(t) = I_1 \sin \alpha t, \qquad i_2(t) = I_2 \sin \beta t \tag{4.12}$$

and $\alpha \neq \beta$ but are otherwise arbitrary.   Then

$$i_{1\text{-rms}}{}^2 = \lim_{T \to \infty} \frac{1}{T} \int_{-T/2}^{T/2} I_1{}^2 \sin^2 \alpha t \, dt = \tfrac{1}{2} I_1{}^2 \tag{4.13}$$

and similarly

$$i_{2\text{-rms}}{}^2 = \tfrac{1}{2} I_2{}^2. \tag{4.14}$$

Thus we may write

$$i_{\text{rms}}{}^2 = \tfrac{1}{2} I_1{}^2 + \tfrac{1}{2} I_2{}^2 + 2 I_1 I_2 \lim_{T \to \infty} \frac{1}{T} \int_{-T/2}^{T/2} \sin \alpha t \sin \beta t \, dt. \tag{4.15}$$

Since $\alpha \neq \beta$,

$$\frac{1}{T} \int_{-T/2}^{T/2} \sin \alpha t \sin \beta t \, dt = \frac{2}{T} \left[\frac{\sin (\alpha - \beta) \dfrac{T}{2}}{\alpha - \beta} + \frac{\sin (\alpha + \beta) \dfrac{T}{2}}{\alpha + \beta} \right] \tag{4.16}$$

and since the numerators are bounded, the limit of the above integral as T approaches infinity is zero.   Thus

$$i_{\text{rms}}{}^2 = i_{1\text{-rms}}{}^2 + i_{2\text{-rms}}{}^2. \tag{4.17}$$

The *average value* of an alternating wave is usually zero, because the positive and negative loops usually have the same area (see Sec. 4.1). Sometimes it is convenient, however, to define the average value of a symmetrical alternating wave as the average value of the *positive* loop. In such cases,

$$I_{\text{av}} = \frac{2}{T} \int_0^{T/2} i \, dt. \tag{4.18}$$

The factor $T/2$ occurs because the waveform is symmetrical, the wave being positive from 0 to $T/2$ and negative from $T/2$ to T.

Example 4.4.   Determine the "average" value of a sine wave.
Solution.

$$I_{\text{av}} = \frac{2}{T} \int_0^T I_{\max} \sin \frac{2\pi t}{T} \, dt = \frac{2 I_{\max}}{\pi} = 0.636 I_{\max}.$$

Occasionally the notions of *form factor* and *peak factor* are employed. The form factor is the ratio of the effective to the average value of a wave.   For a sine wave it is $\pi \sqrt{2}/4 = 1.11$.   The peak factor is the ratio of the maximum to the effective value of a wave.   For a sine wave its value is $\sqrt{2} = 1.414$.

4.3. Solution of the Steady-state Equilibrium Equations.   Having dispensed with the preliminary definitions, we shall focus our attention on the *steady-state response* of the network equations when *sinusoidal forcing functions* (sources) are employed.   In order to avoid repetitious qualifications of our statements it will be understood, unless specifically mentioned otherwise, that we are concerned only with such solutions.

In Sec. 3.4 it was pointed out that the steady-state response is equal to the forced response, provided that the forced response is periodic. It was also shown that the forced response to sinusoidal signals was periodic.   Hence for sinusoidal sources the forced response is the steady-state solution.   Thus the problem of determining steady-state responses is equivalent to that of determining forced responses.

Recall the procedure for determining forced responses when the driving function is of the form $E\epsilon^{j\omega t}$.   We assume that the solution is of the form $I\epsilon^{j\omega t}$ (Remember, it is implicit that only the real parts of these functions are of concern.)   We then write the equilibrium equation and solve for I.   To be specific, consider the series RLC circuit (see Sec. 3.3).   The equilibrium equation is

$$Ri + L\frac{di}{dt} + \frac{1}{C}\int_0^t i\,dt + v_{c0} = e \tag{4.19}$$

or, using the values $I\epsilon^{j\omega t}$ and $E\epsilon^{j\omega t}$ (and neglecting initial conditions),

$$RI\epsilon^{j\omega t} + j\omega L I\epsilon^{j\omega t} + \frac{1}{j\omega C} I\epsilon^{j\omega t} = E\epsilon^{j\omega t}. \tag{4.20}$$

Dividing both sides by $\epsilon^{j\omega t}$ and solving for I give

$$I = \frac{E}{R + j\omega L + 1/j\omega C}. \tag{4.21}$$

By means of these manipulations we have succeeded in converting the integrodifferential equation (4.19) into an algebraic equation (4.21) relating the steady-state response to the forcing function and the circuit parameters.   In particular, we have replaced the *integrodifferential operator*

$$R(\quad) + L\frac{d}{dt}(\quad) + \frac{1}{C}\int(\quad)\,dt$$

by the complex *number*

$$R + j\omega L + \frac{1}{j\omega C}.$$

4.4. Complex Impedance.   We have already observed (Sec. 3.3) that the relationship of Eq. (4.21) is similar to Ohm's law for a d-c circuit. Thus we have defined the complex number $R + j\omega L + 1/j\omega C$ as the (complex) *impedance* Z of a series RLC circuit.   We thus write "Ohm's law for an a-c circuit" as

$$I = \frac{E}{Z} \tag{4.22}$$

by which we really mean†

$$i(t) = \text{Re}\,[I\epsilon^{j\omega t}] = \text{Re}\left[\frac{E}{Z}\,\epsilon^{j\omega t}\right]. \qquad (4.23)$$

Because of the importance of these relationships in steady-state circuit analysis, we shall devote this and the next several sections to further remarks on impedance and to explanations of the methods for its manipulation.

We have defined the complex impedance for the general case of a series RLC circuit. If any of these elements is missing, the expression for Z is correspondingly simplified. In particular, for a resistor,

$$Z = R; \qquad (4.24.1)$$

for an inductor,

$$Z_L = j\omega L; \qquad (4.24.2)$$

for a capacitor,

$$Z_C = \frac{1}{j\omega C} = -\frac{j^2}{j\omega C} = -\frac{j}{\omega C}. \qquad (4.24.3)$$

The latter two equations are frequently written in the form

$$Z_L = jX_L \qquad (4.25.1)$$
$$Z_C = jX_C \qquad (4.25.2)$$

where X, the imaginary component of Z, is called the *reactance*, X_L being the inductive reactance and X_C being the capacitive reactance. Comparing Eqs. (4.24) and (4.25) shows

$$X_L = \omega L$$
$$X_C = -\frac{1}{\omega C}. \qquad (4.26)$$

An extension of the above arguments allows us to define the reciprocal of impedance as (complex) *admittance* Y,

$$Y = \frac{1}{Z}. \qquad (4.27)$$

Hence, for a resistor,

$$Y_R = \frac{1}{R} = G \qquad (4.28.1)$$

where G is called the *conductance* of a resistor. Also, for an inductor,

$$Y_L = \frac{1}{j\omega L} = -\frac{j}{\omega L} \qquad (4.28.2)$$

† It is reemphasized that here we are considering only sinusoidal sources. The results we are about to derive hold only for this case. They may be generalized to any source of the form ϵ^{st}, but this will not be done here, however (see Chap. 10).

and for a capacitor,

$$Y_C = j\omega C. \tag{4.28.3}$$

We may write

$$Y_L = jB_L \tag{4.29.1}$$
$$Y_C = jB_C \tag{4.29.2}$$

where B is defined as the *susceptance*, B_L being the inductive susceptance and B_C being the capacitive susceptance.

$$B_L = -\frac{1}{\omega L}$$
$$B_C = \omega C. \tag{4.30}$$

In the above definitions we have identified inductive reactance with a single inductor, and capacitive reactance with a single capacitor. In general, the susceptance of a circuit results from both inductance and capacitance. Thus, for an RLC circuit

$$Z = R + j\omega L + \frac{1}{j\omega C} = R + j\left(\omega L - \frac{1}{\omega C}\right) = R + jX$$

where $X = \omega L - 1/\omega C$. If the parameters are such that X is positive, it is said to be inductive; if negative, it is said to be capacitive. The converse is true for susceptance.

To continue efficiently our discussion of impedance in circuits involving various series-parallel connections of elements, it will be convenient to consider the manipulation of complex numbers. This will be done in the next section. It need merely be pointed out here that the rules for manipulating resistance developed in Sec. 1.12 also apply to impedance.

4.5. The Arithmetic of Complex Numbers. A complex number A is of the form

$$A = a + j\alpha \tag{4.31}$$

where a and α are real numbers and $j = \sqrt{-1}$. A complex number may be represented graphically as shown in Fig. 4.5. The abscissa (x axis) is called the "real axis" and the ordinate (y axis) is the "imaginary axis." The *conjugate* of a complex number A is written A^* and defined as

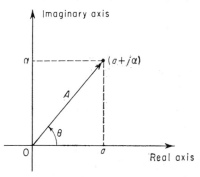

FIG. 4.5. Graphical interpretation of a complex number.

$$A^* = a - j\alpha. \tag{4.32}$$

The *magnitude* of a complex number is written $|A|$ and is defined as

$$|A| = +\sqrt{a^2 + \alpha^2}. \tag{4.33}$$

Geometrically (see Fig. 4.4) it is the length of the line from the origin to the point (a,α). We also call $|A|$ the *modulus* of the complex number A.

Two complex numbers are equal only if their real parts are equal and their imaginary parts are equal. Thus, a complex number is zero only if *both* real and imaginary parts are zero.

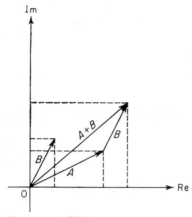

If $A = a + j\alpha$ and $B = b + j\beta$ are two complex numbers, then by the *sum* of A and B we mean the complex number

$$A + B = (a + b) + j(\alpha + \beta) \quad (4.34)$$

obtained by adding the real and imaginary parts separately. This is shown graphically in Fig. 4.6.

The *product* of A and B is

$$
\begin{aligned}
AB &= (a + j\alpha)(b + j\beta) \\
&= ab + j(a\beta + \alpha b) + j^2\alpha\beta \\
&= (ab - \alpha\beta) + j(a\beta + \alpha b) \quad (4.35)
\end{aligned}
$$

Fig. 4.6. Addition of complex numbers.

since $j^2 = -1$.

The *reciprocal* of a nonzero complex number is also a complex number. Suppose that

$$A = \frac{1}{B} = \frac{1}{b + j\beta}. \quad (4.36)$$

If we multiply both numerator and denominator by the conjugate of B, then

$$A = \frac{1}{B}\frac{B^*}{B^*} = \frac{1}{b + j\beta}\frac{b - j\beta}{b - j\beta} = \frac{b - j\beta}{b^2 + \beta^2} = \frac{b}{b^2 + \beta^2} - j\frac{\beta}{b^2 + \beta^2}. \quad (4.37)$$

This development, incidentally, shows that

$$AA^* = |A|^2. \quad (4.38)$$

We may alternatively write

$$\frac{1}{B} = \frac{B^*}{|B|^2} \qquad B \neq 0. \quad (4.39)$$

Division of complex numbers may be performed by taking the reciprocal of the denominator and multiplying by the numerator according to the rules given above. It is generally more convenient, however, to follow the methods to be explained below.

Equation (4.31) represents the *cartesian* form of the complex number. Referring to Fig. 4.5, it is also clear that the complex number can be expressed in *polar* form. In fact,

$$
\begin{aligned}
a &= |A| \cos \theta \\
\alpha &= |A| \sin \theta
\end{aligned}
\quad (4.40)
$$

where
$$|A| = + \sqrt{a^2 + \alpha^2} \tag{4.33}$$

and

$$\theta = \arctan \frac{\alpha}{a} \tag{4.41}$$

so that

$$A = a + j\alpha = |A| \, (\cos \theta + j \sin \theta). \tag{4.42}$$

But by Euler's formula (Sec. 3.5)

$$\cos \theta + j \sin \theta = \epsilon^{j\theta}. \tag{4.43}$$

Thus

$$A = |A|\epsilon^{j\theta}. \tag{4.44}$$

In electrical engineering, this relation is usually written

$$A = |A| \, \underline{/\theta} \tag{4.44a}$$

and is read " A at the angle θ."

Clearly, any complex number can be uniquely expressed in either cartesian form or polar form. The cartesian form of complex numbers is convenient when we wish to add or subtract complex numbers, whereas the polar form is most useful when multiplication or division is to be carried out, since

$$\begin{aligned}
A_1 A_2 &= (|A_1|\epsilon^{j\theta_1})(|A_2|\epsilon^{j\theta_2}) = |A_1 A_2|\epsilon^{j(\theta_1 + \theta_2)} \\
&= |A_1 A_2| \, [\cos (\theta_1 + \theta_2) + j \sin (\theta_1 + \theta_2)].
\end{aligned} \tag{4.45}$$

The above rule is known as *De Moivre's* formula and is frequently written in the form

$$(|A_1| \, \underline{/\theta_1})(|A_2| \, \underline{/\theta_2}) = |A_1 A_2| \, \underline{/\theta_1 + \theta_2}. \tag{4.45a}$$

Similarly,

$$\frac{|A_1| \, \underline{/\theta_1}}{|A_2| \, \underline{/\theta_2}} = \frac{|A_1|}{|A_2|} \, \underline{/\theta_1 - \theta_2} = \left|\frac{A_1}{A_2}\right| \, \underline{/\theta_1 - \theta_2}. \tag{4.46}$$

(It is common to omit the magnitude bars when the sense of the expression is clear without them.)   In order to illustrate concretely the application of the above rules, several illustrative examples follow.

Example 4.5.   Multiply the following numbers together, expressing the result in both cartesian and polar forms:

$$A_1 = 1 + j2, \qquad A_2 = 3 + j4.$$

Solution.   We have

$$A_1 A_2 = (1 + j2)(3 + j4) = (3 - 8) + j(4 + 6) = -5 + j10.$$

This may be written as $A_3\underline{/\theta}$, where

$$A_3 = + \sqrt{(-5)^2 + (10)^2} = 11.18$$

and

$$\theta = \arctan \frac{10}{-5} = 116.56°.†$$

Alternatively,

$$A_1 = \sqrt{(1)^2 + (2)^2}\ \underline{|\arctan \tfrac{2}{1}} = 2.236\underline{|63.43°}$$
$$A_2 = \sqrt{(3)^2 + (4)^2}\ \underline{|\arctan \tfrac{4}{3}} = 5.000\underline{|53.13°}$$

whence

$$A_1 A_2 = 2.236 \times 5.000\underline{|63.43 + 53.13} = 11.18\underline{|116.56°}.$$

This may be expressed as

$$A_1 A_2 = 11.18(\cos 116.56° + j \sin 116.56°)$$
$$= 11.18(-0.4472 + j0.8944) = -5 + j10.$$

Example 4.6. Divide A by B, expressing the result in both cartesian and polar forms:

$$A = 4 + j5, \qquad B = 2 + j3.$$

Solution. We multiply numerator and denominator by the conjugate of B to obtain

$$\frac{A}{B} = \frac{4 + j5}{2 + j3}\frac{2 - j3}{2 - j3} = \frac{(8 + 15) + j(-12 + 10)}{4 + 9} = \frac{23 - j2}{13} = 1.77 - j0.154.$$

This may be written as

$$\frac{A}{B} = 1.78\underline{|-4.99°}.$$

Alternatively,

$$A = 6.40\underline{|51.33°}$$
$$B = 3.61\underline{|56.32°}$$

so that

$$\frac{A}{B} = \frac{6.40}{3.61}\ \underline{|51.33 - 56.32} = 1.78\underline{|-4.99°}$$

which may be expressed as

$$\frac{A}{B} = 1.78[\cos (-4.99°) + j \sin (-4.99°)] = 1.78(0.996 - j0.0870)$$
$$= 1.77 - j0.154.$$

Example 4.7. Develop expressions for the impedance of a resistor, an inductor, and a capacitor, in cartesian and in polar form.
    Solution.   *a.* Resistor,

$$R = R + j0 = R\underline{|0}.$$

---

† In slide-rule computations it is usually most convenient to convert $a + j\alpha$ into $A\underline{|\theta}$ by first finding θ ($= \arctan \alpha/a$) and then using the relation $A = \alpha/\sin \theta$. One must also be careful to obtain θ in the correct quadrant. In the above example, sine is positive and cosine is negative. Thus the angle must lie in the *second* quadrant.

b. Inductor,
$$Z_L = 0 + j\omega L = j\omega L = \omega L \underline{|90°}.$$

c. Capacitor,
$$Z_C = 0 + \frac{1}{j\omega C} = -j\frac{1}{\omega C} = \frac{1}{\omega C} \underline{|-90°}.$$

The foregoing example also points out the familiar but important fact that

$$j = 1\underline{|90°} = \epsilon^{j\pi/2}. \qquad (4.47)$$

Example 4.8. Determine the impedance and admittance of the circuit of Fig. 4.7 at a frequency of 100 cycles.

Solution. From the figure,

$$R = 1000 \ \Omega.$$
$$X_L = \omega L = 2\pi f L = 2\pi 100 \times 1 = 628 \ \Omega$$

and

$$X_C = -\frac{1}{\omega C} = \frac{-1}{2\pi 100 \times 10^{-6}} = -1592 \ \Omega.$$

Thus

$$Z = R + jX = 1000 + j(628 - 1592) = 1000 - j964$$
$$= 1390\underline{|-43.92°} \text{ ohms}.$$

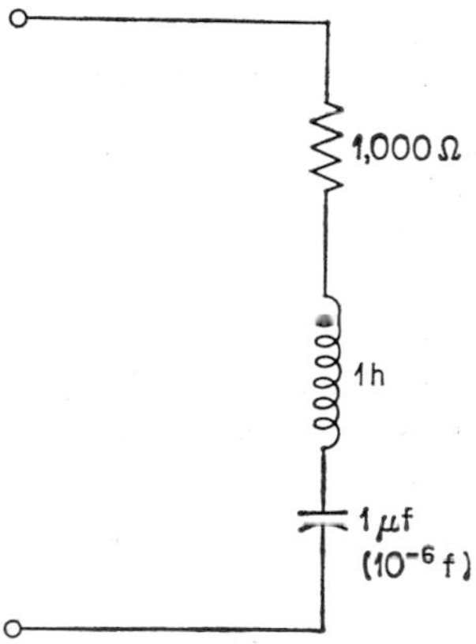

The admittance is then

FIG. 4.7. Circuit for Example 4.8.

$$Y = \frac{1}{Z} = \frac{1}{1390\underline{|-43.92}} = 7.20 \times 10^{-4}\underline{|43.92°} \text{ mhos}$$
$$= 518 + j500 \text{ micromhos}.$$

Thus the conductance is 518 μmhos and the susceptance is 500 μmhos, capacitive.

Example 4.9. Find the impedance and admittance of the circuit of Fig. 4.8 at a frequency of 1000 cps.

Solution. It is easiest to find first the admittance

$$G = \frac{1}{R} = \frac{1}{100} = 0.0100 \text{ mho}$$

$$B_L = -\frac{1}{\omega L} = \frac{-1}{2\pi 1000 \times 16.1 \times 10^{-3}} = -0.0099 \text{ mho}$$

and

$$B_C = \omega C = 2\pi 1000 \times (2 \times 10^{-6}) = 0.0126 \text{ mho}.$$

Thus

$$Y = G + jB = 0.0100 + j(0.0126 - 0.0099) = 0.0100 + j0.0027$$
$$= 0.01036\underline{|15.10°} \text{ mho}.$$

The impedance is

$$Z = \frac{1}{Y} = \frac{1}{0.01036\underline{|15.10}} = 96.6\underline{|-15.10} = 93.2 - j25.2 \text{ ohms}.$$

Alternatively,

$$Z = \frac{1}{0.0100 + j0.0027} \frac{0.0100 - j0.0027}{0.0100 - j0.0027} = \frac{100 - j27}{1 + (0.27)^2} = \frac{100 - j27}{1.073}$$
$$= 93.2 - j25.2 \text{ ohms}.$$

(Multiplying numerator and denominator by a suitable power of 10 is frequently done in order to reduce the possibility of error.) Thus the circuit is equivalent to a resistance of 93.2 ohms in series with a capacitive reactance of 25.2 ohms. The reactance is that of a capacitor given by

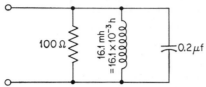

FIG. 4.8. Circuit for Example 4.9.

$$C = \frac{1}{\omega X_C} = \frac{1}{2\pi 1000 \times 25.2} = 6.32 \ \mu f.$$

4.6. Graphical Interpretation of Complex Currents and Voltages.

It is possible now to give a useful interpretation of the expression

$$I = \frac{E}{Z} \tag{4.22}$$

in terms of a graphical illustration known as a "phasor"† diagram. It should first be noted that Eq. (4.22) is merely a shorthand form for

$$i = \text{Re}\left[I\epsilon^{j\omega t}\right] = \text{Re}\left[\frac{E\epsilon^{j\omega t}}{Z}\right] \tag{4.23}$$

or, since I, E, and Z are complex numbers,

$$i = \text{Re}\left[|I|\,\underline{|\phi}\ \epsilon^{j\omega t}\right] = \text{Re}\left[\frac{|E|\,\underline{|\psi}}{|Z|\,\underline{|\theta}}\ \epsilon^{j\omega t}\right]. \tag{4.48}$$

This means that since $|I|$, $|E|$, and $|Z|$ are real numbers

$$i = I\ \text{Re}\left[\epsilon^{j\phi}\epsilon^{j\omega t}\right] = \frac{E}{Z}\ \text{Re}\left[\frac{\epsilon^{j\psi}\epsilon^{j\omega t}}{\epsilon^{j\theta}}\right] = \frac{E}{Z}\ \text{Re}\left[\epsilon^{j(\omega t + \psi - \theta)}\right] \tag{4.49}$$

(the magnitude bars are omitted, since it is understood that only magnitudes of I, E, and Z are implied) or

$$i = I\ \cos\ (\omega t + \theta) = \frac{E}{Z}\ \cos\ (\omega t + \psi - \theta).\ddagger \tag{4.50}$$

Now, $\cos\ (\omega t + \phi)$ is the projection on the real axis of a line (a *phasor*) of unit length rotating about the origin of the complex plane, as shown in Fig. 4.9. In this figure the rotating phasor represents $\epsilon^{j(\omega t + \phi)}$ and the projection on the real axis, $\text{Re}\ [\epsilon^{j(\omega t + \phi)}]$, is $\cos\ (\omega t + \phi)$.

Using the notion of rotating phasors, we may represent the current

† Until recently, the term "vector diagram" was in common use, the entities which we shall call phasors being referred to as vectors. This usage led to confusion with space vectors, and to obviate the confusion the more descriptive term phasor was adopted.

‡ Strictly speaking, we should write $\cos\ (\omega t + \psi - \theta + 2n\pi)$, where n is an integer. However, for simplicity we let $n = 0$.

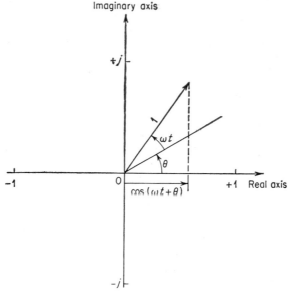

FIG. 4.9. Phasor representation of $\cos(\omega t + \theta)$.

and voltage of Eq. (4.49) by Fig. 4.10 wherein θ has been assumed positive (Z inductive). (The current and voltage are drawn to arbitrary scales.) From Eq. (4.50)

$$\omega t + \phi = \omega t + \psi - \theta \quad (4.51)$$

whence

$$\phi = \psi - \theta \quad (4.52)$$

which is illustrated in the figure.

Usually we are not as interested in the absolute phase of a quantity as we are in its phase relative to other quantities (that is, the phase difference concerned). Thus there is no need explicitly to consider the phasors to be rotating; we need only consider the phasor diagram as existing at a single instant of time, which may be arbitrarily chosen as a matter of

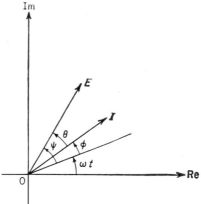

FIG. 4.10. Phasor diagram for E and I in an inductive circuit.

convenience (usually so that one of the variables lies on the real axis, as will be shown in subsequent examples). Furthermore, we are usually concerned more with the effective value (Sec. 4.2) of an alternating wave than with its maximum value. Therefore the length of a phasor is usually made proportional to the effective value of the quantity represented.

The points discussed above can best be appreciated with the aid of some examples.

Example 4.10. A voltage of 10 volts (effective value) is impressed on a series circuit consisting of a resistor having a resistance of 1 ohm and an inductor having a reactance of 2 ohms.   Determine the resulting current, and draw the phasor diagram.

Solution. Since we are not interested in the phase of E (and, indeed, it is not specified) it is convenient to assume it to be zero.   Then

$$E = 10\underline{|0^\circ}.$$

(Remember that this is a much abbreviated shorthand notation for

$$e = \mathrm{Re}\ [10\ \sqrt{2}\ \epsilon^{j(\omega t+0)}].$$

The $\sqrt{2}$ converts the effective to the peak value.)   By definition,

$$I = \frac{E}{Z} = \frac{10\underline{|0}}{1+j2} = \frac{10\underline{|0}}{2.236\underline{|63.43}} = 4.48\underline{|-63.43^\circ}.$$

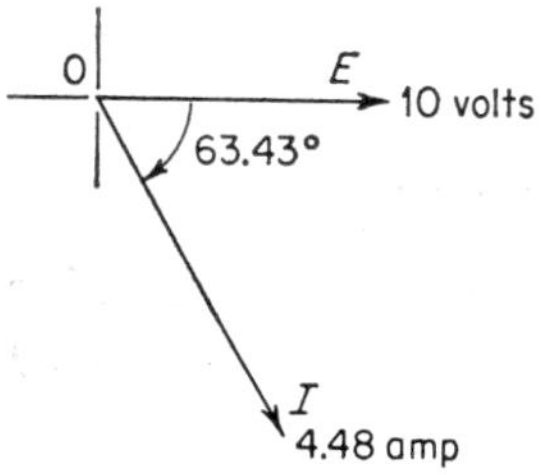

The phasor diagram is shown in Fig. 4.11.

FIG. 4.11. Phasor diagram for E and I in Example 4.10.

In the foregoing example I is said to *lag* E because the rotating phasor representing I crosses the abscissa *after* that representing E. Conversely, E leads I.   In a capacitive circuit, I leads E, or E lags I.   The terms *leading* and *lagging* are generally used only when the phase difference is less than 90°, as confusion might result in other cases.

It should be noted that $E\underline{|\theta}$ represents a phasor, whereas $Z\underline{|\theta}$ is a complex number.   That is, $E\underline{|\theta}$ carries the implication of a rotating line segment while no rotation is associated with Z.   Nevertheless, the rules of complex addition and subtraction apply to E (as well as to I).   This is so because

$$E\underline{|\theta} = E_1\underline{|\theta_1} + E_2\underline{|\theta_2} \tag{4.53}$$

implies

$$\mathrm{Re}\ [\sqrt{2}\ E\epsilon^{j(\omega t+\theta)}] = \mathrm{Re}\ [\sqrt{2}\ E_1\epsilon^{j(\omega t+\theta_1)}] + \mathrm{Re}\ [\sqrt{2}\ E_2\epsilon^{j(\omega t+\theta_2)}]$$
$$= \mathrm{Re}\ [\sqrt{2}\ E_1\epsilon^{j(\omega t+\theta_1)} + \sqrt{2}\ E_2\epsilon^{j(\omega t+\theta_2)}] = \mathrm{Re}\ [\sqrt{2}\ (E_1\epsilon^{j\theta_1} + E_2\epsilon^{j\theta_2})\epsilon^{j\omega t}] \tag{4.54}$$

and the last expression may be evaluated by the rules for manipulating complex numbers.   This result is used in graphical form in the following examples.

Example 4.11.   Draw the phasor diagram for a series RLC circuit.

Solution.   In this example no numerical data are given in order to illustrate that the phasor diagram may often be drawn (though incompletely) with relatively little information.   Here the same current flows in each element of the circuit, and so it proves convenient to take the current phasor as a reference.   The voltage across the resistor, V_R, is in phase with the current; that across the inductance, V_L, leads the current by 90°; and that across the capacitor, V_C, lags the current by 90°.   This is shown in Fig. 4.12, where three cases are considered: (a) $X_L < X_C$, (b) $X_L > X_C$, and (c) $X_L = X_C$.   (In the last case the phenomenon of resonance occurs, which will be treated in detail in Chap. 6.)   The total voltage in each case is the sum of V_R, V_L, and V_C and is represented by the phasor E.

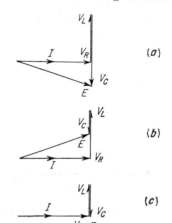

Example 4.12.   Draw the phasor diagram for a circuit consisting of a resistor, an inductor, and a capacitor in parallel.

Solution.   The voltage across each element is the same, and so we shall take the voltage phasor as the reference.   The current in the resistor, I_R, is in phase with the voltage E; that in the inductor, I_L, lags the voltage by 90°; and that in the capacitor, I_C, leads the voltage by 90°.   Three cases, corresponding to (a) $X_L < X_C$, (b) $X_L > X_C$, (c) $X_L = X_C$ are illustrated in Fig. 4.13.   The total current is indicated by the phasor I.

Example 4.13.   Determine the variation of E_{out} as R is varied, in the circuit of Fig. 4.14.   (Here the output voltage may serve

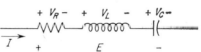

FIG. 4.12. Phasor diagrams for a series *RLC* circuit (Example 4.11).

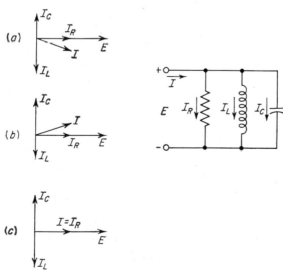

FIG. 4.13. Phasor diagrams for a parallel *RLC* circuit (Example 4.12).

as a source to another network, and so the output voltage is designated by E rather than by V. This is one of many cases where the symbol for voltage may be either E or V, chosen more or less arbitrarily. For simplicity we retain the symbol E for voltage throughout the example.)

Solution. The solution of this example is less straightforward than those given previously, but it serves to illustrate the power of the technique of phasor-diagram analysis.

The voltage E is taken as reference. Then $E_{ab} = E_{bc} = E/2$.† The current I leads E, because the branch *def* is capacitive. The voltage E_{ef} is in phase with I. Also, E_{de} lags I by 90°, and furthermore $E_{ef} + E_{de} = E$. This is shown in Fig. 4.15.

Now a theorem in plane geometry states that, if right triangles are erected on a given hypotenuse, the locus of the vertices of the right angles is a circle, with the

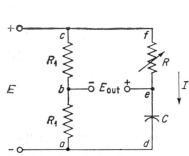
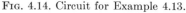

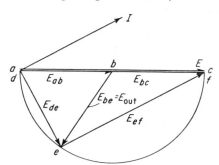

FIG. 4.14. Circuit for Example 4.13.   FIG. 4.15. Phasor diagram for Example 4.13. Arrows indicate voltage rises.

hypotenuse as a diameter. Using this theorem, it follows that the tip of the phasor E_{de} lies on the semicircle shown in Fig. 4.15. Since

$$E_{\text{out}} = E_{be} = E_{ba} + E_{de} = E_{de} - E_{ab}$$

(a and d are the same point) the output voltage is represented by the phasor from the tip of E_{ab} to the tip of the phasor E_{de}. From the geometry of the phasor diagram, then, it is seen that as R is varied the output voltage varies in phase from in phase with E through 180° lagging E, with a constant amplitude of $E/2$. This circuit is frequently employed as a "phase shifter." That is, it is used to provide an output voltage which is shifted in phase relative to the input voltage.

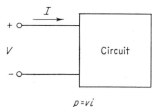

FIG. 4.16. Power relation in a circuit.

4.7. Power Relations in A-C Circuits. It was pointed out in Sec. 1.3 that the power delivered to a circuit is equal to the product of the current through the circuit and the voltage drop across the circuit (see Fig. 4.16). This relationship was developed for constant voltages and varying currents. It may be extended to cover the case of varying voltages as well as varying currents. Then

$$p = iv \qquad (4.55)$$

† Recall that the notation E_{ab} means the voltage *rise* from a to b.

represents the instantaneous value of power being delivered to a circuit, when the reference polarities are as in Fig. 4.16.

Usually we are interested in the average power delivered to a circuit. This is defined by the integral

$$P = P_{av} = \frac{1}{T} \int_0^T iv \, dt \qquad (4.56)$$

where T is the period of the wave.

It is interesting and informative to consider the power relations which apply to simple circuit elements. The power dissipated in a resistor across which a sinusoidal voltage is applied is

$$p = iv = \frac{v^2}{R} = \frac{(\sqrt{2} \, V)^2}{R} \sin^2 \omega t \qquad (4.57)$$

and the average value is

$$P = \frac{1}{T} \int_0^T \frac{2V^2}{R} \sin^2 \omega t = \frac{V^2}{R}. \qquad (4.58)$$

It is instructive to plot the instantaneous power as a function of time (Fig. 4.17a). This plot shows that the instantaneous power varies sinusoidally at twice the frequency of the applied voltage, from zero to twice the average value.

The instantaneous power delivered to an inductor across which a sinusoidal voltage is applied is

$$p = iv = \operatorname{Im} \left[\frac{\sqrt{2} \, V e^{j\omega t}}{\omega L \underline{|90}} \right] \operatorname{Im} [\sqrt{2} \, V e^{j\omega t}]$$

$$= -\frac{2V}{\omega L} \cos \omega t \, V \sin \omega t = -\frac{V^2}{\omega L} \sin 2\omega t. \qquad (4.59)$$

This expression is plotted in Fig. 4.17b. If the average value of p is determined, it is found that

$$P = \frac{1}{T} \int_0^T -\frac{V^2}{\omega L} \sin 2\omega t \, dt = 0. \qquad (4.60)$$

Thus the average value of power delivered to an inductor is zero.

What, then, is the significance of the instantaneous power? Positive instantaneous power represents the rate at which energy is being stored in the magnetic field of the inductor. (Recall that energy is required to change the current in an inductor, because the voltage developed across the inductor tends to oppose the change of current. Since there exists no mechanism to dissipate this energy,† it must be stored in the magnetic field.) Negative instantaneous power represents the rate at which stored energy is being extracted from the magnetic field. Thus, during

† A negligible amount of energy may be radiated, but this need not concern us here.

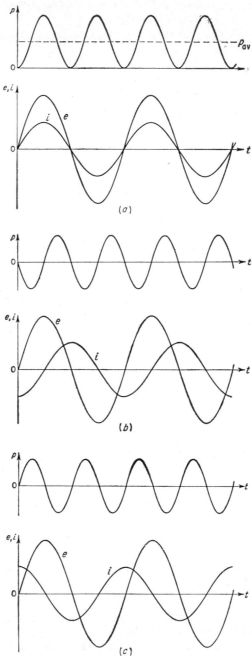

Fig. 4.17. Power relations in simple circuit elements.   (a) Resistor; (b) inductor; (c) capacitor.

a complete cycle of the applied voltage, energy is alternately being stored in and drawn from the magnetic field.

A similar discussion applies to the instantaneous power delivered to a capacitor. In this case,

$$p = iv = \text{Im} \left[\frac{2V\,e^{j\omega t}}{\frac{1}{\omega C} \left\lfloor -90 \right.} \right] \text{Im} \left[\sqrt{2}\, V\, e^{j\omega t} \right] = 2V^2 \omega C \cos \omega t \sin \omega t$$

$$= V^2 \omega C \sin 2\omega t, \tag{4.61}$$

and it follows, as in the inductive case, that

$$P = 0. \tag{4.62}$$

The instantaneous values of voltage, current, and power are plotted in Fig. 4.17c.

A particularly interesting case occurs with an inductor and a capacitor in parallel, when $X_L = -X_C$ (that is, $\omega^2 LC = 1$). Then the current in the inductor is equal to the current in the capacitor. This situation is illustrated in Fig. 4.18, which also shows the instantaneous power for each branch and the values of total instantaneous current and power. It is seen that the total current is zero, as is the power. It might be expected that the total current would be zero, because the sum of the inductive susceptance and the capacitive susceptance is zero, but the behavior of the energy may at first be surprising. In fact, what is happening is this: Energy is stored in the electric field of the capacitor and in the magnetic field of the inductor. The energy is periodically transferred from the electric to the magnetic field, and vice versa. The proportion of energy in each field varies, but the total amount of energy remains constant. The power into either element represents the rate at which energy is transferred from one field to the other. It is clear from an inspection of Fig.

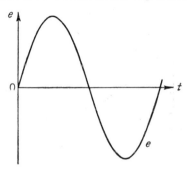

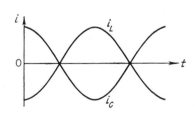

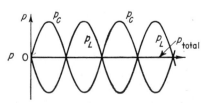

FIG. 4.18. Voltage, currents, and power in a parallel LC circuit.

4.18 that the rate at which energy leaves the electric field is always equal to that at which energy goes into the magnetic field, and conversely.

The current flowing in the inductor and capacitor is frequently referred to as a "circulating current."

In general, impedances which are encountered are not pure resistance, inductance, or capacitance but may be represented by a complex number $Z|\theta$. Although we may, if we wish, plot the instantaneous value of power for such an impedance, we are more interested in the average power in this impedance. Assume an applied voltage of the form Re $[\sqrt{2}\ V\epsilon^{j\omega t}]$ and a current of the form Re $[\sqrt{2}\ I\epsilon^{j(\omega t - \theta)}]$, where θ is the angle by which the current lags the voltage (the angle of the impedance). We thus have

$$P = \frac{1}{T}\int_0^T \text{Re}\ [\sqrt{2}\ I\epsilon^{j(\omega t-\theta)}]\ \text{Re}\ [\sqrt{2}\ V\epsilon^{j\omega t}]\ dt = \frac{2VI}{T}\int_0^T \cos(\omega t - \theta)\cos\omega t\ dt$$

$$= \frac{\omega VI}{\pi}\int_0^T [\cos\omega t\cos\theta + \sin\omega t\sin\theta]\cos\omega t\ dt = VI\cos\theta. \qquad (4.63)$$

This important result tells us that the average power in a circuit is equal

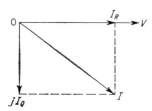

FIG. 4.19. Real (in-phase) and quadrature components of current.

to the product of the effective values of voltage and current times the cosine of the phase angle θ between the current and voltage. The factor $\cos\theta$ is known as the *power factor* of the circuit.

An additional interpretation may be placed on Eq. (4.63). If we draw the phasors representing V and I (Fig. 4.19) it is seen that I may be resolved into two components: a *real* component (that in phase with V) and a *quadrature* component (that lagging V by 90°). Thus

$$I = I_R + jI_Q \qquad (4.64)$$

where (from Fig. 4.19)

$$I_R = I\cos\theta$$
$$I_Q = I\sin\theta. \qquad (4.65)$$

We may then say that

$$P = VI_R \qquad (4.66)$$

since the quadrature component of current does not result in any average power. Now, we may consider any impedance to be made up of two branches in parallel, a resistive branch and a reactive branch (since the admittance Y may be written $G + jB$, G being the conductance of the resistive branch and B being the susceptance of the reactive branch). It then follows from Fig. 4.20 that I_R is the component of current flowing in the resistive branch and jI_Q is the current flowing in the reactive branch.   We consequently define

$$Q = VI_Q = VI \sin \theta \qquad (4.67)$$

as the *reactive volt-amperes* (abbreviated var) and call $\sin \theta$ the reactive factor.† Sometimes Q is called *reactive power*.

The concept of reactive volt-amperes is useful because the limitation on the output of a-c generators is not the total power but rather the

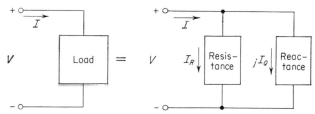

FIG. 4.20. Interpretation of real and reactive currents.

volt-ampere rating (product of rated voltage and maximum output current).   The volt-ampere rating of a load is, from Eqs. (4.64), (4.66), and (4.67),

$$VI = V \sqrt{I_R{}^2 + I_Q{}^2} = \sqrt{V^2 I_R{}^2 + V^2 I_Q{}^2} = \sqrt{P^2 + Q^2}. \qquad (4.68)$$

Frequently the voltage and current are not specified in terms of their magnitudes and relative phase angles but are given in cartesian form. Although we may determine the power by first converting the voltage and current to polar form, there is a convenient expression whereby we may calculate the power directly from the cartesian expressions for voltage and current.   Let

$$\begin{aligned} V_r + jV_q &= V \,\underline{|\theta_V} \\ I_r + jI_q &= I \,\underline{|\theta_I} \end{aligned} \qquad (4.69)$$

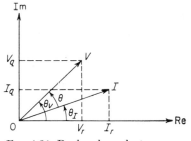

FIG. 4.21. Real and quadrature components of voltage and current.

where now the subscripts r and q refer to the real and quadrature (imaginary) components of V and I (see Fig. 4.21).   Form the product

$$VI^* = V \,\underline{|\theta_V}\, I \,\underline{|-\theta_I} = VI\epsilon^{j(\theta_V - \theta_I)} = VI\epsilon^{j\theta} = VI\,(\cos \theta + j \sin \theta) \qquad (4.70)$$

where θ is the angle by which I lags V.   This becomes, by virtue of Eqs. (4.63) and (4.67),

$$VI^* = P + jQ. \qquad (4.71)$$

† It is again emphasized that θ has been defined as the angle by which the current lags the voltage.   Thus, the reactive power is positive in an inductive circuit.   This convention has only recently been standardized, and many older books use the opposite convention.

This latter quantity is called the *vector power*.   Vector power is a useful concept in power-system calculations.

It is seen that

$$P = \text{Re}\,[VI^*] = \text{Re}\,[(V_r + jV_q)(I_r - jI_q)] \qquad (4.72)$$
$$P = V_r I_r + V_q I_q \qquad\qquad\qquad\qquad\qquad\qquad (4.73)$$

which is a convenient form for calculating power from the cartesian expressions for V and I.

EXERCISES

4.1. (*a*) Determine the effective value of the waveform shown in Fig. 4.22.
(*b*) Determine its average value.

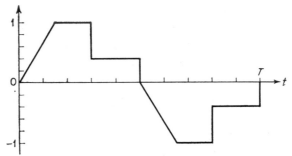

FIG. 4.22. Exercise 4.1.

4.2. (*a*) What is the effective value of the waveform shown in Fig. 4.23?
(*b*) What is its average value?

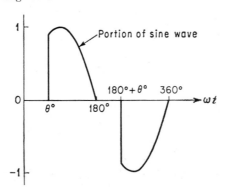

FIG. 4.23. Exercise 4.2.

4.3. Determine the peak factor and form factor of the waveforms of Exercises 4.1 and 4.2.

4.4. Find the sums of the following pairs of complex numbers.

(*a*) $2 - j3,\ 7 + j2$

(b) $0.1 + j6$, $-0.2 + j3.5$
(c) $a + jb$, $-a + jb$
(d) ϵ^{j2}, $2\epsilon^{j\pi}$
(e) $2 + ja$, ϵ^{ja}
(f) $3\underline{|30°}$, $-2\underline{|60°}$
(g) $\cos 3 + j \sin 4$, $\cos 4 + j \sin 3$
(h) $1.7\underline{|16°}$, $2 - j\sqrt{3}$
(i) $\cos a - j2$, $2\underline{|a}$
(j) $2 \cos 3 + j2$, j^3

4.5. Write the following complex numbers in polar form.

(a) $1 + j$
(b) $-2 + j3$
(c) $7 - j6$
(d) $-1 - j\sqrt{2}$
(e) $\cos \pi/4 + j \sin \pi/4$
(f) $\cos 2 + j \sin 2$
(g) $\cos 3 + j \sin 3.5$
(h) $\sin 1 + j \cos 1$
(i) $\sin 2 + j \sin 2$
(j) $2 \cos 0.2\pi - 3j \sin 0.2\pi$

4.6. Write the following complex numbers in cartesian form.

(a) ϵ^{j^2}
(b) $3\epsilon^{j0.3}$
(c) $2\epsilon^{-j} + 3\epsilon^{j}$
(d) $\dfrac{1}{2 + j3} + 7\epsilon^{j\pi}$
(e) $2\underline{|20°}$
(f) $2.5\underline{|10°} - 5\underline{|20°}$
(g) $\cos 2 + j^2 \cos 2$
(h) $\epsilon^{j\,2+\delta}$
(i) $1 + j + j^2 + j^3$
(j) $j\epsilon^{j0.2\pi}$

4.7. Express the following numbers in the form $a + jb$.

(a) $\dfrac{2}{1 - j}$
(b) $(-2 + j)^3$

(c) $(-1 + j)^4$
(d) $\dfrac{2 - j}{\sqrt{3} + j}$

(e) $\dfrac{3\epsilon^{4j}}{1 - \pi j}$
(f) $\dfrac{\cos \theta + j \sin \theta}{\sin \theta + j \cos \theta}$

(g) $j2.2\underline{|15°}$
(h) j^n, n a positive integer

(i) $\dfrac{1}{\cos \theta + j \cos \theta}$
(j) j^j

4.8. Find a complex number whose square is $2 + j3$.   [HINT: Write the number in polar form and recall that $\sqrt{\epsilon^{j\theta}} = \pm\epsilon^{j\theta/2}$.]

4.9. Find the three cube roots of unity.   That is, find three (complex) numbers whose cubes are 1.

4.10. What is the square root of j?

4.11. Write $\log (2 + j)$ as a complex number in the form $a + jb$.

4.12. Prove that

$$\cos \theta + \cos 2\theta + \cdots + \cos N\theta = \frac{\cos \dfrac{N + 1}{2} \theta \sin \dfrac{N\theta}{2}}{\sin \dfrac{\theta}{2}}, \qquad \theta \neq 0.$$

4.13. Prove that
$$(\text{Re } [A])^2 + (\text{Im } [A])^2 = AA^*.$$

4.14. Prove that

(a) $(A + B)^* = A^* + B^*$ (b) $(AB)^* = A^*B^*$

(c) $\left(\dfrac{A}{B}\right)^* = \dfrac{A^*}{B^*}$, $B \neq 0$ (d) $|AB| = |A| \cdot |B|$

(e) $(iA)^* = -iA^*$

4.15. Prove that

$$(\cos \theta + j \sin \theta)(\cos \phi + j \sin \phi) = \cos (\theta + \phi) + j \sin (\theta + \phi).$$

4.16. Prove that, if A and B are complex numbers, then
(a) $|A + B| \leq |A| + |B|$.
(b) $|A + B| \geq | |A| - |B| |$.
4.17. If $A^2 = A^{*2}$, what can you say about A?
4.18. Consider all ordered pairs of real numbers (a,b), where $(a,b) = (c,d)$ if and only if $a = c$ and $b = d$. Define sum as

$$(a,b) + (c,d) = (a + c, b + d)$$

and product as

$$(a,b)(c,d) = (ac - bd, ad + bc).$$

Show that these ordered pairs enjoy all the arithmetic properties of complex numbers. For example, show that
(a) $(a,b) + (c,d) = (c,d) + (a,b)$.
(b) $(a,b)(c,d) = (c,d)(a,b)$.
(c) $(a,b)[(c,d) + (e,f)] = (a,b)(c,d) + (a,b)(e,f)$.
(d) $(0,1)(0,1) = (-1,0)$.
(e) $\dfrac{1}{(a,b)} = \left(\dfrac{a}{a^2 + b^2}, \dfrac{-b}{a^2 + b^2}\right)$, $a^2 + b^2 \neq 0$.

4.19. Show that any root of a complex number is again a complex number.
4.20. Let z be a complex variable. Describe the region in the z plane determined by the following inequalities or equalities.

(a) $|z| = 1$ (b) $|z - 2| < 3$
(c) Re $[z] > 0$ (d) Im $[z] \leq 0$
(e) Re $[z] = $ Im $[z]$

4.21. Let $|z - 1| \leq 1$. Show that the set of points covered by $w = z^2$ in the w plane is bounded by a cardioid.
4.22. Compute the impedance of the circuit shown in Fig. 4.24 at $f = 1$ cps, $f = 10$ cps, $f = 100$ cps.

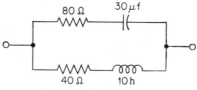

Fig. 4.24. Exercise 4.22.

4.23. (*a*) Determine the equivalent impedance of the circuit of Fig. 4.25, using the rectangular form of all complex impedances.

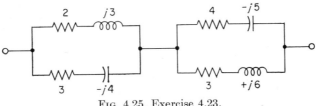

FIG. 4.25. Exercise 4.23.

(*b*) Repeat, using polar forms for multiplication and division.

4.24. Repeat Exercise 4.23 for the impedances shown in Fig. 4.26.

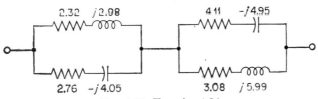

FIG. 4.26. Exercise 4.24.

4.25. Draw a phasor diagram showing the various currents and voltages in Exercise 4.22 at a frequency of 10 cps.

4.26. Draw a phasor diagram showing the various currents and voltages in Exercise 4.24.

4.27. Determine the voltage difference between points *c* and *d* of Fig. 4.27.   Draw the phasor diagram for this circuit.

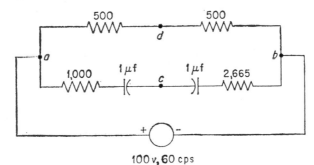

FIG. 4.27. Exercise 4.27.

4.28. An impedance of $12 + j9$ is connected across a 60-cps source.   What values of capacitance must be connected across this impedance to make the power factor unity?   Draw the appropriate phasor diagrams.

4.29. Repeat Exercise 4.28 for a power factor of 0.95.   Find every value of capacitance which will produce the desired result.   Show the phasor diagram.

4.30. If a resistor is to be used in Exercise 4.29 instead of a capacitor, determine every value of resistance which will produce a power factor of 0.95.   Sketch the phasor diagram.

4.31. An impedance dissipates 600 watts at a power factor of 0.7 when the applied voltage is 100 volts.   Determine the effective resistance, the inductive reactance, the current, and the vector power.

4.32. In the circuit of Example 4.13 (Fig. 4.14) what is the effect of replacing R_{bc} by a capacitor equal to $C/2$ and replacing R_{ab} by a resistor which is maintained equal to $2R$?   Draw the phasor diagram.

4.33. (a) Find Z for unity power factor at the input of Fig. 4.28.   Note that Re $[Z] > 0$.

(b) Find the smallest current in Z for which the input power factor is unity.

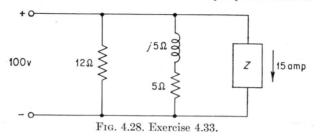

FIG. 4.28. Exercise 4.33.

4.34. Determine the value of L for which the power factor at the input of the circuit shown in Fig. 4.29 is unity.

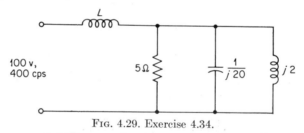

FIG. 4.29. Exercise 4.34.

4.35. With a voltage of $10\underline{|15°}$ volts applied to the circuit of Exercise 4.24, determine the power dissipated in each resistor.   Compare with the total power dissipated calculated from $VI \cos \theta$, Re $[VI^*]$, and $|I|^2$ Re $[Z]$.

4.36. A voltage of 50 volts rms is applied to an impedance $4 + j5$.   Find the vector power, the real power, the reactive power, and the power factor of the circuit.

4.37. An impedance consists of a 5-ohm resistor in parallel with a $j7$-ohm reactor. With 100 volts applied, determine the vector power, the real power, the reactive power, and the power factor of the circuit.

CHAPTER 5

GENERAL STEADY-STATE ANALYSIS OF A-C CIRCUITS

We now wish to generalize the techniques developed for analyzing simple series and parallel circuits in the sinusoidal steady state. We shall proceed by easy stages toward this more general analysis. Such a general analysis may be approached by many routes; we may consider non-sinusoidal periodic waveforms in simple networks, or sinusoidal waveforms in more general networks, or even exponential waveforms. We choose in this chapter to consider first the analysis of general networks in which the waveforms are all sinusoids having the same frequency.

The networks considered are perfectly general. To some extent, then, the problem considered is quite artificial, for in practical problems such generality is rarely encountered. At least two major reasons may be advanced for considering the general problem. In the first place, a method will be developed which permits the complete determination of the current and voltage in each branch of any network in the sinusoidal steady state. Thus we shall have at least *some* method of obtaining answers to problems. Secondly, the general analysis will lay the groundwork for determining general properties of all networks, which properties are important not only in network analysis but in network synthesis as well.

It may be profitable here to dwell for a moment on the matter of network *synthesis*. In network analysis one is presented with a problem in the form of a network whose behavior in some sense is to be determined. In practice, however, problems generally occur in the converse form: A certain behavior is required—what network provides this behavior? One cannot synthesize networks if he cannot analyze them; learning network analysis is a necessary prelude to learning network synthesis. The ability to analyze networks is not alone sufficient to provide the ability to synthesize networks. This is particularly true if one is accustomed to apply blindly the most powerful and general analytical techniques even to simple networks. Networks should always be examined for symmetries and other simplifying factors. One should approach network problems ready to understand a network and not just ready to demolish it. This approach will make one proficient in network theory and not merely in network solving.

In this chapter we shall consistently designate steady-state currents and voltages by their effective values. Thus writing $E|\theta$ implies $e = \text{Re}\,[\sqrt{2}\,E\epsilon^{j(\omega t+\theta)}]$.

5.1. Loop-current Analysis of A-C Circuits. The loop-current method of analysis developed in Chap. 1 for d-c circuits applies also to a-c circuits, provided that we replace the various resistances in the d-c circuit by a-c impedances. In the general case of a network having λ independent loops, the equilibrium equations may be written as

$$
\begin{aligned}
E_1 &= Z_{11}I_1 + Z_{12}I_2 + \cdots + Z_{1\lambda}I_\lambda \\
E_2 &= Z_{21}I_1 + Z_{22}I_2 + \cdots + Z_{2\lambda}I_\lambda \\
&\cdots\cdots\cdots\cdots\cdots\cdots\cdots\cdots\cdots \\
E_\lambda &= Z_{\lambda1}I_1 + Z_{\lambda2}I_2 + \cdots + Z_{\lambda\lambda}I_\lambda.
\end{aligned}
\tag{5.1}
$$

In this set of equations

E_i is the sum of the (complex) voltage rises from voltage sources in the ith loop (the loop being traversed in the direction of I_i).

I_j is the current in the jth loop.

Z_{ij} If Z is the complex impedance common to loops i and j, then $Z_{ij} = Z$ if I_i and I_j traverse Z in the same direction and $Z_{ij} = -Z$ if I_i and I_j traverse Z in the opposite direction. Z_{ij} is called the *mutual impedance* between loops i and j. Clearly, $Z_{ij} = Z_{ji}$. If $I = j$, Z_{ii} is called the *self-impedance* of loop i.

There is one phenomenon peculiar to a-c circuits which does not occur in d-c circuit analysis. This is the effect of mutual inductance, which may lead to mutual impedance between loops which are not conductively connected, or which may modify mutual and self-impedances of loops. These effects are best illustrated by means of examples.

Example 5.1. Determine Z_{12} for the network of Fig. 5.1.

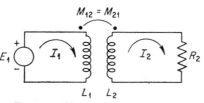

$M_{12} = M_{21}$

FIG. 5.1. Circuit for Example 5.1.

Solution. Two approaches may be used. The first is to write the loop equations for the network,

$$
\begin{aligned}
E_1 &= j\omega L_1 I_1 - j\omega M_{12}I_2 \\
0 &= -j\omega M_{21}I_1 + R_2 I_2.
\end{aligned}
$$

From these equations it is apparent that

$$
Z_{12} = Z_{21} = -j\omega M_{12}.
$$

A more direct approach is to write, by inspection of the circuit diagram, the mutual impedance. Since the only coupling between the two loops is by means of mutual inductances,

$$
Z_{12} = -j\omega M_{12}.
$$

The negative sign is obtained because I_1 enters the dotted end of L_1, whereas I_2 leaves the dotted end of L_2 (see Sec. 2.4).

Example 5.2.   Determine the Z_{ij} for the circuit shown in Fig. 5.2.

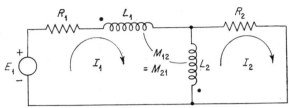

FIG. 5.2. Circuit for Example 5.2.

Solution,   Loop 1 contains a resistor and two inductors.   Note, however, that I_1 flowing in L_1 causes an induced voltage in L_2.   Similarly, I_1 flowing in L_2 induces a voltage in L_1.   Thus

$$Z_{11} = R_1 + j\omega(L_1 + L_2 - 2M_{12}).$$

(The negative sign occurs because I_1 enters the dotted end of L_1 and leaves the dotted end of L_2.)   Also,

$$Z_{12} = Z_{21} = j\omega(L_2 + M_{12}).$$

(Observe the positive sign of M_{12}.)   Finally

$$Z_{22} = R_2 + j\omega L_2.$$

Example 5.3.   Enumerate the Z_{ij} for the network of Fig. 5.3.

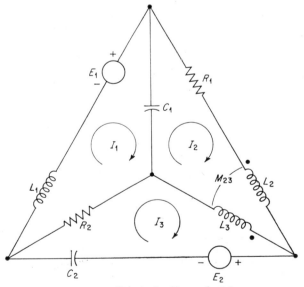

FIG. 5.3. Circuit for Example 5.3.

Solution. The impedances can be conveniently tabulated as in the array below. This array is called an *impedance matrix* (see Chap. 11).

$$\left\| \begin{matrix} Z_{11} & Z_{12} & Z_{13} \\ Z_{21} & Z_{22} & Z_{23} \\ Z_{31} & Z_{32} & Z_{33} \end{matrix} \right\|$$

$$= \left\| \begin{matrix} R_2 + j\omega L_1 - j\dfrac{1}{\omega C_1} & j\dfrac{1}{\omega C_1} & -R_2 \\ j\dfrac{1}{\omega C_1} & R_1 + j\omega(L_2 + L_3 + 2M_{23}) & j\omega(-L_3 - M_{23}) \\ -R_2 & j\omega(-L_3 - M_{23}) & R_2 + j\omega L_3 - j\dfrac{1}{\omega C_2} \end{matrix} \right\|$$

It is worthwhile to compare the simplicity of the expressions for the Z_{ij} with the system of integrodifferential equations obtained in Chap. 2 for the same network (see Example 2.2).

The rules for solving linear algebraic equations may be employed to obtain explicit solutions for the loop currents from Eqs. (5.1). Branch currents are obtained by combining loop currents, and branch voltages by multiplying branch currents by branch impedances. As pointed out in the introduction, such general forms of solution are not necessarily required in real problems, but the general form of the solution is significant in theoretical investigations.

The application of Cramer's rule (see Appendix A) to Eqs. (5.1) yields

$$I_1 = \frac{A_{11}}{D} E_1 + \frac{A_{21}}{D} E_2 + \cdots + \frac{A_{\lambda 1}}{D} E_\lambda$$

$$I_2 = \frac{A_{12}}{D} E_1 + \frac{A_{22}}{D} E_2 + \cdots + \frac{A_{\lambda 2}}{D} E_\lambda$$

$$\cdots \cdots \cdots \cdots \cdots \cdots \cdots \cdots \cdots \tag{5.2}$$

$$I_\lambda = \frac{A_{1\lambda}}{D} E_1 + \frac{A_{2\lambda}}{D} E_2 + \cdots + \frac{A_{\lambda\lambda}}{D} E_\lambda$$

where A_{ij} is the cofactor of Z_{ij} and D is the determinant of the Z_{ij}. The ratios A_{ij}/D have the dimensions of admittance. Hence we may write

$$I_1 = y_{11}E_1 + y_{12}E_2 + \cdots + y_{1\lambda}E_\lambda$$
$$I_2 = y_{21}E_1 + y_{22}E_2 + \cdots + y_{2\lambda}E_\lambda$$
$$\cdots \cdots \cdots \cdots \cdots \cdots \cdots \cdots \cdots \tag{5.3}$$
$$I_\lambda = y_{\lambda 1}E_1 + y_{\lambda 2}E_2 + \cdots + y_{\lambda\lambda}E_\lambda$$

where

$$y_{ij} = \frac{A_{ji}}{D}. \tag{5.4}$$

These y_{ij} have a physical significance which may be explained as follows. If all the voltage sources in the network except E_j are replaced by short circuits, then

$$I_i = y_{ij}E_j \tag{5.5}$$

or y_{ij} is the ratio of current flowing in the ith loop to the voltage applied in the jth loop.   Thus

y_{ij} is termed the *short-circuit transfer admittance* between loops i and j. ($y_{ij} = y_{ji}$ since $A_{ji} = A_{ij}$.)

y_{ii} is termed the *short-circuit admittance* or *short-circuit driving-point admittance* of loop i.

It is often possible to obtain the y_{ij} directly from the circuit diagram without actually solving the equilibrium equations.   Recalling the definition of y_{ij} as the ratio of current in the ith loop to the voltage in the jth loop causing it, we may determine y_{ij} by considering the circuit with all voltage sources removed, then placing a voltage source in the jth loop, and measuring the current in the ith loop.   This procedure is illustrated by means of an example.

Example 5.4.   Determine y_{12} and y_{32} for the circuit shown in Fig. 5.4a.

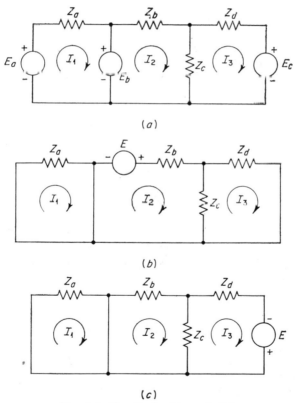

(a)

(b)

(c)

FIG. 5.4. Circuits for Example 5.4.

Solution.   To determine y_{12} we remove all voltage sources and then place a single voltage source in loop 2 (Fig. 5.4b).   Observe that this source cannot be placed in the branch which originally contained E_b, for such a location would make the source contribute to E_2 *and also to* E_1.

It is clear that, with the source placed as shown, $I_1 = 0$ (I_2 is independent of the voltage in loop 2), and so

$$y_{12} = 0.$$

To determine y_{23}, we place a source only in loop 3 (Fig. 5.4c). The current in Z_b is equal to I_2. (That in Z_c is *not*—it is $I_2 - I_3$.) Thus

$$y_{23} = \frac{I_2}{E_c} = \frac{I_{z_b}}{E_c} = \frac{1}{Z_d + \dfrac{Z_b Z_c}{Z_b + Z_c}} \frac{Z_c}{Z_b + Z_c}$$

$$= \frac{Z_c}{Z_d Z_b + Z_d Z_c + Z_b Z_c}.$$

It is left to the reader to verify the results obtained here by actually writing the equilibrium equations for the network and solving for the y_{ij}.

It is seen from the last example that care must be exercised when inserting a source, to be certain that it is placed in one, and only one, loop, and

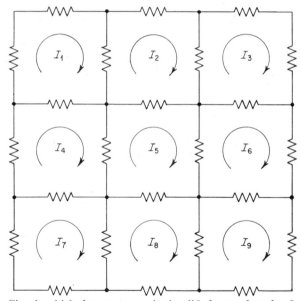

FIG. 5.5. Circuit which does not permit simplified procedure for finding y_{ij}.

when measuring the current, to measure only one loop current, not the sum of two or more. This cannot always be done, as may be seen from Fig. 5.5. With the circuit shown, we cannot use the simple procedure explained above to determine y_{ij}, when $i = 5$ or $j = 5$, because any voltage source inserted in the fifth loop is also part of one other loop. Thus a voltage source cannot be placed in the fifth loop alone, and similarly an ammeter placed in the fifth loop measures not I_5 but the difference between I_5 and some other loop current. However, it is still possible to determine y_{5j} or y_{i5} without solving the whole network problem by making suitable pairs of measurements, as a little study will show.   This is left as an exercise for the reader.

5.2. Node-voltage Analysis of A-C Circuits.   The method of node-voltage analysis for d-c circuits may also be extended to a-c circuits if we replace the conductances by complex admittances.   Then the equilibrium equations of an n-node network may be written

$$
\begin{aligned}
I_1 &= Y_{11}V_1 + Y_{12}V_2 + \cdots + Y_{1n}V_n \\
I_2 &= Y_{21}V_1 + Y_{22}V_2 + \cdots + Y_{2n}V_n \\
&\; \cdots \cdots \cdots \cdots \cdots \cdots \cdots \cdots \\
I_n &= Y_{n1}V_1 + Y_{n2}V_2 + \cdots + Y_{nn}V_n.
\end{aligned}
\tag{5.6}
$$

In the above set of equations

I_i is the (complex) sum of the currents flowing from current sources into the ith node.

V_j is the potential of the jth node with respect to the reference node.

Y_{ii} is the sum of all admittances terminating on the ith node.   It is called the *self-admittance* of the ith node.

Y_{ij} $(i \neq j)$ is the negative of the admittance connecting the ith and jth nodes.   It is called the *mutual admittance* between nodes i and j. Clearly, $Y_{ij} = Y_{ji}$.

It is to be observed that the Y_{ij} are not the y_{ij} of Eq. (5.5).   They are defined differently, and furthermore, since the number of meshes used in analyzing a circuit is not generally equal to the number of nodes used in analyzing the same circuit, there are not necessarily the same number of y_{ij} and Y_{ij}.

Example 5.5.   Write the node-voltage equations for the circuit shown in Fig. 5.6.

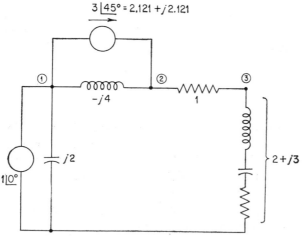

FIG. 5.6. Circuit for Example 5.5.   Admittances are in mhos.

Solution. We have

$$-1.121 - j2.121 = -j2V_1 + \qquad j4V_2$$
$$2.121 + j2.121 = \quad j4V_1 + (1 - j4)V_2 - V_3$$
$$0 = \qquad - V_2 \qquad + (3 + j3)V_3.$$

Mutual inductances prove troublesome in node-voltage analysis, to the extent that mutual inductances cannot be handled, except in a clumsy fashion.† This is so because the voltage of mutual induction which appears across a coil results from a branch current flowing in another coil.

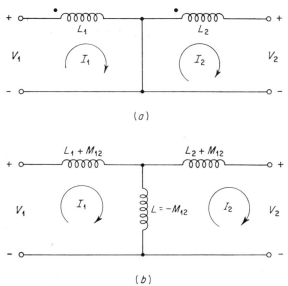

(a)

(b)

Fɪɢ. 5.7. Reduction of circuit containing mutual inductance for node-voltage analysis. (a) Original circuit; (b) equivalent circuit.

However, the branch currents do not appear explicitly in the node equations. The only case involving mutual inductances which is simple to treat occurs when part of the network to be analyzed contains the configuration of inductances shown in Fig. 5.7a. The following set of loop equations applies to that network:

$$V_1 = j\omega L_1 I_1 + j\omega M_{12} I_2$$
$$V_2 = -j\omega M_{12} I_1 - j\omega L_2 I_2. \tag{5.7}$$

This set of equations also applies to the network shown in Fig. 5.7b. Hence, in circuits in which the configuration of Fig. 5.7a appears, we may replace it by that of Fig. 5.7b. This replacement removes the mutual inductance as such, thereby permitting us to analyze the circuit on a node basis.

† M. F. Gardner and J. L. Barnes, "Transients in Linear Systems," vol. 1, John Wiley & Sons, Inc., New York, 1942, pp. 40ff.

The general solution of Eq. (5.6) may be written with the aid of Cramer's rule. Then

$$V_1 = \frac{A_{11}}{D} I_1 + \frac{A_{21}}{D} I_2 + \cdots + \frac{A_{n1}}{D} I_n$$

$$V_2 = \frac{A_{12}}{D} I_1 + \frac{A_{22}}{D} I_2 + \cdots + \frac{A_{n2}}{D} I_n \qquad (5.8)$$

$$\cdots\cdots\cdots\cdots\cdots\cdots\cdots\cdots\cdots$$

$$V_n = \frac{A_{1n}}{D} I_1 + \frac{A_{2n}}{D} I_2 + \cdots + \frac{A_{nn}}{D} I_n$$

where A_{ij} is the cofactor of Y_{ij} and D is the determinant of the Y_{ij}. We may write the above set of equations as

$$V_1 = z_{11}I_1 + z_{12}I_2 + \cdots + z_{1n}I_n$$
$$V_2 = z_{21}I_1 + z_{22}I_2 + \cdots + z_{2n}I_n \qquad (5.9)$$
$$\cdots\cdots\cdots\cdots\cdots\cdots\cdots$$
$$V_n = z_{n1}I_1 + z_{n2}I_2 + \cdots + z_{nn}I_n$$

where

$$z_{ij} = \frac{A_{ji}}{D}. \qquad (5.10)$$

Like the y's encountered in loop analysis, the z_{ij} may be given physical significance. If all the current sources except I_j are open-circuited, then, from Eqs. (5.9),

$$V_i = z_{ij}I_j$$

where

z_{ij} ($i \neq j$) is called the *open-circuit transfer impedance* between nodes i and j ($z_{ij} = z_{ji}$ since $A_{ji} = A_{ij}$).

z_{ii} is called the *open-circuit impedance* or *open-circuit driving-point impedance* of node i.

There is some temptation to write $z_{ij} = 1/y_{ij}$. This temptation must be resisted. The z's refer to impedances between nodes; the y's refer to admittances between loops.

As was the case with the y_{ij}, we may often determine the z_{ij} directly from the circuit diagram by removing all current sources and then measuring the voltage of the ith node which results from a current being injected into the jth node.

5.3. Network Geometry. The presence of mutual inductance in a-c circuits modifies somewhat the relationships of network geometry developed in Chap. 1. In particular, a circuit may now have *separate parts*, each separate part being a network which is coupled only magnetically to one or more other parts of the circuit. Examples are shown in Fig. 5.8. If

B = the total number of branches
N = the total number of nodes
m = the total number of meshes
λ = the number of independent loop equations which may be written
n = the number of independent node equations which may be written
s = the number of separate parts

then the relations of Chap. 1 become (provided that each separate part is mappable)

$$\lambda = m - s \qquad (5.11)$$
$$n = N - s \qquad (5.12)$$

[since Eqs. (1.19) and (1.20) hold for *each* separate part]. The relation

$$B = \lambda + n \qquad (5.13)$$

still holds regardless of the number of separate parts. Equation (5.12) is not of much utility, however, since almost all circuits involving mutual inductance are analyzed on a loop basis, using Eq. (5.11) to indicate the proper number of equations to be written.

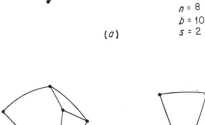

(a)

$n = 8$
$b = 10$
$s = 2$

$n = 8$
$b = 11$
$s = 1$

(b)

Fig. 5.8. Illustration of separate parts of a network.

5.4. Network Theorems. The simple relationships developed in Secs. 1.12 and 1.13 also hold for a-c circuits, wherein Z is substituted for R. The more important theorems which were merely stated in the latter section will be repeated here with proofs.

I. *The Principle of Superposition.* The principle of superposition states that the response of a network to several simultaneously acting forcing functions is equal to the sum of the responses to each forcing function acting individually. This principle follows directly from the linearity of the circuit elements. It is merely a restatement of Cramer's rule for finding the solution of a set of simultaneous linear algebraic equations.

The principle of superposition may be employed as in Sec. 1.13 as an alternative to the usual methods of solving simple networks. A more useful, although less obvious, application is to the case where the sources in a network produce sine waves of different frequencies, as will be seen in the following example.

Example 5.6. Determine the current i in the circuit of Fig. 5.9a if

$$e_1 = 1 \sqrt{2} \cos (t + \theta_1)$$
$$e_2 = 2 \sqrt{2} \cos (2t + \theta_2).$$

Solution. Using the principle of superposition, we shall first determine the component of i resulting from e_1 and then that from e_2. The sum of these is the current i.

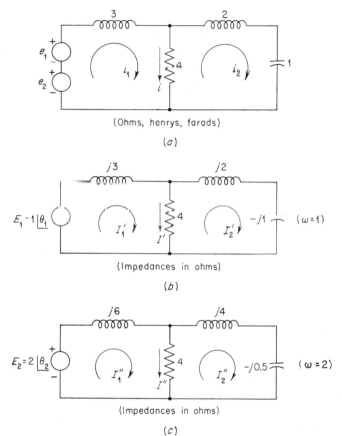

(Ohms, henrys, farads)

(a)

(Impedances in ohms)

(b)

(Impedances in ohms)

(c)

FIG. 5.9. Circuit showing application of superposition theorem. (a) Original circuit, (b) circuit for variables of frequency $\omega = 1$; (c) circuit for variables of frequency $\omega = 2$.

Since we are now dealing with a single frequency ω ($=1$) we may use the shorthand notation of complex voltages and impedances to write

$$E_1 = 1|\theta_1.$$

The network may be redrawn as in Fig. 5.9b, where the impedances are shown in ohms.

The equilibrium equations are

$$1\underline{|\theta_1} = (4 + j3)I_1' - 4I_2'$$
$$0 = -4I_1' + (4 + j1)I_2'$$

whence

$$I' = I_1' - I_2' = \frac{(4 + j1) - (-4)}{(4 + j3)(4 + j1) - 16} \, 1\underline{|\theta_1} = \frac{8 + j1}{-3 + j16} \, 1\underline{|\theta_1}$$

$$= \frac{8.06\underline{|7.12}}{16.27\underline{|100.62}} \, 1\underline{|\theta_1} = 0.496\underline{|-93.50} \times 1\underline{|\theta_1} = 0.496\underline{|\theta_1 - 93.50}.$$

To obtain the component of current resulting from E_2 we may use the circuit shown in Fig. 5.9c, wherein the impedances at $\omega = 2$ are now shown, and for which

$$E_2 = 2\underline{|\theta_2}.$$

Then

$$2\underline{|\theta_2} = (4 + j6)I_1'' - 4I_2''$$
$$0 = -4I_1'' + (4 + j3.5)I_2''$$

and so

$$I'' = I_1'' - I_2'' = \frac{(4 + j3.5) - (-4)}{(4 + j6)(4 + j3.5) - 16} \, 2\underline{|\theta_2} = \frac{8 + j3.5}{-21 + j38} \, 2\underline{|\theta_2}$$

$$= \frac{8.74\underline{|23.63}}{43.4\underline{|108.94}} \, 2\underline{|\theta_2} = 0.207\underline{|-85.31} \times 2\underline{|\theta_2} = 0.414\underline{|\theta_2 - 85.31°}.$$

The total current i may then be written

$$i = 0.496 \sqrt{2} \cos (t + \theta_1 - 93.50°) + 0.414 \sqrt{2} \cos (2t + \theta_2 - 85.31°).$$

We cannot write the current i as $0.496\underline{|\theta_1 - 93.50} + 0.414\underline{|\theta_2 - 85.31}$ because this implies the same frequency for each term, which is not the case. Notice also that we cannot speak meaningfully of the phase of i relative to e_1 or e_2, because phase is meaningful only if all our variables have the same frequency. Finally, $\theta_1 = \theta_2$ does not imply, in general, that e_1 and e_2 pass through zero at the same time, as 1° of e_1 corresponds, in time, to 2° of e_2.†

II. *The Principle of Reciprocity.* This principle is usually stated in terms of the *reciprocity theorem:* The current in any loop in a circuit (say loop i) caused by an ideal voltage source in another loop in the circuit (say loop j) is the same as the current in loop j which would be caused were the ideal voltage source placed in loop i. That is, an ideal voltage source and an ammeter may be interchanged in a circuit without changing the reading of the ammeter, provided that no other voltage sources exist in the circuit.‡ The reciprocity theorem follows directly from the fact that $y_{ij} = y_{ji}$, which in turn stems from the equality of Z_{ij} and Z_{ji}. Indeed, rather than consider reciprocity as a theorem it is often considered

† It is interesting to observe that, if ω_2 is not an integral multiple of ω_1 (for example, $\omega_2 = \sqrt{3} \, \omega_1$), i is not truly a periodic waveform, and so its steady state appears non-existent. Nonetheless, this aperiodic waveform is a true steady-state response (see Sec. 3.4), and the type of analysis used above is proper.

‡ See the footnote comment to Sec. 1.13, II, p. 30.

as a definition of the class of networks under consideration. That is, *reciprocal networks* are those in which $Z_{ij} = Z_{ji}$. (For an example of a nonreciprocal network, see Sec. 5.5.)

There does exist a more general principle of reciprocity applied to electromagnetic fields from which we obtain the relationship $M_{ij} = M_{ji}$. Unfortunately, a proper discussion of the general principle of reciprocity is beyond the scope of this book.

III. *Thévenin's Theorem.*   This theorem states that if measurements are made at two terminals of any network the network is indistinguishable from a network consisting of a voltage source in series with an impedance,

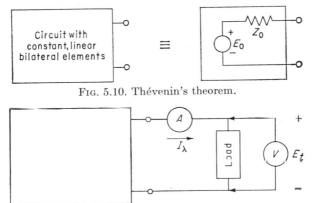

FIG. 5.10. Thévenin's theorem.

FIG. 5.11. Circuit employed in development of Thévenin's theorem.

if the voltage source is equal to the open-circuit voltage across the two terminals of the circuit (E_0) and the impedance is equal to the ratio of the open-circuit voltage to the short-circuit current (I_0) between the two terminals.   Figure 5.10 illustrates the equivalent circuit obtained by Thévenin's theorem.

The theorem may be proved as follows: All the electrical measurements which can be made at the two terminals are essentially simultaneous measurements of voltage across these terminals and current entering the terminals.   The load which may be placed across the terminals may be a combination of impedances and sources; however, in terms of its effect on the network it may be described completely by its terminal voltage and the current which it draws.   Thus we may represent it merely by a two-terminal box (see Fig. 5.11).   The current and voltage may be measured by the ideal† ammeter and voltmeter shown.   We assume that these instruments can show phase angles as well as magnitude, which is not generally the case with real instruments.

† An ideal ammeter has no impedance.   An ideal voltmeter has infinite impedance. Hence, their presence does not at all disturb the circuit.   This is not true of real ammeters and voltmeters.

Now let us proceed to analyze the whole circuit (the original circuit plus the external components connected to it) on a loop basis. For convenience we shall call the external circuits part of the λth loop, where λ is the number of independent loops in the circuit. Then we may write the loop equations, all of which are written conventionally [see Eqs. (5.1)] except for the one for the λth loop which becomes

$$E_\lambda = Z_{\lambda 1} I_1 + Z_{\lambda 2} I_2 + \cdots + Z_{\lambda \lambda} I_\lambda + E_t \qquad (5.14)$$

or

$$E_\lambda - E_t = Z_{\lambda 1} I_1 + Z_{\lambda 2} I_2 + \cdots + Z_{\lambda \lambda} I_\lambda. \qquad (5.14a)$$

Here E_λ is the sum of the *internal* voltage sources in the λth loop, and E_t is the terminal voltage of the network. By measuring E_t we do not have to consider possible sources or $I_\lambda Z$ drops in the load. Hence, we do not have to add the load impedance to $Z_{\lambda\lambda}$; the load impedance is absorbed in E_t.

If we solve the set of λ-loop equations of which Eq. (5.14a) is one, we obtain, for I_λ [see Eqs. (5.3)],

$$I_\lambda = y_{\lambda 1} E_1 + y_{\lambda 2} E_2 + \cdots + y_{\lambda\lambda}(E_\lambda - E_t) \qquad (5.15)$$

where the E_j are the internal voltage sources of the jth loops and the $y_{\lambda j}$ are defined by Eq. (5.4).

If the two terminals of the network are open-circuited, then the current is zero,

$$I_\lambda = 0 = y_{\lambda 1} E_1 + \cdots + y_{\lambda\lambda}(E_\lambda - E_t). \qquad (5.16)$$

In this case E_t is what we have called the open-circuit voltage E_0, and so, from Eq. (5.16),

$$E_0 = E_{t_{\text{open}}} = \frac{y_{\lambda 1}}{y_{\lambda\lambda}} E_1 + \cdots + \frac{y_{\lambda\lambda}}{y_{\lambda\lambda}} E_\lambda. \qquad (5.17)$$

Thus Eq. (5.15) may be written

$$I_\lambda = y_{\lambda\lambda} E_0 - y_{\lambda\lambda} E_t. \qquad (5.18)$$

If the two terminals of the network are short-circuited, the value of I_λ which flows is called I_0, and since E_t is then zero,

$$I_0 = I_{\lambda_{\text{short}}} = y_{\lambda\lambda} E_0. \qquad (5.19)$$

We may call $1/y_{\lambda\lambda}$ the impedance Z_0,

$$Z_0 = \frac{E_0}{I_0} \qquad (5.20)$$

which, combined with Eq. (5.17), yields

$$E_t = E_0 - I_\lambda Z_0. \qquad (5.21)$$

This is, however, merely the equation for the equivalent circuit shown in Fig. 5.9, which proves the theorem.†

It should be noted that $y_{\lambda\lambda}$ is the short-circuit input admittance of the λth loop. Its reciprocal, Z_0, which might be called the "short-circuit input impedance" but is usually called the *internal impedance*, may thus be obtained alternatively‡ by measuring the input impedance of the circuit when all the voltage sources are replaced by short circuits.

The example given below merely illustrates the technique of forming Thévenin's equivalent circuit. The power and utility of this theorem will be illustrated in later sections.

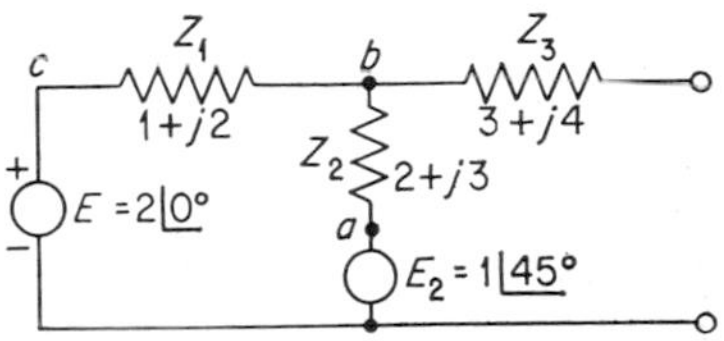

Example 5.7. Find Thévenin's equivalent circuit for the circuit shown in Fig. 5.12.

FIG. 5.12. Circuit for Example 5.7.

Solution. By inspection, the open-circuit voltage is

$$E_0 = E_2 + E_{ab} = E_2 + \frac{Z_2}{Z_1 + Z_2} V_{ac} = E_2 + \frac{Z_2}{Z_1 + Z_2} (E_1 - E_2)$$

$$= 0.707 + j0.707 + \frac{2 + j3}{3 + j5} (2 - 0.707 - j0.707)$$

$$= 1.484 + j0.232 = 1.502 | 8.88°.$$

In this case it is simple to determine Z_0 directly:

$$Z_0 = Z_3 + \frac{Z_1 Z_2}{Z_1 + Z_2} = 3 + j4 + \frac{(1 + j2)(2 + j3)}{3 + j5}$$

$$= 3.677 + j5.207 = 6.37 | 54.8°.$$

We may now obtain I_0 as

$$I_0 = \frac{1.502 | 8.88}{6.37 | 54.8} = 0.236 | -45.9°.$$

I_0 could have been obtained directly from the following equations (but in this case it is a more lengthy approach; it is done here as an illustration):

$$E_1 - E_2 = Z_{11}I_1 + Z_{12}I_0 = (3 + j5)I_1 + (-2 - j3)I_0$$
$$E_1 = Z_{21}I_1 + Z_{22}I_0 = (-2 - j3)I_1 + (5 + j7)I_0$$

---

† The foregoing proof does not explicitly consider current sources in the network. However, it is easy to show that a single current source in parallel with an impedance is equivalent to a voltage source in series with an impedance so that current sources may be replaced by voltage sources. (If the impedance paralleling the current source is infinite, fictitious equal impedances of opposite sign may have to be introduced to complete the proof.)

‡ The remarks of Sec. 5.5 should be noted before using this alternative method of calculating Z_0.

and by Cramer's rule

$$I_0 = \frac{(3 + j5)E_2 + (2 + j3)(E_1 - E_2)}{(3 + j5)(5 + j7) - (2 + j3)^2}$$

$$= \frac{(3 + j5)(0.707 + j0.707) + (2 + j3)(2 - .707 - j.707)}{-20 + j46 + 5 - j12}$$

$$= \frac{3.293 + j8.121}{-15 + j34} = 0.237\underline{|-45.9}$$

which is in good agreement with the previously obtained answer.

IV. *Norton's Theorem.* A variant of Thévenin's theorem known as Norton's theorem states that a two-terminal network is equivalent to a current source in parallel with an impedance, where the current source is equal to the short-circuit current of the network I_0 and the impedance is the Z_0 previously defined for Thévenin's theorem.

This theorem may be proved in a manner similar to the proof of Thévenin's theorem using node-voltage analysis. Since Thévenin's theorem has already been proved, it is simpler to show that a voltage source in series with an impedance is equivalent to a suitable current source in series with the same impedance. The proof of this theorem is left as an exercise for the reader.

V. *The Maximum-power-transfer Theorem.* The maximum-power-transfer theorem states that if a variable impedance (the *load* impedance)

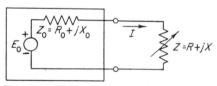

is connected to two terminals of a network the maximum power will be dissipated in that impedance when it is equal to the conjugate of the internal impedance of the network.

FIG. 5.13. Circuit for maximum-power-transfer theorem.

First, it should be noted that the two-terminal network may be replaced according to Thévenin's theorem by a voltage source in series with the internal impedance of the network. This situation is shown in Fig. 5.13.

Now the power dissipated in R is

$$P = \text{Re}\,[VI^*] = \text{Re}\,[II^*R] = |I|^2R. \qquad (5.22)$$

[The power is *not* I^2R, for I^2R is a complex number (see Sec. 4.7).]   Now

$$I = \frac{E_0}{(R_0 + R) + j(X_0 + X)}. \qquad (5.23)$$

Thus

$$P = II^*R = \frac{|E_0|^2R}{(R_0 + R)^2 + (X_0 + X)^2}. \qquad (5.24)$$

In order to find what values of R and X yield maximum power transfer, we must differentiate Eq. (5.24) with respect to R and X and set the resulting partial derivatives equal to zero:

$$\frac{\partial P}{\partial R} = \frac{|E_0|^2\{[(R_0 + R)^2 + (X_0 + X)^2] - [2R(R_0 + R)]\}}{[(R_0 + R)^2 + (X_0 + X)^2]^2} = 0 \tag{5.25}$$

and

$$\frac{\partial P}{\partial X} = \frac{|E_0|^2[-2R(X_0 + X)]}{[(R_0 + R)^2 + (X_0 + X)^2]^2} = 0. \tag{5.26}$$

Since in real circuits the denominators of the above expressions are never zero, we may equate the numerators to zero,

$$(R_0 + R)^2 + (X_0 + X)^2 - 2R(R_0 + R) = 0 \tag{5.27}$$
$$-2R(X_0 + X) = 0. \tag{5.28}$$

From Eq. (5.28)

$$X = -X_0.$$

(The solution $R = 0$ corresponds to a minimum of power transfer.)   Substituting this expression in Eq. (5.27) and solving for R yields

$$R = R_0 \tag{5.29}$$

which proves the theorem.   (The solution $R = -R_0$ is extraneous.) When the load impedance satisfies the requirements of the theorem it is said to be *matched* to the network.

Sometimes the load impedance is only a resistor, and we are unable to provide it with a reactive component (that is, $X = 0$).   In that case the reader may verify that maximum power is transferred when

$$R^2 = R_0^2 + X_0^2, \tag{5.30}$$

that is, when the magnitude of R is equal to the magnitude of the internal impedance of the network.   This condition of the load resistor is also referred to as a matched condition.

We repeat here for emphasis the dictum laid down at the beginning of this chapter, that often various network theorems can be used to provide sufficient information about the behavior of a network without resort to the often more ponderous and obfuscating general methods.

5.5. Active Circuits.   In certain types of circuits, notably those containing vacuum tubes or transistors, there exist voltage sources which are not independent.   That is, their voltages are proportional to the voltage drop across some other branch in the circuit.   As a simple illustration we have shown the equivalent circuit† (more aptly termed an *incremental linear model*) for a vacuum-tube triode in Fig. 5.14.

† We are not concerned here with how the equivalent circuit was obtained or in what sense it is equivalent—merely that it exists.

The loop equations for Fig. 5.14 are

$$E_1 = (Z_1 + R_g)I_1 + 0$$
$$-\mu E_{gk} = 0 + (r_p + Z_L)I_2. \qquad (5.31)$$

These equations cannot be solved in the same manner as Eqs. (5.1), because the voltage drop E_{gk} is not an independent variable. Rather,

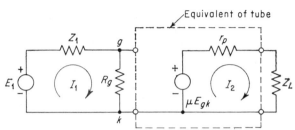

FIG. 5.14. Network including equivalent circuit of a vacuum tube. E_{gk} is the drop from g to k.

it is given by the expression

$$E_{gk} = I_1 R_g. \qquad (5.32)$$

We may now write Eqs. (5.31) as

$$E_1 = (Z_1 + R_g)I_1 + 0$$
$$0 = \mu R_g I_1 + (r_p + Z_L)I_2. \qquad (5.33)$$

The usual methods of solving simultaneous linear algebraic equations apply to this set of equations.

In general, the nonindependent voltage sources encountered in vacuum-tube circuits may be represented by expressions of the form

$$E'_i = Z'_{i1}I_1 + Z'_{i2}I_2 + \cdots + Z'_{im}I_m \qquad (5.34)$$

where

E'_i is the nonindependent voltage generated in the ith loop. (Voltage drops in the direction of I_i are taken as positive.)

Z'_{ij} is a factor (having the dimensions of impedance) giving the ratio of the value of the voltage generated in the ith loop to the current in the jth loop. It is called the *trans-impedance* from the jth to the ith loop. If $i = j$, there is no special name for Z'_{ii}. It should not be called the self-impedance, as this name is already in use for something different. (Actually E'_i is usually proportional to a branch current. It is more convenient for a general analysis to write the branch current as the sum of appropriate loop currents.) It is very important to note that generally Z'_{ij} is *not* equal to Z'_{ji}.

I_j is the current in the jth loop.

We may now write our equilibrium equations as

$$E_1 = (Z_{11} + Z'_{11})I_1 + (Z_{12} + Z'_{12})I_2 + \cdots + (Z_{1\lambda} + Z'_{1\lambda})I_\lambda$$
$$E_2 = (Z_{21} + Z'_{21})I_1 + (Z_{22} + Z'_{22})I_2 + \cdots + (Z_{2\lambda} + Z'_{2\lambda})I_\lambda \quad (5.35)$$
$$\cdots\cdots\cdots\cdots\cdots\cdots\cdots\cdots\cdots\cdots\cdots\cdots$$
$$E_\lambda = (Z_{\lambda 1} + Z'_{\lambda 1})I_1 + (Z_{\lambda 2} + Z'_{\lambda 2})I_2 + \cdots + (Z_{\lambda\lambda} + Z'_{\lambda\lambda})I_\lambda.$$

The solution of these equations proceeds as before except that the symmetry of the array of Z's is usually destroyed. Hence, the symmetry of the array of y's [see Eqs. (5.3)] is also destroyed. Furthermore, the reciprocity theorem no longer generally holds. Thus, the network may be *nonreciprocal*.

A further consequence of this analysis is the constraint on Thévenin's theorem mentioned in Sec. 5.5, III. If Eqs. (5.35) rather than Eqs. (5.1) are used in the analysis in that section, it is seen that Z_0, the internal impedance, is not obtained by measuring the impedance of the network with all voltage sources shorted, for this would short all the E'_i, which would imply that the Z'_{ij} are set equal to zero. This, of course, completely alters the network. In obtaining Z_0, then, one must only short-circuit the *independent* voltage sources. As a matter of convenience, however, it is usual in electronic circuits to obtain Z_0 as the ratio E_0/I_0, which avoids the problem of which sources are independent and how they should be shorted.

A similar analysis can be developed on the node basis, using *transadmittance* parameters Y'_{ij}.

EXERCISES

5.1. For the circuit shown in Fig. 5.15, find the steady-state values of the following quantities by the loop method: the loop current I_1; the loop current I_2; the total average power supplied to the 48-ohm resistor.

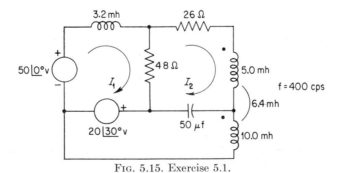

FIG. 5.15. Exercise 5.1.

5.2. (*a*) Write the mesh equations for the circuit shown in Fig. 5.16. (*b*) Solve these equations for the current in each branch.

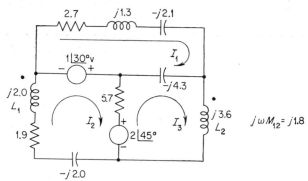

FIG. 5.16. Exercise 5.2.

5.3. Determine y_{12} for the circuit shown in Fig. 5.17.

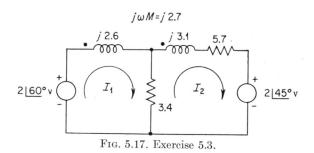

FIG. 5.17. Exercise 5.3.

5.4. Determine z_{12} for the circuit illustrated in Fig. 5.18.

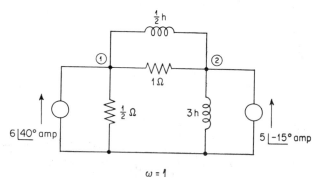

FIG. 5.18. Exercise 5.4.

5.5. For the circuit shown in Fig. 5.19 find the steady-state values of the following quantities by the node method: the potential of node 2 with respect to node 4; the potential of node 3 with respect to node 4; the current I in L_1.

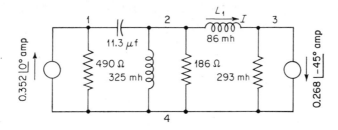

f = 50 cps

FIG. 5.19. Exercise 5.5.

5.6. (*a*) Write the node equations for the network shown in Fig. 5.20.
(*b*) Determine the voltage of each node with respect to ground.

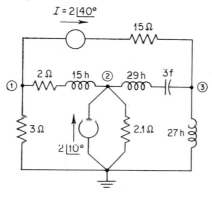

$\omega = 0.1/\text{sec}$

FIG. 5.20. Exercise 5.6.

5.7. (*a*) Write the node equations for the network drawn in Fig. 5.21.   Evaluate all admittances and express them in cartesian form.
(*b*) Determine the potential of each node with respect to ground.

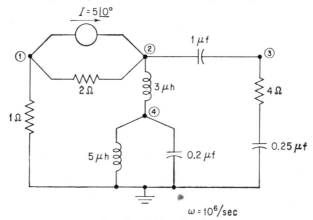

$\omega = 10^6/\text{sec}$

FIG. 5.21. Exercise 5.7.

5.8. Write the loop equations for the network sketched in Fig. 5.22.   Evaluate all impedances and express them in cartesian form.

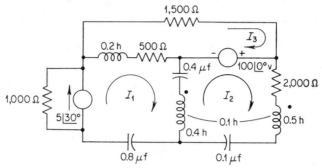

FIG. 5.22. Exercise 5.8.

5.9. Write the node equations for the circuit shown in Fig. 5.23.   Reduce the expressions to their simplest form.

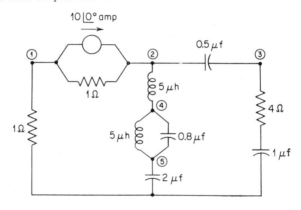

$\omega = 5 \times 10^5/\text{sec}$

FIG. 5.23. Exercise 5.9.

5.10. Write the node-voltage equations for the network of Fig. 5.24.

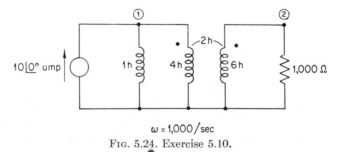

$\omega = 1,000/\text{sec}$

FIG. 5.24. Exercise 5.10.

5.11. Determine the current-voltage relations at the terminals of each circuit shown in Fig. 5.25.

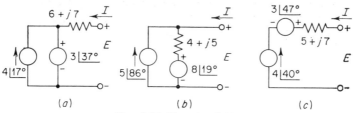

FIG. 5.25. Exercise 5.11.

5.12. For each circuit in Exercise 5.11 determine the simplest equivalent circuit based on (a) voltage sources; (b) current sources.

5.13. Prove Eq. (5.30).

5.14. The generalization of the Y-Δ transformation is the star-mesh transformation. A star is an n-terminal network each terminal of which (the ith terminal) is joined to a common point by an admittance Y_i. A mesh is an n-terminal network each terminal of which is joined to every other by admittances Y_{rs} (for terminals r and s). Show that for a mesh to be equivalent to a star,

$$Y_{rs} = \frac{Y_r Y_s}{\Sigma Y_i}.$$

[HINT: If a set of terminal voltages V_i is applied to either network, the currents I_i will be the same. Since this is true for all V_i, it is convenient to choose those V_i which simplify computations. Also note that $\Sigma I_i = 0$ and let the voltage of the common point of the star be V_0.]

5.15. A vacuum-tube amplifier has the equivalent circuit illustrated in Fig. 5.26.
(a) Write the node-voltage equations for V_1 and V_2 in terms of $j\omega$.
(b) For $\omega = 5 \times 10^6$, what is V_2?

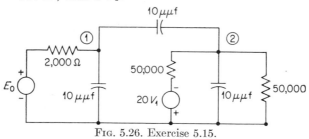

FIG. 5.26. Exercise 5.15.

5.16. Determine Thévenin's equivalent for the circuit shown in Fig. 5.27.

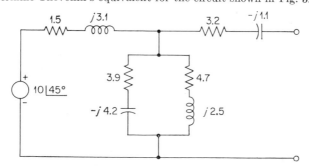

FIG. 5.27. Exercise 5.16.

5.17. Determine Norton's equivalent for the circuit of Exercise 5.16.

5.18. The circuit shown in Fig. 5-28 is an Anderson bridge. It is desired to determine the conditions for balance (no current in R_g) at any frequency. Write the necessary equations and solve them for the required relations among the various elements of the bridge.

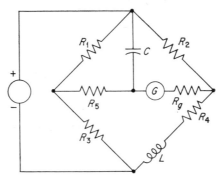

FIG. 5.28. Exercise 5.18.

5-19. The switch in the circuit shown in Fig. 5-29 is suddenly closed at $t = 0$. The capacitor is initially uncharged, and there is no initial current in the inductor. Find i, e_1, and e_2 as functions of time.

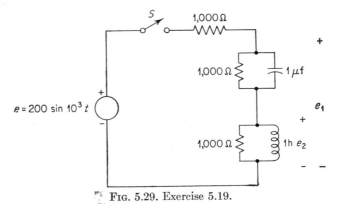

FIG. 5.29. Exercise 5.19.

5.20. (a) Develop the theory of circuits containing only inductors which initially carry no current. Show that the branch voltages everywhere in such a circuit are the same as in a circuit which has the same geometry but in which each inductor is replaced by a resistor whose value in ohms is equal to the inductance in henries.

(b) Repeat the above for circuits composed entirely of initially uncharged capacitors. Show that the branch voltages may be determined by replacing the capacitors with resistors, the conductance of which in mhos is equal to the capacitance of the capacitors in farads.

CHAPTER 6

TWO-TERMINAL NETWORKS

In the previous chapter we analyzed networks in the sinusoidal steady state, extending our methods from simple networks to ones of arbitrarily great complexity. Here we shall return to simple networks and consider generalizations in a different direction, namely, wherein the frequency of the voltages and currents is made to vary. The reader may ask: "Is this not merely a matter of repeating previous analyses at various frequencies?" It will be found that the proposed generalization is of much greater significance than that.

In order to keep the analysis within manageable limits we restrict it to simple networks. The simplest class of networks which is nontrivial is the two-terminal network. This is one which consists only of resistors, capacitors, and inductors (that is, it has no sources) with the constraint that only two points of the network are brought to terminals to which sources or measuring instruments are (hypothetically) connected. Thus the only variables of interest in such networks are the voltage differences between the terminals and the current into a terminal. Since the current is proportional to the voltage (there being only one source), only their ratio is a significant variable. Thus, the impedance (or, equivalently, the admittance) of a two-terminal network is investigated herein; the study of two-terminal networks is the study of general impedances. These impedances are often referred to as *driving-point impedances* because they are indeed driving-point impedances of *some* network (see Sec. 5.2).

6.1. The Variation of Impedance with Frequency. The specification of the impedance of a two-terminal network actually tells us very little about the nature of the network. A network having an impedance of $j100$ ohms at a frequency of 400 cps may consist of an inductor having an inductance of 0.0796 henry or a 1-henry inductor in series with a 1.36-μf capacitor; or, indeed, an infinite number of combinations of inductance and capacitance arranged in equally varied configurations would provide the same result. On the other hand, if it is known that the impedance of a circuit varies linearly with frequency, that circuit can consist only of a single inductor (or of trivial variations, such as several inductors in series or in parallel). From even this simple case it is seen that the dependence

148   INTRODUCTORY ELECTRIC CIRCUITS

of impedance upon frequency carries a great deal of information about a network.

In general, networks contain resistance as well as reactance. Thus, as frequency is varied a total of three quantities must be considered: the frequency itself, the resistance of the network, and the reactance of the network. Since we wish to use the variation of impedance to convey information about the network it is important to present these data in the most useful form possible. A difficulty lies in the fact that the sheet of paper on which we draw graphs is two-dimensional, and there are three variables to present. "This is quibbling;" the reader may say, "plot the resistance as a function of frequency on one graph, and the reactance as a function of frequency on another." This does indeed present all the data, but it dismisses the generality of the problem. It may be interesting to plot the magnitude and the angle of the impedance as functions of frequency—or reactance and frequency as functions† of the resistance.

For a while we shall consider the variation of resistance and reactance with frequency, but we shall also return later in this chapter to the alternative approach of considering reactance and frequency as functions of resistance.

6.2. Impedance Variation of a Simple Series Circuit. As an example, the variation of the series RLC network of Fig. 6.1 will be considered. The impedance of that network is given by

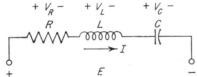

FIG. 6.1. Series RLC circuit.

$$Z = R + j\omega L + \frac{1}{j\omega C}. \quad (6.1)$$

In this case the resistive component of impedance Re $[Z]$ remains constant at the value R. The reactive component Im $[Z]$, on the other hand, is $(\omega L - 1/\omega C)$ and varies from $-\infty$ to $+\infty$ (see Fig. 6.2). At a frequency ω_0 given by

$$\omega_0 = \frac{1}{\sqrt{LC}} \quad (6.2)$$

the reactance is zero, and the impedance is a pure resistance. The impedance also has its minimum magnitude at $\omega = \omega_0$. The condition of Z being purely resistive is known as *resonance*.‡

Because the impedance of a series RLC circuit may be quite small at resonance compared with other frequencies, the circuit may act as a frequency-selective network by allowing significant current to pass through

† These will not generally be single-valued functions.

‡ Resonance is sometimes erroneously defined as the condition of minimum (or maximum) impedance. Such a definition is difficult to apply to networks more complicated than that being considered.

only when the source frequency is close to ω_0. Conversely, at resonance the current is limited only by R and so may be very large. Also, with I large, V_C and V_L may also be quite large. Thus, if a circuit is unwittingly arranged so that series resonance occurs, excessive currents may exist which will damage (melt) wires, or excessive voltages may exist which may break down insulation or which may be hazardous to life.

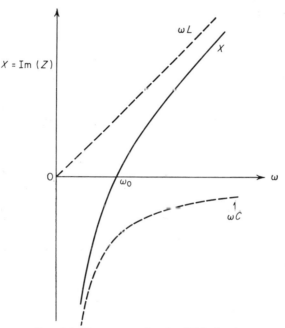

FIG. 6.2. Reactance of series RLC circuit.

It might appear that with a constant applied voltage E the maximum values of V_L and V_C, when frequency is varied, occur at resonance. However, X_L increases with frequency and X_C decreases with frequency, so that V_L $(= IX_L)$ reaches a maximum at $\omega > \omega_0$, and V_C $(= IX_C)$ reaches a maximum at $\omega < \omega_0$. The variations of I, V_L, and V_C with frequency are shown in Fig. 6.3. In this figure the scale is *normalized*; that is, the variables are presented as ratios with respect to some normal value. It is natural to normalize frequency with respect to ω_0 and thereby use ω/ω_0 as the frequency variable. Similarly, the voltages are normalized with respect to the applied voltage and the current with respect to the resonant current E/R. Normalizing variables converts the values to reasonable ranges; even more important, the curves of Fig. 6.3 are now *universal curves*. They describe the behavior of any series RLC circuit regardless of the values of R, L, C, provided only that they have the same "lossiness" as discussed below.   Observe also that the normalized-current curve is also a graph of the magnitude of the normalized admittance.

Normalization is a particularly useful tool in describing the general behavior of networks.   The resonant frequency is an important normalizing factor.   Clearly, though, it is not alone sufficient.   A circuit having a large value of R is not expected to behave as one having an extremely small value.   This difference in behavior can be accounted for by introducing a new parameter, the *quality factor*, or Q, of the circuit.   The Q is a

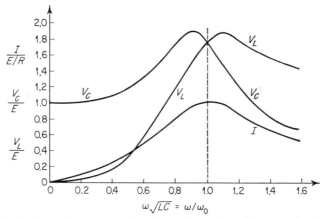

Fig. 6.3. Variations of current and voltage (normalized) in a series *RLC* circuit.

measure of the "lossiness" of a circuit.   It is defined by

$$Q_0 = \pi \, \frac{\text{maximum energy stored in } L \text{ (or } C\text{) during a cycle}}{\text{energy loss per half cycle in } R}. \qquad (6.3)$$

(The subscript zero indicates that the evaluation is to be made at $\omega = \omega_0$.) Proceeding with the evaluation yields

$$Q_0 = \pi \, \frac{\tfrac{1}{2}I_{max}^2 L}{\displaystyle\int_0^{T/2} (I_{max}^2 \cos \omega_0 t)^2 R \, dt} = \pi \, \frac{\tfrac{1}{2}I_{max}^2 L}{\tfrac{1}{2}I_{max}^2 \dfrac{\omega_0 T R}{2\omega_0}} = \frac{\omega_0 L}{R}. \qquad (6.4)$$

Alternatively,

$$Q_0 = \frac{1}{\omega_0 R C}. \qquad (6.4a)$$

A high-Q circuit is a low-loss circuit, and a low-Q circuit is a lossy circuit.   The curves in Fig. 6.3 are for a circuit having a fairly low value of Q ($Q_0 \doteq 2$).

By making use of the factor Q it is possible to construct a single curve which describes the admittance of a series *RLC* in the vicinity of its resonant frequency.   The admittance rather than the impedance is chosen in order that we may deal with values which approach zero instead of infinity at frequencies far removed from resonance.

The admittance of the series RLC circuit is given by

$$Y = \frac{1}{Z} = \frac{1}{R + j\omega L + 1/j\omega C} \qquad (6.5)$$

which may be expressed as

$$Y = \frac{1}{R}\frac{1}{1 + jQ_0\dfrac{\omega}{\omega_0} - jQ_0\dfrac{\omega_0}{\omega}}. \qquad (6.5a)$$

Since it is frequencies near ω_0 which are of interest, it is convenient to

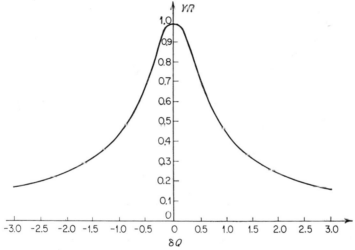

FIG. 6.4. Normalized admittance of a series resonant circuit.

represent the frequency variable in terms of the fractional frequency deviation δ defined by

$$\delta = \frac{\omega - \omega_0}{\omega_0} = \frac{\omega}{\omega_0} - 1. \qquad (6.6)$$

Then

$$Y = \frac{1}{R}\frac{1}{1 + jQ_0\left[1 + \delta - \dfrac{1}{1 + \delta}\right]}. \qquad (6.7)$$

Since for small δ

$$\frac{1}{1 + \delta} \doteq 1 - \delta \qquad (6.8)$$

Eq. (6.7) becomes

$$YR \doteq \frac{1}{1 + j2\delta Q_0}, \qquad |\delta| \ll 1. \qquad (6.9)$$

Here YR is the normalized admittance, which is plotted in Fig. 6.4.

In discussing the "sharpness" of the resonance region the notion of *half-power* frequencies is useful. The maximum power is dissipated in R when $\omega = \omega_0$, because then the current is greatest. When the current is $1/\sqrt{2}$ of its maximum value, one-half the maximum power is dissipated in R. From Eq. (6.9)† this occurs when $|2\delta Q_0| = 1$. Thus the half-

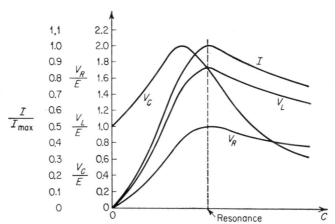

FIG. 6.5. Variation of current and voltages in a series RLC circuit as C is varied.

power deviation $\delta_{1/2}$ is given by

$$\delta_{1/2} = \pm \frac{1}{2Q_0} \tag{6.10}$$

and the *half-power* frequencies $\omega_{1/2}$ are given by

$$\omega_{1/2} = \omega_0(1 \pm \delta_{1/2}) = \omega_0(1 \pm 1/2Q_0). \tag{6.11}$$

The *bandwidth* BW of the circuit is defined in the present case as the frequency range between the half-power frequencies.

$$\mathrm{BW} = \omega_{1/2\,\mathrm{upper}} - \omega_{1/2\,\mathrm{lower}} = \frac{\omega_0}{Q_0}. \tag{6.12}$$

A series RLC circuit may also be analyzed by investigating its behavior at a fixed frequency as one or more of the parameters R, L, C is varied. Typical results of such an analysis are plotted in Fig. 6.5. It should be observed that such an approach is not essentially different from that already presented and really conveys no new information. Varying C, as in Fig. 6.5, merely varies ω_0, and so the normalized frequency ω/ω_0 is varied even though ω remains constant. The approach does differ from that already presented in that Q_0 is no longer constant (because ω_0 varies).

† As it is assumed in deriving Eq. (6.9) that $|\delta| \ll 1$, it follows that $|2\delta Q_0| = 1$ only if $2Q_0 \gg 1$.

6.3. The Impedance of Simple Parallel Circuits. The simplest general form of a parallel circuit is a parallel combination of R, L, and C. This circuit, however, is merely the dual of the series RLC circuit already considered, and nothing is to be gained from a repetitious discussion of this circuit. A simple parallel circuit of considerable practical interest consists of a real inductor in parallel with a real capacitor. Because, in practice, resistance is always associated with inductance, the entire circuit has the configuration of Fig. 6.6. The impedance of this circuit is given by

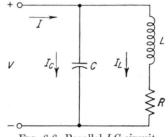

FIG. 6.6. Parallel LC circuit.

$$Z = \frac{(1/j\omega C)(R + j\omega L)}{R + j\omega L + 1/j\omega C}. \qquad (6.13)$$

The condition of resonance exists when Z is purely resistive. This occurs when

$$\frac{\text{Re [numerator]}}{\text{Re [denominator]}} = \frac{\text{Im [numerator]}}{\text{Im [denominator]}} \qquad (6.14)$$

or at a frequency ω_0 such that

$$\frac{L}{RC} - \frac{-R}{\omega_0 C(\omega_0 L - 1/\omega_0 C)} \qquad (6.15)$$

whence, after some manipulations,

$$\omega_0 = \frac{1}{\sqrt{LC}} \sqrt{1 - \frac{R^2 C}{L}}. \qquad (6.16)$$

The parameter Q can also be utilized to simplify the form of this expression. Here the Q of the coil is defined by†

$$Q = \pi \frac{\text{maximum energy stored in } L \text{ during a cycle}}{\text{loss per half cycle in } R} \qquad (6.17)$$

which becomes upon evaluation

$$Q = \frac{\omega L}{R}. \qquad (6.18)$$

For sufficiently small R (high Q), Eq. (6.16) becomes

$$\omega_0 \doteq \frac{1}{\sqrt{LC}} \qquad (6.19)$$

and this combined with Eq. (6.18) leads to

$$Q_0 = \frac{\omega_0 L}{R} \doteq \frac{1}{R\omega_0 C} \qquad (6.20)$$

† There is a subtle difference between the Q of a coil, defined by Eq. (6.17), and the Q_0 of the series circuit defined by Eq. (6.3). The Q of a coil is defined at all frequencies and at ω_0 is designated Q_0. The Q_0 of the series circuit is defined only for $\omega = \omega_0$.

which also shows

$$\frac{1}{Q_0{}^2} \doteq \frac{R^2C}{L}. \tag{6.21}$$

This latter expression may be introduced back into Eq. (6.16) yielding

$$\omega_0 = \frac{1}{\sqrt{LC}} \sqrt{1 - \frac{1}{Q_0{}^2}}. \tag{6.22}$$

This expression is shown as an equality because the assumptions made affect Q directly but cause only second-order errors in ω_0 for reasonably high Q's.

Because the resonant frequency of the parallel circuit is nearly equal to $1/\sqrt{LC}$, this latter is sometimes, erroneously, referred to as the resonant frequency. Certain writers also define resonance as the condition where the impedance of the circuit is maximum, or where $I_L = I_C$. All these conditions occur at almost the same frequency when the coil has a high Q, and some are easier to measure than others; but at low Q's the frequencies at which these conditions occur differ greatly, and only the condition of purely resistive impedance is sensible as a definition of resonance.

Let us now return to the expression for the impedance of the parallel circuit [Eq. (6.13)]. By using the expressions for Q_0 of Eq. (6.20) and introducing the fractional frequency deviation δ [using Eq. (6.19) to define ω_0], the impedance may be expressed as

$$Z = \frac{RQ_0{}^2 \left[1 + \delta - j\frac{1}{Q_0} \right]}{1 + \delta + jQ_0\delta(2 + \delta)}. \tag{6.23}$$

[This expression is exact for all values of δ, to the extent that Eq. (6.20) is correct.] Near resonance, $|\delta| \ll 1$ so that

$$Z \doteq \frac{RQ_0{}^2 \left[1 - j\frac{1}{Q_0} \right]}{1 + j2\delta Q_0}. \tag{6.24}$$

This expression, which is plotted in Fig. 6.7, shows that the maximum impedance occurs for $\delta = 0$. However, because ω_0 is only approximated by $1/\sqrt{LC}$, the impedance is not purely resistive at this point; that is, resonance does not truly occur at $\delta = 0$. This occasions no practical difficulties with high-Q circuits.

Although the normalizing factors are different, the foregoing expression has the same frequency dependence as the *admittance* of the series RLC circuit [Eq. (6.9)]. Thus it is possible to define half-power frequencies given by

$$\omega_{1/2} = \omega_0 \left(1 \pm \frac{1}{2Q_0} \right) \tag{6.25}$$

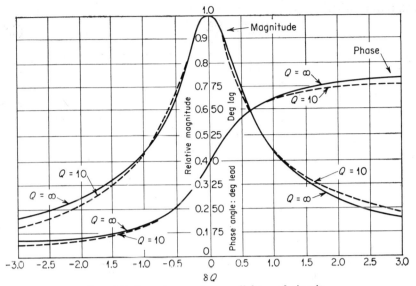

FIG. 6.7. Impedance of a parallel tuned circuit.

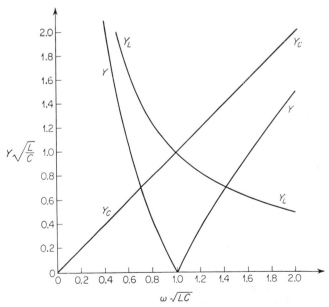

FIG. 6.8. Admittance of a lossless parallel resonant circuit.

and a bandwidth

$$\text{BW} = \frac{\omega_0}{Q_0}. \tag{6.26}$$

These quantities, however, do not have the simple physical significance of the corresponding quantities in the simple series RLC circuit.

The variation of the admittance of each branch of a lossless parallel circuit and of the entire circuit is shown in Fig. 6.8. Because the admittance is a minimum at resonance, a parallel resonant circuit is sometimes referred to as an *antiresonant* circuit.

6.4. Impedance Loci. In the previous sections the variation of the impedance of simple networks with frequency was considered. It

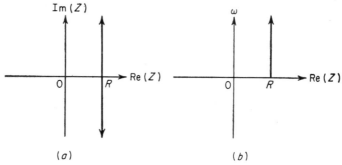

FIG. 6.9. Alternative methods of plotting behavior of series RLC circuit as frequency varies.

appeared in that analysis that the results were most logically presented as curves showing the variation of the magnitude and angle of the impedance with frequency. Alternatively, the real and imaginary parts of the impedance might be presented as functions of frequency.

There are, however, other forms in which the results of such analyses may be given. There exist three interdependent variables in the analysis: the frequency, the real part of Z, and the imaginary part of Z. Any one of these may be plotted as the independent variable. Thus we may plot Im $[Z]$ and ω as functions of Re $[Z]$. Although this is now offered merely as an academic exercise, the value and significance of this form of presentation will soon emerge.

As an example, we consider the impedance of the series RLC circuit of Fig. 6.1. The impedance of this circuit is

$$Z = R + j\left(\omega L - \frac{1}{\omega C}\right). \tag{6.1a}$$

It is seen that Im $[Z]$ may assume any value from $-\infty$ to $+\infty$ at Re $[Z] = R$. Similarly, ω may assume any positive value at Re $[Z] = R$. (Possible negative frequencies are considered later.) These facts lead to the plots shown in Fig. 6.9. These plots are not particularly informative

as they stand.   However, it is possible to add a frequency scale to the plot of Im [Z] vs. Re [Z] to indicate the frequency at which Z assumes each of the values on the line.   This is done in Fig. 6.10.   (The frequency scale is not linear, as will be better seen in the next example.)   The plot of ω vs. Re [Z] is not now really necessary, as it contains no new informa-
tion on Z not already shown in Fig. 6.10.   Alternatively, a reactance scale could be added to Fig. 6.9b, but this would not be found to be as useful as the present procedure.

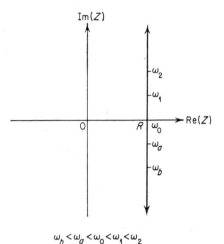

The plot of Im [Z] vs. Re [Z], with or without the auxiliary frequency scale, is known as an *im-
pedance locus*, since it is the locus of all points representing values which Z may assume as ω is varied. Although it was developed here as a plot of reactance vs. resistance, it is quite clearly also the plot of magnitude vs. angle if a polar coor-
dinate system is assumed.

$$\omega_b < \omega_a < \omega_0 < \omega_1 < \omega_2$$

Fig. 6.10. Impedance locus of series RLC circuit.

As a further example, consider the parallel RLC circuit of Fig. 6.11. Its impedance is

$$Z = \frac{1}{1/R + j(\omega C - 1/\omega L)}. \qquad (6.27)$$

We shall not here attempt to unscramble the real and imaginary parts of Z, since this is done more effectively in the next section.   We content ourselves with laboriously plotting out the locus of Z shown in Fig. 6.12.

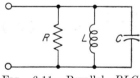

Fig. 6.11.   Parallel RLC circuit.

6.5. Circle Diagrams.   The remarkable re-
semblance to a circle of the impedance locus of a parallel RLC circuit is more than a coincidence. It is indeed a circle, as also are many other loci encountered in circuit analysis.   That it is a circle may be shown as follows: Consider a function of the form

$$Z(\omega) = \frac{1}{1 + jf(\omega)} \qquad (6.28)$$

where f is any *real* function of ω.   This may be written in polar form as

$$Z(\omega) = Z\underline{\big|-\theta} \qquad (6.29)$$

where

$$\theta = \arctan \frac{f(\omega)}{1} \qquad (6.30)$$

Since $f(\omega)$ is therefore equal to $\tan \theta$ we may write Eq. (6.28) as

$$Z(\omega) = \frac{1}{1 + j \tan \theta} = \frac{1}{\sqrt{1 + \tan^2 \theta}} \underline{|-\theta} = \cos \theta \underline{|-\theta}. \qquad (6.31)$$

The elegance of this method lies in the use of an exponential expression

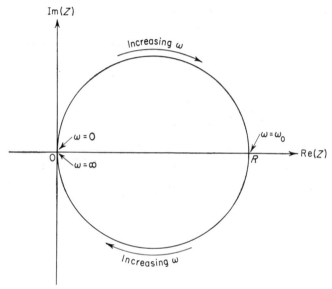

Fig. 6.12. Locus of impedance of parallel RLC circuit.

for $\cos \theta$, for then Eq. (6.31) becomes

$$Z(\omega) = (\cos \theta)\epsilon^{-j\theta} = \frac{\epsilon^{j\theta} + \epsilon^{-j\theta}}{2} \epsilon^{-j\theta} = \frac{1}{2} + \frac{1}{2} \epsilon^{-j2\theta}. \qquad (6.32)$$

This equation is recognized as the sum of two complex numbers, one fixed in both magnitude and angle, and one fixed in magnitude but of variable angle. This form of equation evidences directly that as ω takes on various real values, $Z(\omega)$ traces out an arc of a circle, with its center at $(\frac{1}{2}, 0)$ and of radius $\frac{1}{2}$, in the complex plane.

If there are limits on the range of $f(\omega)$, for example,

$$a \leqq f(\omega) \leqq b \qquad (6.33)$$

then the range of θ is also limited by

$$\arctan a \leqq \theta \leqq \arctan b. \qquad (6.34)$$

Generalizing, if a function can be expressed in the form $A + Be^{j\phi}$, where A and B are complex numbers and where ϕ varies, the function is an arc of a circle with center A and magnitude B. The portion of the circle of physical interest is determined by the limits of ϕ and by the value of the phase angle of B. Any function of the form

$$\frac{C}{D + jE(\omega)},$$

where C is a fixed complex number, D a fixed real number, and $E(\omega)$ a real function of ω (or of any other variables), may be reduced to the required form for a circle.

The foregoing procedures may now be applied to Eq. (6.27) to show that the impedance locus is indeed a circle. That equation may be written

$$Z = R\frac{1}{1 + jR(\omega C - 1/\omega L)} \tag{6.27a}$$

or

$$Z = R(\tfrac{1}{2} + \tfrac{1}{2}\epsilon^{-j2\theta})$$

where, since $0 \leqq \omega < \infty$, $-\infty < R(\omega C - 1/\omega L) < \infty$; and as

$$\theta = \arctan R\left(\omega C - \frac{1}{\omega L}\right), \qquad -180 > -2\theta > 180.$$

A simple example now follows to demonstrate the generality of the circle-diagram approach and one of its less obvious applications. Another application is illustrated in Example 7.6.

Example 6.1. In Fig. 6.13, what is Z at resonance (defined here as E in phase with I) and what is the minimum value

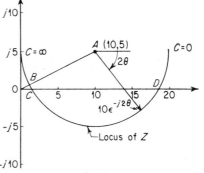

FIG. 6.14. Locus of Z in Fig. 6.13.

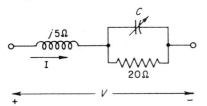

FIG. 6.13. Circuit for Example 6.1.

of Z as C is varied from 0 to ∞ (ω is not, and need not be, specified)?

Solution. Here

$$Z = j5 + \frac{20}{1 + j\omega 20C} = j5 + 20(\tfrac{1}{2} + \tfrac{1}{2}\epsilon^{-j2\theta})$$
$$= 10 + j5 + 10\epsilon^{-j2\theta}$$

where $0 \leqq \tan \theta < \infty$ or $-180 \leqq -2\theta \leqq 0$. The above expression is plotted in

Fig. 6.14. From this figure,

$$Z_{\text{res}} = \overline{OC} \qquad\qquad \text{or} \qquad = \overline{OD}$$
$$= 10 - \sqrt{10^2 - 5^2} \qquad \text{or} \qquad = 10 + \sqrt{10^2 - 5^2}$$
$$= 1.34\ \Omega \qquad\qquad \text{or} \qquad = 18.66\ \Omega$$

and

$$Z_{\text{min}} = \overline{OB} = \sqrt{10^2 + 5^2} - 10 = 1.16\ \Omega.$$

6.6. A General Interpretation of Impedance Functions. Greater insight into the variation of impedance of two-terminal networks with frequency is obtained if a more general case of the frequency variable is considered.   In Sec. 3.6 the concept of frequency was extended from the imaginary frequency $j\omega$ to the complex frequency s $(= \sigma + j\omega)$.   Similarly, the concept of impedance can be extended to include impedances at complex frequencies by expressing the impedance of an inductor as Ls and that of a capacitor as $1/Cs$.

In this manner the generalized impedance of the series RLC circuit of Fig. 6.1 is

$$Z(s) = R + Ls + \frac{1}{Cs} = \frac{L\left(s^2 + \dfrac{R}{L}s + \dfrac{1}{LC}\right)}{s}. \tag{6.35}$$

Now, a polynomial in s may be written as a product of factors of the form $s - s_i$, where s_i is a zero of the polynomial.   Thus, Eq. (6.35) can be expressed as

$$Z(s) = \frac{L(s - s_1)(s - s_2)}{s} = \frac{L(s - \alpha_1 - j\omega_1)(s - \alpha_1 + j\omega_1)}{s} \tag{6.36}$$

where

$$s_{1,2} = \alpha_1 \pm j\omega_1 = -\frac{R}{2L} \pm \sqrt{\frac{R^2}{4L^2} - \frac{1}{LC}}. \tag{6.37}$$

When the frequency s of the applied voltage is equal to one of the zeros of the numerator of Z, the impedance is zero, and an "infinite" current flows when finite voltage is applied.   The values of s for which $Z(s)$ is zero are termed the zeros of Z.   These are also the natural frequencies of the circuit.

Considerable significance attends the plot of the zeros of Z in the s plane. Illustrating, consider Fig. 6.15.   The circles represent locations of the zeros of Z, and the dot, the location of s representing the applied frequency.   The vector drawn from the origin to s_1 represents s_1, whereas that from the origin to the dot represents s.   Thus, that from s_1 to s represents $s - s_1$, one of the terms in the numerator of Z.   Similarly, we find $s - s_2$.   Clearly, if s is constrained to remain on the $j\omega$ axis (the condition of Sec. 6.2), Z will near a minimum as s nears its position of closest approach to s_1. Z is zero only when the forcing function has the same frequency as that of the natural response. This equality may be achieved either by exciting the circuit with a damped sine wave or by reducing the series resistance to zero.

Because zeros occur on the real axis or as complex conjugates, the behavior of the circuit at negative values of ω is the mirror image of that at positive values and is generally ignored.†

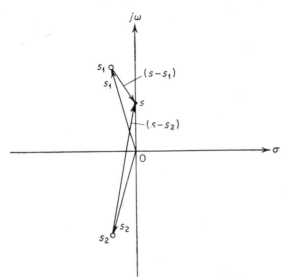

FIG. 6.15. s plane, showing zeros of Z.

It is interesting to note that the "infinite" response which occurs when a lossless series resonant circuit is excited at its natural frequency actually has the form‡ $te^{j\omega t}$, so that its modulus (or envelope) becomes infinite only at $t = \infty$. Because this response is neither constant nor periodic, no steady state exists for the condition of series resonance.

Let us also apply this general form of analysis to the parallel resonant circuit already analyzed in Sec. 6.3. Equation (6.13) may be generalized

† Since only the real part of ϵ^{st} has any physical significance, either s or its conjugate may be taken as the frequency variable, for Re $[\epsilon^{st}]$ = Re $[\epsilon^{s*t}]$. This indicates also why zeros must occur either on the real axis or as conjugate pairs; only in such cases will the response of a circuit be the same regardless of whether s or s^* is chosen. (In transmission-line theory the sign of s denotes the direction of travel of a wave, but transmission lines are distributed-parameter circuits, beyond the scope of this book.)

‡ This has not been shown but is related to the form of solution obtained when $Z(s)$ has multiple zeros. A forcing function whose frequency is a natural frequency of the circuit results in a response similar to the natural response, but with the order of that zero increased by 1.

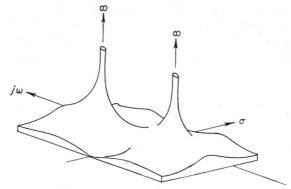

FIG. 6.16. Representation of $|Z(s)|$.

to

$$Z(s) = \frac{R + Ls}{LCs^2 + RCs + 1} = \frac{1}{C}\frac{s + R/L}{s^2 + (R/L)s + 1/LC} \qquad (6.38)$$

which may be written as

$$Z(s) = \frac{1}{C}\frac{s - s_0}{(s - s_a)(s - s_b)} \qquad (6.39)$$

where $s_0 = -R/L$ and $s_{a,b}$ are given by

$$s_{a,b} = -\frac{R}{2L} \pm \sqrt{\frac{R^2}{4L^2} - \frac{1}{LC}}. \qquad (6.40)$$

The frequencies s_a and s_b are zeros of the admittance of the network. At these frequencies the impedance is infinite. This infiniteness is indicated by terming s_a and s_b *poles* of the impedance. This notation stems from the fact that a plot of $|Z(s)|$ in the s plane gives rapidly rising infinite peaks, looking like slender poles, at s_a and s_b (see Fig. 6.16).

Poles are indicated on the s plane by crosses, as in Fig. 6.17. It is to be observed that Z also has a zero at $s = -R/L$, as designated by the circle in the figure. (It may be noted that the impedance function of the series RLC circuit has a pole

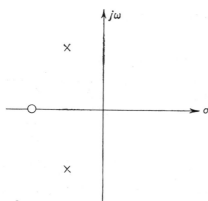

FIG. 6.17. Complex plane, showing poles and zero of Z.

at $s = 0$, which fact was not previously mentioned.)

The expression for the values of $s_{a,b}$ [Eq. (6.40)] is identical with that for the values of $s_{1,2}$ [Eq. (6.37)]. The values s_1, s_2 represent the natural frequencies of the series RLC circuit when analyzed on a loop basis. That is, they are the natural frequencies of the circuit formed by replacing the voltage source by a short circuit. The values s_a and s_b, on the other hand, represent the natural frequencies of the parallel circuit when analyzed on a node basis, with the terminals open-circuited (that is, with a presumed current source replaced by an open circuit). It is only a coincidence that these two cases degenerate to the same RLC circuit having the same natural frequencies in each case. This is shown in Fig. 6.18.

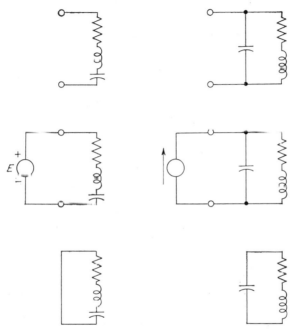

Fig. 6.18. Showing how two networks assume the same form when connected to sources.

The results of this section may be generalized. The impedance of any two-terminal circuit may be represented by a fraction, the numerator and denominator of which are polynomials in s. The zeros of the numerator are zeros of the impedance, whereas the zeros of the denominator are poles of the impedance. A more general definition of resonance than that previously given is, then, the condition that the frequency of the forcing function be a zero of the impedance. The condition that the frequency of the forcing function be a pole of the impedance may be termed antiresonance.

6.7. The Reactance of Reactive Networks. By confining our attention to networks which contain no resistance, that is, to *reactive networks*, certain additional generalizations may be made. These results are of more than academic interest, for reactive networks play a significant role in the design of filters (see Sec. 7.12).†

The driving-point impedance of a (sourceless) two-terminal network is generally designated by the symbol Z_{11} (even though this may cause confusion with the self-impedance of loop 1, which uses the same symbol; the meaning of Z_{11} must be inferred from its context). From Eqs. (5.2) it is seen that (since $Z_{11} = E_1/I_1$ for $E_2 = E_3 = \cdots = 0$)

$$Z_{11} = \frac{D}{A_{11}}. \tag{6.41}$$

Here D is the determinant of the loop impedances and A_{11} the cofactor of the element in the first row and first column.

Each term of D (and of A_{11}) is of the form $Ls + 1/Cs$. It is more convenient to deal only with positive powers of s. Let us therefore consider a new determinant formed from D by multiplying each element by s. The elements then have the form $Ls^2 + 1/C$. This new determinant we call D'. The two determinants are related by

$$D' = s^n D \tag{6.42}$$

where n is the order of the determinants, for each time we multiply D by s, the elements of one column are multiplied by s, and repeating this n times multiplies every element of D by s_1. Similarly, the elements of A_{11} can each be multiplied by s to yield a new determinant A'_{11}. This is related to A_{11} by

$$A'_{11} = s^{n-1} A_{11}. \tag{6.43}$$

(Recall that A_{11} is of one lower order than D.)   Now Z_{11} may be written

$$Z_{11} = \frac{D'}{s^n} \frac{s^{n-1}}{A'_{11}} = \frac{D'}{sA'_{11}}. \tag{6.44}$$

The determinants D' and A'_{11} contain only even powers of s. Consequently, the numerator of Z_{11} is a polynomial in even powers of s and the denominator a polynomial in odd powers of s. Furthermore, in the general case where each mesh of the circuit contains an independent inductance and capacitance, each element of D' and A' is of the form $Ls^2 + 1/C$, where neither L nor $1/C$ is zero, so that the numerator of Z_{11} is of one degree higher than the denominator. Also, the final term of the numerator is a constant and that of the denominator is a constant multiple

† It must be admitted that we are to some degree begging the question when we say reactive networks are important because they are used in filter design. The fact is that the techniques of design are incapable of adequately treating resistive networks, and so reactive networks must be used.

of s. Thus

$$Z_{11} = \frac{a_{2n}s^{2n} + a_{2n-2}s^{2n-2} + \cdots + a_0}{b_{2n-1}s^{2n-1} + b_{2n-3}s^{2n-3} + \cdots + b_1 s}. \tag{6.45}$$

Each of these polynomials may be factored in terms of its roots. Since the factor s^2 occurs so frequently it is generally most convenient to take it as a variable. Then

$$Z_{11} = H \frac{(s^2 - s_1{}^2)(s^2 - s_3{}^2) \cdots (s^2 - s_{2n-1}{}^2)}{s(s^2 - s_2{}^2)(s^2 - s_4{}^2) \cdots (s^2 - s_{2n-2}{}^2)} \tag{6.46}$$

where H is a constant. The roots in s^2 are all real and negative, for both the zeros and poles of Z_{11} represent natural frequencies of the network, and the natural frequencies of a resistanceless network have the form $\pm j\omega_i$. Thus, we may replace the $s_i{}^2$ by $(j\omega_i)^2 = -\omega_i{}^2$ and write

$$\begin{aligned}
Z_{11}(\omega) &= H \frac{(-\omega^2 + \omega_1{}^2)(-\omega^2 + \omega_3{}^2) \cdots (-\omega^2 + \omega_{2n-1}{}^2)}{j\omega(-\omega^2 + \omega_2{}^2)(-\omega^2 + \omega_4{}^2) \cdots (-\omega^2 + \omega_{2n-2}{}^2)} \\
&= j\omega H \frac{(\omega^2 - \omega_1{}^2)(\omega^2 - \omega_3{}^2) \cdots (\omega^2 - \omega_{2n-1}{}^2)}{\omega^2(\omega^2 - \omega_2{}^2)(\omega^2 - \omega_4{}^2) \cdots (\omega^2 - \omega_{2n-2}{}^2)}.
\end{aligned} \tag{6.47}$$

It is to be noted that the above expression applies to a general network in which every mesh has independent inductance and capacitance. Such an impedance has a pole at the origin, but it also has one at infinity. This pole at infinity occurs because the numerator is of higher degree than the denominator. (A simple inductor has a pole at infinity.) In the case of less general networks it is possible to have zeros either at the origin or at infinity, or at both.

The entire behavior of the network is specified by giving the location of its poles and zeros and the value of H. This remarkable result is known as *Foster's reactance theorem*.

Another important property of reactive two-terminal impedances is based on the fact that the slope of reactance with frequency is always positive. The proof of this is beyond the scope of this text but is clearly true for inductance and capacitance and for simple combinations of these.[†] That is,

$$\frac{d}{d\omega} X_{11} > 0. \tag{6.48}$$

This implies that the poles and zeros of Z_{11} separate each other:

$$\omega_1 < \omega_2 < \omega_3 < \omega_4 \cdots < \omega_{2n-2} < \omega_{2n-1}. \tag{6.49}$$

This is the *separation property* of the poles and zeros. Its truth can be inferred from Fig. 6.19.

[†] See, for example, E. A. Guillemin, "Communication Networks," vol. 2, John Wiley & Sons, Inc., New York, 1935, pp. 226–229.

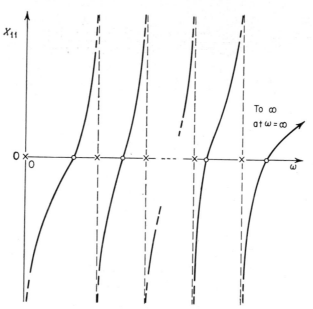

FIG. 6.19. Illustrating separation of poles and zeros.

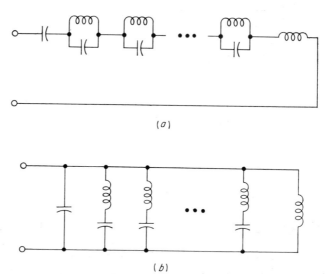

(a)

(b)

FIG. 6.20. (a) First Foster form for synthesis of reactive networks; (b) second Foster form.

In order to design, or *synthesize*, a reactive network one needs to know only the location of its poles and zeros and the value of H.   The given poles and zeros must possess the separation property.   There also exist some simple procedures for synthesizing reactive networks.   An obvious one, due to Foster, is to expand Eq. (6.47) in partial fractions† as

$$Z_{11} = j\omega H \left(1 + \frac{A_0}{\omega^2} + \frac{A_1}{\omega^2 - \omega_2{}^2} + \cdots + \frac{A_{2n-2}}{\omega^2 - \omega_{2n-2}{}^2} \right). \quad (6.50)$$

The first term, $j\omega H$, is an inductance $L = H$.   The second, $-HA_0/j\omega$, is a capacitor $C = -1/HA_0$.   (A_0 will be negative.)   All other terms may

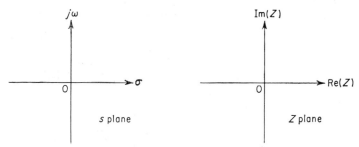

FIG. 6.21. Showing s plane and Z plane.

be represented by parallel combinations of L and C.   The final network has the form of Fig. 6.20a.   An alternative method is to synthesize $1/Z_{11}$ as an admittance.   This leads to a network of the form of Fig. 6.20b. These networks have exactly the same impedance function, although practical considerations of construction may lead to favoring one over the other.   Other methods of synthesis, of course, also exist.‡

6.8. Mapping of Functions.   The reintroduction of complex frequency enables us to take a more general view of the plotting of impedance loci, as done in the beginning of this chapter.   It is now realized that the problem which exists is to plot the complex variable Z as a function of the complex variable s.

In plotting real functions of real variables we merely *graph* one as a function of the other.   This procedure is possible because graph paper is two-dimensional.   This simple procedure is not now available to us because at best we have three dimensions available for plotting, and in fact only two are practical.

A method of circumventing this difficulty is the following: Draw the s plane and the Z plane (see Fig. 6.21).   Arbitrarily select points s_i in the s plane and determine the corresponding values of $Z(s_i)$.   Plot and

† See Appendix B.
‡ Guillemin, *op. cit.*, pp. 198ff.

label these points. This is done in Fig. 6.22 for a 1-farad capacitor.†
This procedure is known as mapping the s plane into the Z plane.
(Analogously, in a slide rule, the x line is mapped into the log x line.)
Thus, an impedance function is one which maps the s plane into the Z
plane. In principle, the point-by-point plot may be carried to any
desired degree of completion. However, it is a cumbersome method to
apply. It is often sufficient to map some curve in the s plane into the Z
plane. The curve which is most convenient is generally one of the s axes.

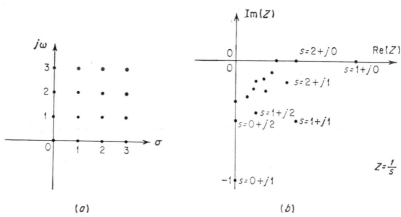

FIG. 6.22. Mapping of s plane onto Z plane.

In particular, the map of the $j\omega$ axis into the Z plane is what was previously considered the impedance locus.

Mapping the $j\omega$ axis into the Z plane separates the Z plane into two
regions, one of which includes values of Z which apply to values of s having positive real parts (the *right-half s plane*) and one of which includes
values of Z which apply to values of s having negative real parts (the
left-half s plane). An analysis of such plots and their implications is of
great value in determining the physical realizability of impedance functions or in designing feedback systems for stability.

EXERCISES

6.1. A circuit consists of three elements in parallel: a conductance G, an inductor L,
and a capacitor C.
  (*a*) Determine the impedance as a function of ω.
  (*b*) Determine Re [Z] as a function of ω.
  (*c*) Determine Im [Z] as a function of ω.
6.2. Show that Eq. (6.4) follows from Eq. (6.3).

† The fact that Z may have a real part does not mean that there is dissipation.
Rather, the average energy stored in the capacitor may be increasing, so that average
energy is delivered by the source.)

6.3. A series circuit consists of a 0.26-ohm resistor in series with a 1.33-henry inductor and a 1.50-farad capacitor. Using Fig. 6.4, determine the admittance of the circuit at $\omega = 1.5$ radians/sec. Verify this value by a direct calculation.

6.4. Using Fig. 6.7, determine the impedance at 1627 cps, expressed in polar form, of a 1-μf capacitor in parallel with a 10-mh coil having a Q of 50.

6.5. Show that the impedance locus of the circuit of Exercise 6.1 is a circle.

6.6. Determine and sketch the locus of the impedance shown in Fig. 6.23. Indicate the points corresponding to impedance magnitudes of one-half the maximum value.

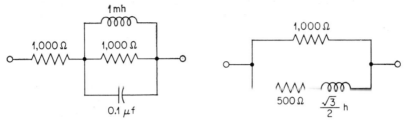

FIG. 6.23. Exercise 6.6.   FIG. 6.24. Exercise 6.7.

6.7. For the circuit shown in Fig. 6.24 determine the maximum and minimum values of Z as ω is varied. At what frequency does the maximum phase of Z occur?

6.8. (a) Show that if an impedance locus is a circle which does not intersect the origin then the corresponding admittance locus is also a circle which does not intersect the origin. That is,

$$\frac{1}{A + Be^{j\theta}} = C + De^{j\phi}, \qquad |A| \neq |B|, \qquad |C| \neq |D|.$$

(b) Show that if an impedance locus is a circle through the origin the corresponding admittance locus is a straight line not through the origin, and vice versa.

(c) Show that if an impedance locus is a straight line through the origin the corresponding admittance locus is also a straight line through the origin.

(The foregoing results follow directly from the theory of bilinear transformations.)

6.9. Sketch the variation of reactance with frequency for the circuit shown in Fig. 6.25. Determine the values of ω at the poles and zeros of this circuit.

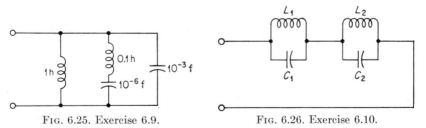

FIG. 6.25. Exercise 6.9.   FIG. 6.26. Exercise 6.10.

6.10. Can the circuit drawn in Fig. 6.26 have the same poles and zeros as the circuit of Exercise 6.9? Explain.

6.11. A network consisting entirely of reactive elements has a pole at $\omega = 150$ radians/sec and either poles or zeros at $\omega = 100, 300, \infty$. Sketch the variation of reactance with frequency. Have all the poles and zeros been specified?

6.12. Write the impedance of the network described in Exercise 6.11 as a function of s.

6.13. Synthesize a network whose impedance is

$$Z(s) = \frac{2s^2 + 4}{s^3 + 4s}.$$

6.14. Synthesize a network whose impedance is

$$Z(s) = \frac{s}{s^2 + 4} + \frac{s}{s^2 + 2}.$$

6.15. Another way of synthesizing a network represented by Eq. (6.45) is to recognize that, because the numerator is of one higher degree than the denominator, the denominator may be divided into the numerator, yielding a function of the form

$$Z_{11}(s) = k_1 s + \frac{N_1(s)}{D(s)}$$

where $N_1(s)$, the remainder, is of one degree less than $D(s)$. This expression represents an inductor $L = k$ in series with an impedance $N_1(s)/D(s)$. This latter impedance may be represented by an admittance $D(s)/N_1(s)$ which may be written

$$Y'_{11}(s) = k_2 s + \frac{R_2(s)}{N_1(s)}$$

where $R_2(s)$ is the new remainder. This represents a capacitor $C = k_2$ in parallel with an admittance $R_2(s)/N_1(s)$. This admittance may be represented by an impedance $N_1(s)/R_2(s)$.

Continue the development of this method of synthesis, justifying each step. It leads to a *ladder* or *Cauer* form of synthesis.

6.16. Apply the results of Exercise 6.15 to synthesize the network represented by Exercise 6.14.

CHAPTER 7

TWO-TERMINAL-PAIR NETWORKS

An important class of networks having even greater generality than the two-terminal networks already considered is the *two-terminal-pair network*. Two terminals constitute a pair if the current leaving one terminal is identically equal to the current entering the other. This definition implies that impedance measurements are made only at a pair of terminals and not between two terminals of different pairs. A two-terminal-pair network, then, should not be called a four-terminal network, which is a more general form of network.

The two-terminal-pair network is of great practical importance. Such networks include those in which the pairs of terminals are widely separated, such as telephone lines, communication circuits (wire or wireless), or power-transmission lines; or those where the pairs of terminals are close together physically, as filters or audio amplifiers.

The description "two-terminal-pair" network is cumbersome, and so the term *port*, borrowed from microwave circuitry where a terminal pair is merely an opening, has achieved popularity as a synonym for *terminal pair*. Thus we speak of *two-port networks* or even of "two-ports." The term *coupling networks* is often also used.

7.1. The Two-terminal-pair Network. The basic two-terminal-pair network is shown in Fig. 7.1. By

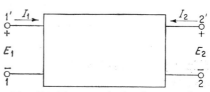

FIG. 7.1. Two-terminal-pair network.

definition we are limited to measurements of the voltages E_1 and E_2 and the currents I_1 and I_2. For example, we are not permitted to measure the difference of potential between terminals 1 and 2. In practice, a source is usually connected to one pair of terminals, and a load to the other pair; however, since we are concerned with the network and not with the external circuits, we consider only the terminal voltages and currents, thus preserving generality. The particular choice of reference polarities used, which appears to imply (but actually does not) that energy is fed into both ends of the network, is selected in order to take advantage of any symmetric properties of the network.

171

The networks which we shall consider in this chapter are passive. That is, they do not contain any sources, but only resistors, capacitors, and inductors. (Later in this chapter a broader definition of passivity will be considered.)

7.2. Impedance and Admittance Parameters. The two pairs of terminals may be considered as being formed by breaking into two meshes of a network, as shown in Fig. 7.2. Then the currents I_1 and I_2 are mesh currents, and we may analyze the network using general mesh analysis.

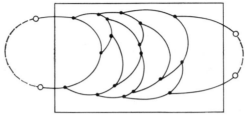

FIG. 7.2. Formation of two-terminal-pair network from a general network.

For convenience we designate the two meshes as mesh 1 and mesh 2. The two voltages E_1 and E_2 may exist across voltage sources, current sources, impedances, or combinations of these. However, if we consider these voltages as the pertinent variables, it is immaterial how they are caused. That is, we may treat the voltages as though they were both sources. Thus, following the procedure of Sec. 5.1, we write

$$\begin{aligned}
E_1 &= Z_{11}I_1 + Z_{12}I_2 + \cdots + Z_{1\lambda}I_\lambda \\
E_2 &= Z_{21}I_1 + Z_{22}I_2 + \cdots + Z_{2\lambda}I_\lambda \\
0 &= Z_{31}I_1 + Z_{32}I_2 + \cdots + Z_{3\lambda}I_\lambda \\
&\cdots\cdots\cdots\cdots\cdots\cdots\cdots\cdots \\
0 &= Z_{\lambda 1}I_1 + Z_{\lambda 2}I_2 + \cdots + Z_{\lambda\lambda}I_\lambda.
\end{aligned} \tag{7.1}$$

(Since we are dealing with passive networks, all the sources except E_1 and E_2 are zero.) Applying Cramer's rule yields

$$I_1 = \frac{1}{\Delta}
\begin{vmatrix}
E_1 & Z_{12} & Z_{13} & \cdots & Z_{1\lambda} \\
E_2 & Z_{22} & Z_{23} & \cdots & Z_{2\lambda} \\
0 & Z_{32} & Z_{33} & \cdots & Z_{3\lambda} \\
\cdot & \cdot & \cdot & \cdots & \cdot \\
0 & Z_{\lambda 2} & Z_{\lambda 3} & \cdots & Z_{\lambda\lambda}
\end{vmatrix}$$

$$\tag{7.2}$$

$$I_2 = \frac{1}{\Delta}
\begin{vmatrix}
Z_{11} & E_1 & Z_{13} & \cdots & Z_{1\lambda} \\
Z_{21} & E_2 & Z_{23} & \cdots & Z_{2\lambda} \\
Z_{31} & 0 & Z_{33} & \cdots & Z_{3\lambda} \\
\cdot & \cdot & \cdot & \cdots & \cdot \\
Z_{\lambda 1} & 0 & Z_{\lambda 3} & \cdots & Z_{\lambda\lambda}
\end{vmatrix}$$

where Δ is the determinant of the coefficients of Eq. (7.1). Since we are concerned only with I_1 and I_2 we need not write the expressions corresponding to Eq. (7.2) for I_3, I_4, . . . , I_λ. If we expand the above determinants we may write

$$I_1 = y_{11}E_1 + y_{12}E_2$$
$$I_2 = y_{21}E_1 + y_{22}E_2$$

$$(7.3)$$

where y_{ij} is the cofactor of Z_{ij} in Δ, divided by Δ. The quantities y_{11}, y_{12}, y_{21}, y_{22} are called the *short-circuit admittances* of the network (see Sec. 5.1) for

$$y_{11} = \frac{I_1}{E_1} \qquad \text{when } E_2 = 0 \text{ (short circuit)}$$

$$y_{12} = \frac{I_1}{E_2} \qquad \text{when } E_1 = 0 \text{ (short circuit)}$$

$$y_{21} = \frac{I_2}{E_1} \qquad \text{when } E_2 = 0 \text{ (short circuit)}$$

$$y_{22} = \frac{I_2}{E_2} \qquad \text{when } E_1 = 0 \text{ (short circuit)}.$$

Now Eqs. (7.3) may be solved for E_1 and E_2 and written as†

$$E_1 = z_{11}I_1 + z_{12}I_2$$
$$E_2 = z_{21}I_1 + z_{22}I_2$$

$$(7.4)$$

where

$$z_{11} = \frac{y_{22}}{Y}, \qquad z_{12} = -\frac{y_{12}}{Y}, \qquad z_{21} = -\frac{y_{21}}{Y}, \qquad z_{22} = \frac{y_{11}}{Y}$$

and Y is the determinant

$$Y = \begin{vmatrix} y_{11} & y_{12} \\ y_{21} & y_{22} \end{vmatrix}.$$

The z's are *open-circuit impedances* for

$$z_{11} = \frac{E_1}{I_1} \qquad \text{when } I_2 = 0 \text{ (open circuit)}$$

$$z_{12} = \frac{E_1}{I_2} \qquad \text{when } I_1 = 0 \text{ (open circuit)}$$

and so forth. These appear to be the same z_{ij} that might be obtained from a node analysis of the network (see Sec. 5.2). Indeed, the network could have been originally analyzed on a node basis to give the same results, but the analysis is less straightforward and is left as an exercise for the reader.

There are only three independent open-circuit impedances since, as will

† It is possible to write Eqs. (7.4) directly from the network by use of the superposition theorem, but this does not yield the values of the z's in terms of the network parameters.

be seen, $z_{12} = z_{21}$. There are also only three independent short-circuit admittances, because $y_{12} = y_{21}$.

It is important to note the difference between the Z's and the z's. Using Z's,

$$E_1 = Z_{11}I_1 + Z_{12}I_2 + \cdots + Z_{1\lambda}I_\lambda. \tag{7.5}$$

The last $\lambda - 2$ terms in this expression are not generally zero even when voltage sources exist only in meshes 1 and 2. However, the first of Eqs. (7.4) states that

$$E_1 = z_{11}I_1 + z_{12}I_2. \tag{7.4.1}$$

To reconcile these two equations we note that in Eq. (7.5), because of superposition, we may write (regarding I_1 and I_2 as the sources)

$$\begin{aligned} I_3 &= \alpha_3 I_1 + \beta_3 I_2 \\ I_4 &= \alpha_4 I_1 + \beta_4 I_2 \\ &\cdots\cdots\cdots\cdots \end{aligned} \tag{7.6}$$

and so Eq. (7.5) becomes

$$E_1 = Z_{11}I_1 + Z_{12}I_2 + Z_{13}(\alpha_3 I_1 + \beta_3 I_2) + \cdots$$

or

$$E_1 = (Z_{11} + \alpha_3 Z_{13} + \alpha_4 Z_{14} + \cdots)I_1 + (Z_{12} + \beta_3 Z_{13} + \beta_4 Z_{14} + \cdots)I_2. \tag{7.7}$$

Comparing this with Eqs. (7.4) we see that z_{11} includes factors which account for the various components of E_1 resulting from all the mesh currents.

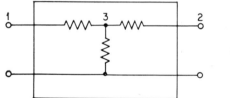

Fig. 7.3. Two-mesh two-terminal-pair network.

Fig. 7.4. Reference polarities for $ABCD$ parameters.

It is clear that in general

$$z_{ij} \neq Z_{ij}.$$

However, in a two-mesh circuit having a common ground node (see Fig. 7.3) the corresponding z's and Z's are equal, which may lead one to lose sight of the foregoing inequality.

7.3. $ABCD$ **Parameters.** There are four variables of interest in a two-terminal-pair network. Also, two independent relations may be written among these variables, for example, Eqs. (7.4). In practical problems it is often convenient to express these relations in a different form, using the current and voltage at one pair of terminals as the independent variables.

This manner of expression gives rise to the so-called *ABCD parameters* or *general circuit constants.*

In defining these parameters a different convention than before is used for the current at terminal pair 2, as shown in Fig. 7.4. This is done because the *ABCD* parameters were originally introduced in the study of power-transmission lines, with terminals 1 considered as the *sending end* and terminals 2 as the *receiving end.* The reference polarities adopted thus always resulted in positive signs for the variables.

Referring to Fig. 7.4, we define the *ABCD* parameters by

$$E_1 = AE_2 + BI_2'$$
$$I_1 = CE_2 + DI_2' \tag{7.8}$$

where

$$A = \frac{E_1}{E_2} \quad \text{with } I_2' = 0 \text{ (open circuit)}$$

$$B = \frac{E_1}{I_2'} \quad \text{with } E_2 = 0 \text{ (short circuit)}$$

$$C = \frac{I_1}{E_2} \quad \text{with } I_2' = 0 \text{ (open circuit)} \tag{7.9}$$

$$D = \frac{I_1}{I_2'} \quad \text{with } E_2 = 0 \text{ (short circuit)}.$$

These parameters are not particularly named, but they may be interpreted as follows:

A^{-1} is the open-circuit voltage gain.
B^{-1} is the short-circuit transfer admittance.
C^{-1} is the open-circuit transfer impedance.
D^{-1} is the short-circuit current gain.

The general circuit constants may be expressed in terms of the open-circuit impedance by making use of Eqs. (7.4):

$$E_1 = z_{11}I_1 + z_{12}I_2 = z_{11}I_1 - z_{12}I_2'$$
$$E_2 = z_{21}I_1 + z_{22}I_2 = z_{12}I_1 - z_{22}I_2'. \tag{7.4a}$$

(Here we have made use of the relations $z_{12} = z_{21}$ and $I_2 = -I_2'$). Now, from the second of these equations,

$$I_1 = \frac{E_2}{z_{12}} + I_2'\frac{z_{22}}{z_{12}}. \tag{7.10.1}$$

Substituting this value of I_1 into the first yields

$$E_1 = \frac{z_{11}}{z_{12}} E_2 + \frac{z_{11}z_{22}}{z_{12}} I_2' - z_{12}I_2' = \frac{z_{11}}{z_{12}} E_2 + \frac{z_{11}z_{22} - z_{12}^2}{z_{12}} I_2'$$

$$= \frac{z_{11}}{z_{12}} E_2 + \frac{\Delta_z}{z_{12}} I_2' \tag{7.10.2}$$

where Δ_z is the determinant of the z's.

Comparing Eqs. (7.10) with Eqs. (7.8) shows that

$$A = \frac{z_{11}}{z_{12}}$$

$$B = \frac{\Delta_z}{z_{12}} = -\frac{1}{y_{12}}$$

$$C = \frac{1}{z_{12}}$$

$$D = \frac{z_{22}}{z_{12}}.$$

Now, it is to be observed that only three independent open-circuit imped-ances exist, whereas there are four general circuit constants. Hence, only three general circuit constants may be specified independently. The relation which consequently exists among the general circuit constants may be found, for example, by solving for B in terms of the other circuit parameters:

$$B = \frac{\Delta_z}{z_{12}} = \frac{z_{11}z_{22} - z_{12}{}^2}{z_{12}} = \frac{Az_{12}{}^2D - z_{12}{}^2}{z_{12}} = \frac{AD - 1}{C}$$

whence

$$AD - BC = 1. \tag{7.11}$$

This relation may be expressed in determinantal form as

$$\begin{vmatrix} A & B \\ C & D \end{vmatrix} = 1. \tag{7.11a}$$

The $ABCD$ constants are particularly useful in the analysis of intercon-nected networks, as may be seen by the following example.

Example 7.1.   Two networks whose general circuit constants are

$$\begin{matrix} A_1 & B_1 & \quad & A_2 & B_2 \\ C_1 & D_1 & \quad & C_2 & D_2 \end{matrix}$$

are connected in cascade (see Fig. 7.5).   Determine the new set of general circuit constants for the combined network.

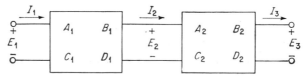

FIG. 7.5. Circuit for Example 7.1.

Solution.   For the first network we may write

$$E_1 = A_1 E_2 + B_1 I_2$$
$$I_1 = C_1 E_2 + D_1 I_2$$

and for the second

$$E_2 = A_2E_3 + B_2I_3$$
$$I_2 = C_2E_3 + D_2I_3.$$

Substitute the second set of values for E_2 and I_2 into the first set of equations to obtain

$$E_1 = (A_1A_2 + B_1C_2)E_3 + (A_1B_2 + B_1D_2)I_3 = AE_3 + BI_3$$
$$I_1 = (C_1A_2 + D_1C_2)E_3 + (C_1B_2 + D_1D_2)I_3 = CE_3 + DI_3.$$

The unmarked constants A, B, C, D are those of the complete network.

It is also possible to write a modified set of general circuit constants for the network taking the receiving-end current and voltage as dependent variables and the sending-end current and voltage as independent variables. This set of constants is defined by

$$E_2 = A'E_1 + B'I_1$$
$$I'_2 = C'E_1 + D'I_1. \tag{7.12}$$

It is not difficult to show that if we solve Eqs. (7.8) for E_2 and I'_2 we obtain

$$E_2 = DE_1 - BI_1$$
$$I'_2 = -CE_1 + AI_1. \tag{7.13}$$

Because E_1 and I_1 are independent variables, each may in turn be set equal to zero. Thus the corresponding coefficients of E_1 and I_1 in Eqs. (7.12) and (7.13) are equal. That is,

$$D = A', \qquad B = -B'$$
$$C = -C', \qquad A = D'.$$

(The reader may at first wonder how the input voltage and current can be independent. Recall that the load may be arbitrary—even a voltage source. Thus, although E_1 may be fixed, I_1 may be varied by changing the load.) Further exploration of the interrelations among these and other sets of parameters is left to the ingenuity of the reader.

7.4. Hybrid Parameters. In the preceding development we considered the relations among the four variables of a two-terminal-pair network with the currents as independent variables and the voltages dependent, and vice versa; with the receiving-end variables independent and the sending-end dependent, and vice versa. There remains another method of pairing the variables: E_1 with I_2, and E_2 with I_1. This approach leads to two new sets of *hybrid parameters*, the first of which is defined by Eqs. (7.14).

$$I_1 = g_{11}E_1 + g_{12}I_2$$
$$E_2 = g_{21}E_1 + g_{22}I_2. \tag{7.14}$$

Hence

$$g_{11} = \frac{I_1}{E_1} \text{ (with } I_2 = 0) = \frac{1}{z_{11}}$$

$$g_{12} = \frac{I_1}{I_2} \text{ (with } E_1 = 0) = -\frac{1}{D'}$$

$$g_{21} = \frac{E_2}{E_1} \text{ (with } I_2 = 0) = \frac{1}{A}$$

$$g_{22} = \frac{E_2}{I_2} \text{ (with } E_1 = 0) = \frac{1}{y_{22}}.$$

Since only three parameters are necessary to describe a two-terminal-pair network, there must exist an additional constraint on these parameters. Inspection of Eqs. (7.12) and (7.13) shows that $D' = A$. Hence

$$g_{12} = -g_{21}. \tag{7.15}$$

A second set of hybrid parameters is defined by

$$E_1 = h_{11}I_1 + h_{12}E_2$$
$$I_2 = h_{21}I_1 + h_{22}E_2. \tag{7.16}$$

It is clear that

$$h_{11} = \frac{E_1}{I_1} \text{ (with } E_2 = 0) = \frac{1}{y_{11}}$$

$$h_{12} = \frac{E_1}{E_2} \text{ (with } I_1 = 0) = \frac{1}{A'}$$

$$h_{21} = \frac{I_2}{I_1} \text{ (with } E_2 = 0) = -\frac{1}{D}$$

$$h_{22} = \frac{I_2}{E_2} \text{ (with } I_1 = 0) = \frac{1}{z_{22}}.$$

It may be noted that $h_{12} = -h_{21}$, for, from Eqs. (7.12) and (7.13), $A' = D$. Additional relations among the various sets of parameters may be worked out by the reader.

The hybrid parameters may appear to be only of academic interest. This is not true. The h parameters are used extensively in the analysis of transistor circuits.

7.5. Passive Equivalent Networks. When the parameters of a two-terminal-pair network are known, it is possible to construct an equivalent network having a very simple form with the same parameters. Since only three parameters are needed to describe a coupling network, it transpires that only three impedance elements are required to construct the equivalent network. This will be illustrated first with the open-circuit parameters. These are defined by Eqs. (7.4) as

$$E_1 = z_{11}I_1 + z_{12}I_2$$
$$E_2 = z_{12}I_1 + z_{22}I_2. \tag{7.4a}$$

(Here it is explicitly recognized that $z_{21} = z_{12}$.)

The circuit shown in Fig. 7.6 also satisfies these equations. This is called a T network. (The convention of using the symbol previously reserved for resistance as the general symbol for impedance is employed.) The elements of this network are single fixed impedances, so that the equivalence between this network and that described by Eqs. (7.4a) exists only at a single frequency.

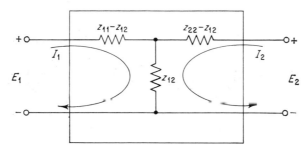

FIG. 7.6. General T circuit.

In general, the parameters of the original network are functions of frequency. Sometimes it is possible to form each arm of the equivalent network from a group of elements (that is, each arm of the network is not a single element but rather a two-terminal network) so that the equivalent network is equivalent at all frequencies. The impedance functions $z_{11} - z_{12}$, $z_{22} - z_{12}$, and z_{12} may not always be realized by two-terminal networks, so that in general we cannot construct a network of the form of Fig. 7.6 which is equivalent at all frequencies.

Another equivalent circuit may be derived if the short-circuit parameters are taken as a starting point. Recognizing that $y_{12} = y_{21}$ we write Eqs. (7.3) as

$$I_1 = y_{11}E_1 + y_{12}E_2$$
$$I_2 = y_{12}E_1 + y_{22}E_2. \quad (7.3a)$$

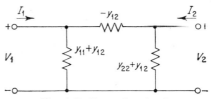

FIG. 7.7. General π circuit.

It is seen that the circuit of Fig. 7.7 also satisfies these equations. This circuit is called, from its appearance, the equivalent pi (π) network. The remarks made above regarding the behavior with frequency of T networks are equally applicable to π networks.

Since a T network and a π network can be constructed equivalent to a given network, they are, of course, equivalent to each other. Indeed, the equivalence of the two networks may be shown by the familiar Y-Δ transformation.

Sometimes it is found, when determining the parameters of equivalent circuits, that z_{12} contains a negative resistance. This does not bother us in a mathematical sense but raises problems if we try to construct an actual equivalent circuit. The difficulty often arises only because the reference polarities of the original network were assigned somewhat arbitrarily, and the problem disappears if we transpose (say) the output terminals of the equivalent circuit.

Example 7.2. Determine the equivalent T network for Fig. 7.8. (Since the only parameter which will cause difficulty is z_{12}, we shall determine only this one.)

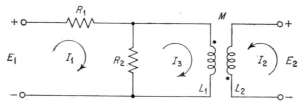

FIG. 7.8. Circuit for Example 7.2.

Solution. The mesh equations for this circuit are

$$
\begin{aligned}
E_1 &= I_1(R_1 + R_2) && + I_3(-R_2) \\
E_2 &= && I_2(j\omega L_2) && + I_3(-j\omega M) \\
0 &= I_1(-R_2) && + I_2(-j\omega M) + I_3(R_2 + j\omega L_1).
\end{aligned} \qquad (a)
$$

Determining the y's and z's by Cramer's rule is laborious. A more direct approach is the following. Write

$$
z_{12} = \frac{E_1}{I_2} \qquad \text{with } I_1 = 0.
$$

But if $I_1 = 0$, the mesh equations become

$$
\begin{aligned}
E_2 &= I_2(j\omega L_2) + I_3(-j\omega M) \\
0 &= I_2(-j\omega M) + I_3(R_2 + j\omega L_1)
\end{aligned}
$$

whence

$$
I_2 = \frac{E_2(R_2 + j\omega L_1)}{\Delta_z}, \qquad I_3 = -\frac{E_2(-j\omega M)}{\Delta_z}
$$

where $\Delta_z = \omega^2(M^2 - L_1 L_2) + j\omega L_2 R_2$. Now from the first of Eqs. (a), with $I_1 = 0$,

$$
z_{12} = \frac{E_1}{I_2} = -\frac{R_2 I_3}{I_2} = -\frac{j\omega M R_2}{R_2 + j\omega L_1} = \frac{-\omega^2 M L_1 R_2 - j\omega M R_2{}^2}{R_2{}^2 + \omega^2 L_1{}^2}.
$$

It is seen that the real part of this expression is always negative, which leads to a physically nonrealizable quantity. However, let us transpose terminals 2 of the equivalent circuit, as in Fig. 7.9a. It is seen that a positive Z acts as a negative z_{12}.

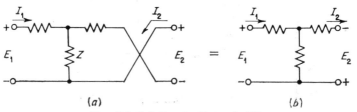

(a) (b)

FIG. 7.9. Solution to Example 7.2.

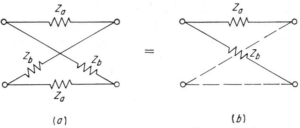

FIG. 7.10. (a) Symmetrical lattice network; (b) simplified representation.

Thus, in cases where negative z_{12} is required, we often need merely to use the modified equivalent circuit of Fig. 7.9a, which may be redrawn as Fig. 7.9b. In the case in hand, the particular choice of reference polarities for M is equivalent to transposing our output reference polarities.

A class of networks frequently encountered in practice is symmetrical networks, wherein $z_{11} = z_{22}$ (or $y_{11} = y_{22}$). In advanced analyses of such networks it often proves convenient to represent them by the *symmetrical lattice networks* shown in Fig. 7.10.

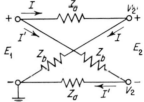

FIG. 7.11. Polarities and current designations used in determining parameters of lattice.

The equivalence between the symmetrical lattice and a symmetrical network may be shown by straightforward application of loop analysis to each network. It is simpler, though, to use the following approach (see Fig. 7.11). Write

$$z_{11} = \frac{E_1}{I_1} \qquad \text{with terminals 2 open-circuited.}$$

Since $I_1 = I + I'$ and $I = I'$,

$$I_1 = \frac{2E_1}{Z_a + Z_b}$$

$$z_{11} = \frac{Z_a + Z_b}{2}. \tag{7.17}$$

Now

$$z_{21} = \frac{E_2}{I_1} \qquad \text{with terminals 2 open-circuited}$$

$$= \frac{V_{2'} - V_2}{I_1}.$$

But

$$V_{2'} = IZ_b, \qquad V_2 = I'Z_a$$

and

$$I = I' = \tfrac{1}{2}I_1$$

so that

$$z_{21} = \frac{Z_b - Z_a}{2}. \tag{7.18}$$

It follows from the symmetry of the lattice that

$$z_{22} = \frac{Z_a + Z_b}{2} = z_{11} \quad \text{and} \quad z_{12} = \frac{Z_b - Z_a}{2} = z_{21}$$

or

$$Z_a = z_{11} - z_{12} \tag{7.19}$$
$$Z_b = z_{11} + z_{12}. \tag{7.20}$$

It is possible to develop circuits directly from the general circuit constants ($ABCD$ parameters) and from the hybrid parameters, but this is infrequently done in practice. Instead, equivalent T and π networks are used.

7.6. Equivalent Circuits Using Active Elements. If *dependent* voltage and current sources are permitted, it is possible to introduce a new class of

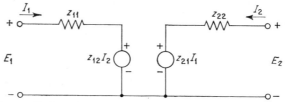

FIG. 7.12. Active equivalent circuit for two-port networks, employing voltage sources.

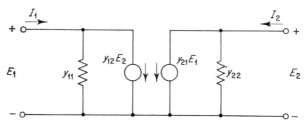

FIG. 7.13. Active equivalent circuit for two-port networks, employing current sources.

equivalent circuits. In a dependent voltage source, the voltage is independent of load current but is proportional to the value of some variable (current or voltage) in the circuit. A dependent current source is defined similarly. Thus, by using two dependent voltage sources, Eqs. (7.4),

$$E_1 = z_{11}I_1 + z_{12}I_2$$
$$E_2 = z_{21}I_1 + z_{22}I_2, \tag{7.4}$$

may be represented by Fig. 7.12. The output voltage of each source is proportional to one of the mesh currents, and so the constant of proportionality is an impedance.

By using dependent sources we can also construct equivalent circuits based on short-circuit admittance parameters (Fig. 7.13). An interesting type of equivalent circuit results if we use dependent sources with the hybrid parameters. We may use Fig. 7.14 to represent Eqs. (7.16). Observe that the input circuit uses a dependent voltage source in a series equivalent circuit, whereas the output circuit uses a dependent current source in a shunt equivalent circuit.

One may inquire: Of what use are these equivalent circuits, and can they actually be constructed? These equivalent circuits sometimes simplify certain computations. They are essential, however, when it is

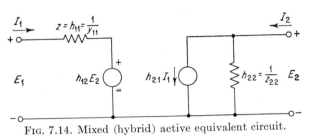

FIG. 7.14. Mixed (hybrid) active equivalent circuit.

desired to construct equivalent circuits for nonreciprocal networks (those wherein $z_{12} \neq z_{21}$). Many networks using electron devices are nonreciprocal. Conversely, it is possible, through the use of circuits containing electron devices, to construct dependent voltage and current sources suitable for physically implementing the equivalent circuits discussed.

7.7. The Transformer. We have previously considered the effects of magnetic coupling between various coils. When two or more coils are deliberately coupled magnetically, the arrangement is known as a *transformer*. Although in many applications the coils are coupled merely by

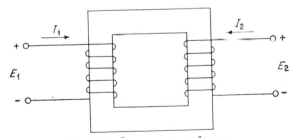

FIG. 7.15. Iron-core transformer.

being placed in proximity to each other, the most important class of transformer is that in which the flux linking the coils is guided by an iron core (which displays only little opposition to the development of magnetic flux) so that substantially all the flux links each coil (Fig. 7.15).

In order properly to appreciate the subsequent discussion of the transformer it is necessary to consider the actual fluxes involved. Referring to Fig. 7.16, the flux developed by the current in coil 1 may be considered to consist of two components:

ϕ_{11}, that component of flux created by i_1, which links only coil 1;

ϕ_{21}, that component of flux created by i_1, which links coil 2 as well as coil 1.

(The total flux developed by i_1 is thus $\phi_{11} + \phi_{21}$.) It is important to note that the diagram is only symbolic; no attempt is made to show any actual plots of the flux lines. The flux shown is an average value of flux considered to link all the turns—actually, some turns are linked by more than the average flux, and others by less.

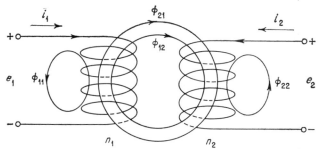

FIG. 7.16. Idealized representation of flux lines in a transformer.

The actual values of flux may be obtained from the expressions

$$\phi_{11} = c_{11}n_1i_1 \qquad (7.21.1)$$
$$\phi_{21} = c_{21}n_1i_1. \qquad (7.21.2)$$

The fluxes are proportional to the exciting ampere turns. The c's are constants dependent on the geometry and the permeability of the media involved.

Similarly,

ϕ_{22} is that component of flux created by i_2, which links only coil 2;

ϕ_{12} is that component of flux created by i_2, which links coil 1 as well as coil 2;

and

$$\phi_{22} = c_{22}n_2i_2 \qquad (7.21.3)$$
$$\phi_{12} = c_{12}n_2i_2. \qquad (7.21.4)$$

Neglecting, for the nonce, the losses in the transformer, we may write by Faraday's law the expression for the voltage at terminals 1 of the transformer as

$$e_1 = n_1\frac{d}{dt}\phi_{11} + n_1\frac{d}{dt}\phi_{21} + n_1\frac{d}{dt}\phi_{12} \qquad (7.22)$$

$$e_1 = n_1\frac{d}{dt}c_{11}n_1i_1 + n_1\frac{d}{dt}c_{21}n_1i_1 + n_1\frac{d}{dt}c_{12}n_2i_2$$

$$= n_1{}^2c_{11}\frac{d}{dt}i_1 + n_1{}^2c_{21}\frac{d}{dt}i_1 + n_1n_2c_{12}\frac{d}{dt}i_2. \qquad (7.22a)$$

The expressions $n_i n_j c_{ij}$ have the dimensions of inductance, and so we define

$$L_{11} = n_1{}^2 c_{11}$$
$$L_{21} = n_1{}^2 c_{21} \tag{7.23}$$
$$M_{12} = n_1 n_2 c_{12}.$$

The first term is called the *leakage inductance;* the last is called the *mutual inductance.* There is no established name for L_{21}. We may now write Eq. (7.22a) as

$$e_1 = (L_{11} + L_{21}) \frac{d}{dt} i_1 + M_{12} \frac{d}{dt} i_2. \tag{7.24}$$

It is recognized that $L_{11} + L_{21}$ is merely the self-inductance of coil 1, L_1. Similarly,

$$e_2 = M_{21} \frac{d}{dt} i_1 + (L_{22} + L_{12}) \frac{d}{dt} i_2 \tag{7.25}$$

where

$$L_{22} = n_2{}^2 c_{22}$$
$$L_{12} = n_2{}^2 c_{12} \tag{7.26}$$
$$M_{21} = n_2 n_1 c_{21}.$$

and $L_{22} + L_{12}$ is the self-inductance of coil 2, L_2.

Now the principle of reciprocity implies that

$$M_{21} = M_{12} = \text{(say)}\ M$$

whence

$$c_{12} = c_{21}. \tag{7.27}$$

We define the coefficient of coupling, k, by

$$k^2 = \frac{M_{12} M_{21}}{L_1 L_2} \tag{7.28}$$

$$k^2 = \frac{(n_1 n_2 c_{12})(n_2 n_1 c_{21})}{n_1{}^2 (c_{11} + c_{21}) n_2{}^2 (c_{22} + c_{12})}$$

$$= \frac{c_{12}{}^2}{(c_{11} + c_{21})(c_{22} + c_{12})}. \tag{7.29}$$

From the manner in which we have defined the c's they are all positive quantities.† Thus, from Eq. (7.29), the minimum value of k is zero, corresponding to no mutual flux, and the maximum value is unity, corresponding to no leakage flux (that is, the same flux links both coils and $c_{11} = c_{22} = 0$).

From Eqs. (7.24) and (7.25) it is seen that a lossless transformer may be

---

† We have so chosen our polarities that the sign of M is positive in the circuit equations. Were the sign of M negative, some of the c's would be negative, but Eq. (7.29) would still read the same.

represented by the circuit shown in Fig. 7.17. The coils L_{11} and L_{22} represent the leakage inductances of the transformer. The coefficient of coupling between coils L_{21} and L_{12} is

$$k = \sqrt{\frac{M^2}{L_{21}L_{12}}} = \left[\frac{(n_1 n_2 c_{12})^2}{(n_1{}^2 c_{21})(n_2{}^2 c_{12})} \right]^{\frac{1}{2}} = 1, \qquad (7.30)$$

so that the coils L_{12} and L_{21} are perfectly coupled. We have thus succeeded in separating the two windings of the transformer into uncoupled and coupled parts.

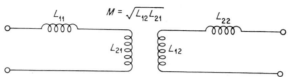

FIG. 7.17. Representation of transformer in terms of uncoupled and perfectly coupled parts.

7.8. The Ideal Transformer. The lossless transformer with unity coupling is of particular interest because it leads to the notion of the *ideal transformer*. First, let us develop a relationship between the voltages at the terminals of each coil of a transformer with unity coupling,

$$e_1 = n_1 \frac{d}{dt} \phi_1$$
$$e_2 = n_2 \frac{d}{dt} \phi_2 \qquad (7.31)$$

where ϕ_1 is the total flux linking coil 1 ($\phi_{11} + \phi_{12}$) and ϕ_2 is the total flux linking coil 2 ($\phi_{22} + \phi_{21}$). However, unity coupling means that there is no leakage flux for either coil, or

$$\phi_1 = \phi_{12} = \phi_{21} = \phi_2. \qquad (7.32)$$

Alternatively, unity coupling means that the same flux links both coils, or $c_{11} = c_{22} = 0$. Thus, from Eqs. (7.31),

$$\frac{e_1}{e_2} = \frac{n_1}{n_2}. \qquad (7.33)$$

An ideal transformer is defined as a unity-coupled transformer whose primary (and hence secondary) inductance approaches infinity (that is, $c_{12} = c_{21} \rightarrow \infty$). This, of course, requires that the core of the transformer have infinite permeability μ, since the geometric factors entering c_{12} and c_{21} are finite. Very large values of μ can be attained in practice, and the ideal transformer also proves to have widespread theoretical application, so that its discussion is well justified.

For the unity-coupled transformer, we may write Eq. (7.24) as

$$e_1 = L_{21} \frac{d}{dt} i_1 + M_{12} \frac{d}{dt} i_2. \tag{7.34}$$

But by virtue of Eqs. (7.23) and (7.27),

$$M_{12} = \frac{n_2}{n_1} L_{21}. \tag{7.35}$$

Hence

$$e_1 = L_{21} \left(\frac{d}{dt} i_1 + \frac{n_2}{n_1} \frac{d}{dt} i_2 \right)$$

or

$$\frac{e_1}{L_{21}} = \frac{d}{dt} i_1 + \frac{n_2}{n_1} \frac{d}{dt} i_2. \tag{7.36}$$

Because L_{21} becomes infinite in the limit, $e_1/L_{21} \rightarrow 0$, and

$$\frac{d}{dt} i_1 = - \frac{n_2}{n_1} \frac{d}{dt} i_2. \tag{7.37}$$

This implies that

$$i_1 = - \frac{n_2}{n_1} i_2 + c. \tag{7.38}$$

The constant of integration may be neglected if we consider only time-varying currents, and so

$$\frac{i_1}{i_2} = - \frac{n_2}{n_1}. \tag{7.39}$$

We may eliminate the negative sign if we reassign reference polarities as in Fig. 7.18, which also shows the symbol for an ideal transformer.

Physically, infinite inductance means that an infinitesimal magnetizing force (ampere turns) gives rise to the finite flux. Hence the total magnetizing force on the core is (almost) zero, and $n_1 i_1 = n_2 i_2$.

By using an ideal transformer it is now possible to develop a new equivalent cir-

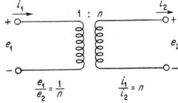

$$\frac{e_1}{e_2} = \frac{1}{n} \qquad \frac{i_1}{i_2} = n$$

FIG. 7.18. An ideal transformer.

cuit for a transformer. This is shown in Fig. 7.19. That this is indeed an equivalent circuit for a transformer may be shown by considering the various voltage-current relationships. First we note that, from the nature of the ideal transformer,

$$e_1' = \frac{n_1}{n_2} e_2' \tag{7.40}$$

$$i' = \frac{n_2}{n_1} i_2. \tag{7.41}$$

Thus

$$e_1 = L_{11} \frac{d}{dt} i_1 + L_{21} \frac{d}{dt} (i_1 + i') = (L_{11} + L_{21}) \frac{d}{dt} i_1 + L_{21} \frac{n_2}{n_1} \frac{d}{dt} i_2.$$

Since $(L_{11} + L_{21}) = L_1$ and, from Eqs. (7.23), $L_{21} n_2/n_1 = M$,

$$e_1 = L_1 \frac{d}{dt} i_1 + M \frac{d}{dt} i_2. \tag{7.42}$$

Also

$$e_2 = L_{22} \frac{d}{dt} i_2 + e_2' = L_{22} \frac{d}{dt} i_2 + \frac{n_2}{n_1} e_1'$$

$$= L_{22} \frac{d}{dt} i_2 + \frac{n_2}{n_1} L_{21} \frac{d}{dt} \left(i_1 + i_2 \frac{n_2}{n_1} \right)$$

$$= \frac{n_2}{n_1} L_{21} \frac{d}{dt} i_1 + \left(L_{22} + \frac{n_2{}^2}{n_1{}^2} L_{21} \right) \frac{d}{dt} i_2.$$

From Eqs. (7.23) and (7.26)

$$\frac{n_2{}^2}{n_1{}^2} L_{21} = L_{12}; \qquad \frac{n_2}{n_1} L_{21} = M \tag{7.43}$$

and therefore

$$e_2 = M \frac{d}{dt} i_1 + (L_{22} + L_{12}) \frac{d}{dt} i_2 = M \frac{d}{dt} i_1 + L_2 \frac{d}{dt} i_2. \tag{7.44}$$

Hence the circuit which we have drawn satisfies the same equations as a transformer. A similar equivalent circuit may be drawn by placing L_{12}

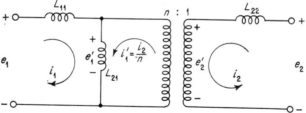

FIG. 7.19. Equivalent circuit for real (but lossless) transformer, employing ideal transformer.

on the secondary side of the transformer. It might be wondered why the equivalent circuit is not symmetrical, with shunt coils on both the primary and secondary sides of the ideal transformer. This is because the secondary current is transformed to the primary side and passes through L_{21}. Hence there is no need of a coil on the secondary side. As an exercise, the reader may show that a symmetrical equivalent circuit results if an inductance of $2L_{21}$ is placed across the primary of the transformer and an inductance of $2L_{12}$ across the secondary.

In real transformers there are losses to be considered, and so the equivalent circuit of a real transformer must include, in addition to the various inductances already considered, resistors to account for the losses. The losses in a transformer consist of the I^2R losses in the windings and the core losses. The core losses are hysteresis and eddy-current losses in the iron core of the transformer. These losses depend in a complex way on the frequency at which the transformer operates and on the maximum flux density in the core. However, these losses are generally of concern

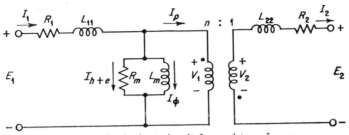

FIG. 7.20. Equivalent circuit for real transformer.

only in power transformers, which are operated at constant voltage and fixed frequency. Thus, for practical purposes they may be represented by a resistor in parallel with L_{21} (the voltage across that coil being a better measure of the peak magnetizing flux than the voltage at the terminals of the transformer).

Thus, the equivalent circuit of an actual power transformer is given by Fig. 7.20. This is the same as Fig. 7.19, with the addition of resistances R_1 and R_2 representing the I^2R losses of the windings and R_m representing the core losses (hence the subscript $h + e$ on I). The inductance L_{21} has also been redesignated I_m, the *magnetizing* inductance (since it accounts for the current which sets up the magnetic field). Observe the particular choice of dots. This has been made so that phasor diagrams to be discussed below will be spread out and easy to draw.

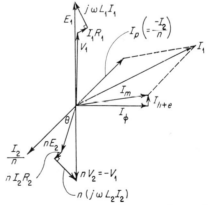

FIG. 7.21. Phasor diagram for real transformer.

The construction of the phasor diagram of the transformer (Fig. 7.21) sheds light on the operation of the transformer and is quite useful in the analysis of power circuits. It is customary to start with the current in L_m, denoted I_ϕ, as reference.† Since $V_1 = j\omega L_m I_\phi$, this is shown leading I_ϕ by 90°. Also V_2 is equal to $-V_1/n$. It is usual for the sake of clarity

† It is suggested that the student reconstruct on paper the phasor diagram as he reads the following procedure. This will help to clarify the various steps.

to multiply the secondary voltage by n before plotting.   Likewise, secondary currents are divided by n before plotting.

Now in order to continue with our diagram we must assume something about the load connected to the secondary terminals.   We shall take it to be inductive, having a phase angle θ.   The voltage E_2 and the current I_2 as well as the drops I_2R_2 and $j\omega L_2 I_2$ are now drawn in.†   To complete the diagram we add I_{h+e} to I_ϕ to obtain I_m.   Then the current through the primary, I_p, which is $-I_2/n$, is added to I_m to give I_1.   The voltages I_1R_1 and $j\omega I_1L_1$ are added to V_1 to give E_1.   This completes the diagram.

7.9. The Transformer as a Matching Device.   If we connect an impedance to the secondary terminals of an ideal transformer, the impedance measured at the primary terminals is no longer the original impedance but depends on the turns ratio of the transformer.   This is readily seen, for

$$V_1 = nV_2 \tag{7.40a}$$

$$I_1 = \frac{I_2}{n} \tag{7.41a}$$

and so the primary impedance Z_1 is given by

$$Z_1 = \frac{V_1}{I_1} = \frac{nV_2}{I_2/n} = n^2\frac{V_2}{I_2} = n^2 Z_2. \tag{7.45}$$

Thus, the ideal transformer acts as an impedance transforming device. Hence, an ideal transformer can be used to match a load to a generator

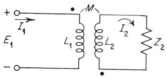

(see Sec. 5.4) in the sense that the magnitude of the transformed impedance can be made equal to that of the generator impedance (although a transformer, alone, is inadequate to change the phase angle of an impedance).

FIG. 7.22. Reflected impedance in an air-core transformer.

This impedance-transforming property is possessed by any transformer, although the analysis of real transformers is more complicated.   Transformers used for impedance matching may generally be considered, as a first approximation, to behave as ideal transformers.

In the general case of loosely coupled transformers, impedance is reflected from one coil to another.   We shall consider the case of an air-core transformer (Fig. 7.22) wherein core losses need not be considered. (The I^2R losses may be considered separately, as will be seen in the subsequent example.)   For that circuit

$$\begin{aligned} E_1 &= j\omega L_1 I_1 + j\omega M I_2 \\ 0 &= j\omega M I_1 + (j\omega L_2 + Z_2)I_2 \end{aligned} \tag{7.46}$$

† Clearly, it is actually easier to start the diagram with E_2 and I_2, rather than I_ϕ.

whence

$$I_1 = \frac{(j\omega L_2 + Z_2)E_1}{(j\omega L_1)(j\omega L_2 + Z_2) + \omega^2 M^2}$$

or

$$Z_1 = \frac{E_1}{I_1} = j\omega L_1 + \frac{\omega^2 M^2}{j\omega L_2 + Z_2}. \qquad (7.47)$$

The term $j\omega L_1$ is the impedance of the primary coil alone. Thus, the term

$$\frac{\omega^2 M^2}{j\omega L_2 + Z_2}$$

represents the *reflected impedance*, that impedance reflected from the secondary winding to the primary winding. (There is a similar impedance reflected from the primary winding to the secondary winding.)

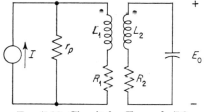

FIG. 7.23. Circuit for Example 7.3.

Example 7.3. Find the output voltage of the circuit of Fig. 7.23 by using the reflected impedance. (This circuit represents a single-tuned transformer-coupled amplifier.) It may be assumed that $r_p \gg |R_1 + j\omega L_1|$.

Solution Since $r_p \gg |R_1 + j\omega L_1|$, essentially all the current I passes through L_1, and so the induced voltage in the secondary of the transformer is

$$E_{ind} = j\omega M I_1.$$

Therefore, the voltage which appears across C is

$$E_c = E_{ind} \frac{Z_c}{R_2 + j\omega L_2 + Z_c + Z_{refl}}$$

where Z_{refl} is the impedance reflected from the primary into the secondary winding. Thus

$$Z_{refl} = \frac{\omega^2 M^2}{r_p + R_1 + j\omega L_1} \doteq \frac{\omega^2 M^2}{r_p}$$

(because $r_p \gg |R_1 + j\omega L_1|$). Therefore,

$$E_c = \frac{j\omega M I_1/j\omega C}{R_2 + j\omega L_2 + 1/j\omega C + \omega^2 M^2/r_p}.$$

7.10. Image Parameters. Another way of describing two-terminal-pair networks is in terms of *image parameters*. Before proceeding with a development of these parameters, it is necessary to introduce the concept of *mismatch ratio*. Consider a two-terminal-pair network $\mathfrak{N}$ to be connected between a source of internal impedance Z_S and a load of impedance Z_L (Fig. 7.24a). The internal voltage of the source is E_S. Let E_L be the load voltage. Now let $\mathfrak{N}$ be replaced by an ideal transformer which matches the source impedance to the load impedance (Fig. 7.24b). Let

E_L' be the load voltage under these new conditions. We then define the mismatch ratio of the network $\mathfrak{N}$ by

$$\text{Mismatch ratio} = \frac{E_L}{E_L'}. \qquad (7.48)$$

The mismatch ratio is generally used only when Z_S and Z_L are resistive. Thus, the mismatch ratio is less than or equal to unity. The value of

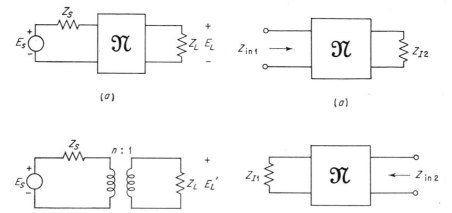

FIG. 7.24. Circuits used in defining mismatch ratio. (a) Two-port network connected between source and load; (b) network replaced by ideal transformer.

FIG. 7.25. Definitions of image impedance.

mismatch ratio may be obtained as follows. From Fig. 7.24b,

$$E_L' = \frac{1}{2} E_S \frac{1}{n} = \frac{1}{2} E_S \sqrt{\frac{Z_L}{Z_S}}.$$

Hence

$$\text{Mismatch ratio} = \frac{E_L}{E_L'} = 2 \frac{E_L}{E_S} \sqrt{\frac{Z_S}{Z_L}}. \qquad (7.49)$$

An important property of the mismatch ratio can be developed with the aid of Eq. (7.49). Since the load current I_L is E_L/Z_L and since the input current I_S is $E_S/2Z_S$, Eq. (7.49) may be written

$$\text{Mismatch ratio} = \sqrt{\frac{E_L I_L}{(E_S/2) I_S}}. \qquad (7.50)$$

If we call the voltage and current at the input terminals E_1 and I_1, and those at the output terminals E_2 and I_2, Eq. (7.50) reduces to

$$\text{Mismatch ratio} = \sqrt{\frac{E_2 I_2}{E_1 I_1}}. \qquad (7.50a)$$

Thus, the mismatch ratio relates the volt-amperes at the output terminals to the volt-amperes at the input terminals.

The image impedance of a network may be defined in terms of Fig. 7.25. The image impedances Z_{I1} and Z_{I2} are two impedances such that

$$Z_{in\ 1} = Z_{I1}$$

when Z_{I2} is connected to terminals 2, where $Z_{in\ 1}$ is the impedance looking into terminals 1, and

$$Z_{in\ 2} = Z_{I2}$$

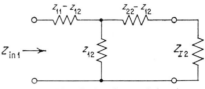

when Z_{I1} is connected to terminals 1, where $Z_{in\ 2}$ is the impedance looking into terminals 2.

We shall now develop expressions for Z_{I1} and Z_{I2} showing, incidentally, that they are uniquely defined. Let

Fig. 7.26. Circuit for determining image impedance in terms of impedance parameters.

us replace $\mathfrak{N}$ in Fig. 7.25a by its equivalent circuit, using the impedance parameters (see Fig. 7.26). Then

$$Z_{in\ 1} = z_{11} - z_{12} + \frac{(z_{22} - z_{12} + Z_{I2})z_{12}}{z_{22} + Z_{I2}}$$

$$- z_{11} - \frac{z_{12}^2}{z_{22} + Z_{I2}} = Z_{I1}. \tag{7.51}$$

Similarly, considering $Z_{in,\ 2}$,

$$Z_{I2} = z_{22} - \frac{z_{12}^2}{z_{11} + Z_{I1}}. \tag{7.52}$$

Substituting Eq. (7.52) into Eq. (7.51) and solving for Z_{I1} yields

$$Z_{I1}^2 = \frac{(z_{11}z_{22} - z_{12}^2)z_{11}}{z_{22}}.$$

But from Sec. 7.3

$$\frac{z_{22}}{z_{11}z_{22} - z_{12}^2} = y_{11}$$

so that

$$Z_{I1}^2 = \frac{z_{11}}{y_{11}}$$

or

$$Z_{I1} = \sqrt{\frac{z_{11}}{y_{11}}}. \tag{7.53.1}$$

Likewise,

$$Z_{I2} = \sqrt{\frac{z_{22}}{y_{22}}}. \tag{7.53.2}$$

Now, z_{11} is the impedance looking into terminals 1 with terminals 2 open-circuited and so is frequently written Z_{oc1}. Also, y_{11} is the admittance looking into terminals 1 with terminals 2 shorted. Hence its reciprocal is often written Z_{sc1}. Using this notation,

$$Z_{I1} = \sqrt{Z_{oc1}Z_{sc1}} \qquad (7.54.1)$$

and

$$Z_{I2} = \sqrt{Z_{oc2}Z_{sc2}}. \qquad (7.54.2)$$

These two parameters are insufficient to define a network, and so a third parameter is needed, the *image transfer constant* θ. This quantity is defined by†

$$\epsilon^{-\theta} = \text{mismatch ratio} = \sqrt{\frac{E_2 I_2}{E_1 I_1}}.$$

The image parameters are useful primarily in filter design. Their use in this application will be indicated in a subsequent section.

7.11. Frequency Response. Until now the discussion of two-ports has been limited, at least implicitly, to single-frequency sinusoidal excitation. Just as a consideration of the behavior of two-terminal networks when frequency is varied proved illuminating (see Chap. 6), so does a discussion of the *frequency response* of two-ports.

We have previously employed the term *response* to denote, in general, all the loop currents or node voltages resulting from a sinusoidal voltage or current source. When we speak of frequency response, however, we usually are considering a more restricted case, namely, a single loop current or node voltage, the *output*, and a single source, the *input*. In particular, the source at one port of a two-port is the input, and the voltage (or current) at the other pair of terminals is the output. The *frequency response* is defined as the ratio of output to input as a function of frequency. The output and input are usually, although not necessarily, measured in the same form (voltage or current), and their ratio is called the *gain* of the network. The impedance which may be placed across the output terminals must be specified in order that the frequency response be meaningful.

Theoretically we measure the frequency response by applying a sinusoidal forcing function of one frequency, waiting an infinite time for the steady state to exist, measuring the desired quantities and repeating the procedure for each frequency. In practice, the steady-state response is effectively reached in a very short time. Also, we may compute the fre-

---

† Often the *insertion ratio* is used in conjunction with image parameters, rather than the mismatch ratio. The insertion ratio of a network is defined as the ratio of the load voltage with the source connected directly to the load, to the load voltage with the network connected between the source and the load. (See W. C. Johnson, "Transmission Lines and Networks," McGraw-Hill Book Company, Inc., New York, 1950, chap. 13, p. 120.)

quency response analytically without even theoretically having to take infinite time.

Since the frequency response is a complex function of frequency, we present it graphically as two real functions of frequency: the *amplitude* response and the *phase* response, these being the amplitude of the frequency response and the phase angle of the frequency response, respectively.

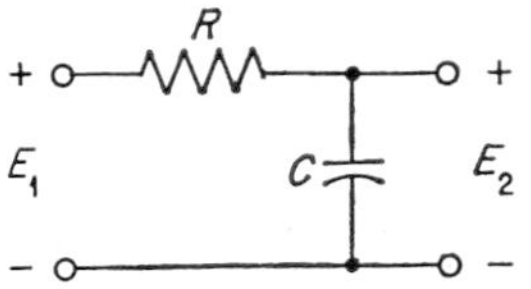

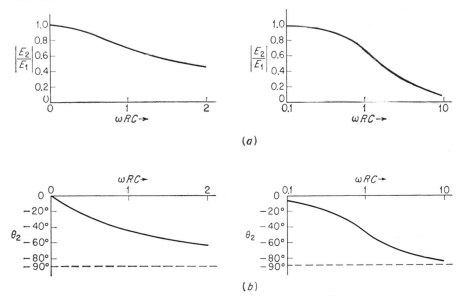

Fig. 7.27. Circuit for Example 7.4.

Example 7.4. Determine the frequency response, and plot the amplitude and phase responses of the network of Fig. 7.27, where E_1 is the input and E_2 is the output.

Solution. We have

$$\frac{E_2(j\omega)}{E_1(j\omega)} = \frac{1/j\omega C}{R + 1/j\omega C} = \frac{1}{1 + j\omega RC}.$$

The amplitude response is

$$A(\omega) = \frac{1}{\sqrt{1 + \omega^2 R^2 C^2}}$$

and the phase response is

$$\theta(\omega) = -\arctan\frac{\omega RC}{1}.$$

These expressions are plotted in Fig. 7.28*a* and *b*, respectively. (These curves are plotted with ωRC as abscissa. It is customary to define RC as $1/\omega_0$ and use ω/ω_0 as the abscissa. This technique normalizes the curves, permitting them to be used as

Linear frequency scales   Logarithmic frequency scales

Fig. 7.28. Amplitude and phase response of circuit of Fig. 7.27. (*a*) Amplitude response; (*b*) phase response.

universal curves for any values of R and C.) A logarithmic frequency scale is also shown. It will be seen later that this scale often brings out various symmetries in the response curves.

Example 7.5. Determine the frequency response and the amplitude and phase response of the circuit shown in Fig. 7.29a.

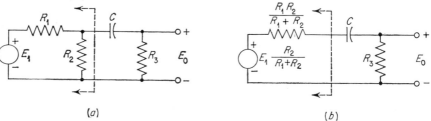

(a)   (b)

FIG. 7.29. Circuits for Example 7.5. (a) Original circuit; (b) circuit simplified by use of Thévenin's theorem.

Solution. As a first step, Thévenin's theorem applied to the portion of the circuit to the left of the broken line enables us to redraw the circuit as in Fig. 7.29b. Then

$$\frac{E_0(j\omega)}{E_1(j\omega)} = \frac{R_2}{R_1 + R_2} \frac{R_3}{\dfrac{R_1 R_2}{R_1 + R_2} + \dfrac{1}{j\omega C} + R_3}$$

$$= \frac{R_2 R_3}{R_1 R_2 + R_1 R_3 + R_2 R_3} \frac{1}{1 + \dfrac{1}{j\omega C} \dfrac{R_1 + R_2}{R_1 R_2 + R_1 R_3 + R_2 R_3}}.$$

A common technique in making such expressions meaningful is to introduce new parameters which simplify the expressions without obscuring essential data. Thus, we may let

$$A_0 = \frac{R_2 R_3}{R_1 R_2 + R_1 R_3 + R_2 R_3}$$

and

$$\omega_0 = \frac{R_1 + R_2}{C(R_1 R_2 + R_1 R_3 + R_2 R_3)}.$$

Thus

$$\frac{E_0(j\omega)}{E_1(j\omega)} = A_0 \frac{1}{1 - j\omega_0/\omega}$$

whence†

$$A(\omega) = A_0 \left[1 + \left(\frac{\omega_0}{\omega}\right)^2\right]^{-\frac{1}{2}}$$

and

$$\theta(\omega) = -\arctan\left(-\frac{\omega_0}{\omega}\right) = \arctan\frac{\omega_0}{\omega}.$$

In plotting amplitude-response characteristics, use is frequently made of a logarithmic, or *decibel*, scale. This scale is defined in terms of the

† Note that A_0 is a dimensionless number, whereas ω_0 has the dimensions of $1/RC$ or sec^{-1}. Thus E_0/E_1 is dimensionless. It is often worthwhile to determine the dimensions of equations as a check on the correctness of solutions.

logarithm of a power ratio. Although a logarithm is a dimensionless number, we specify the ratio in terms of the "bel" (after Alexander Bell) † or more usually in "decibels" (tenths of bels, abbreviated "db") in order to designate the base of the logarithms.

$$\text{Power ratio (in bels)} = \log_{10} \frac{P_2}{P_1}$$

$$\text{Power ratio (db)} = 10 \log_{10} \frac{P_2}{P_1}. \tag{7.55}$$

A power ratio of 10, then, is 1 bel, or 10 db. (In practice, decibels are always used, rather than bels.‡)

Decibel expressions are also used for expressing voltage gains or ratios. If, in response to an input power P_1, a circuit delivers into a resistor R_2 an output power P_2, the decibel gain is $10 \log (P_2/P_1)$. If the input resistance of the circuit is R_1 and the input voltage V_1, then the input power is V_1^2/R_1. Similarly, $P_2 = V_2^2/R_2$. Thus

$$\text{Gain (db)} = 10 \log \frac{V_2^2 R_1}{V_1^2 R_2} = 20 \log \frac{V_2}{V_1} + 10 \log \frac{R_1}{R_2}. \tag{7.56}$$

If $R_2 = R_1$, then

$$\text{Gain (db)} = 20 \log \frac{V_2}{V_1}. \tag{7.57}$$

Common usage has led to the convention of using the expression of Eq. (7.57) even if the resistances are unequal, and so by conventional usage it is possible to have a positive voltage gain even if there is no power gain. Also, this expression is often used in connection with reactive circuits where there may be no question of power. Thus, we may merely accept Eq. (7.57) as a defining relation for voltage gain, without consideration of its origin.

Equation (7.57) also may be used to express *relative gain*. If a constant input voltage having a variable frequency is applied to a network and if V_1 is the output voltage at some reference frequency (generally that corresponding to maximum gain), then the relative gain at frequency f_2, at which the output voltage is V_2, is given by Eq. (7.57). Relative gain is frequently used as ordinate in plotting amplitude response. As an example, the data of Fig. 7.28a are replotted in Fig. 7.30 on a decibel scale,

† The use of logarithmic power measurements stems from experiments in hearing. It is found that, if a sound having a certain level impinges on the ear and if this power is gradually increased, the smallest increase which can be detected is a fixed percentage of the original power, rather than a fixed amount of power. On a logarithmic scale, addition of a fixed number corresponds to multiplication by a fixed percentage.

‡ A system based on natural logarithms and voltage ratios is sometimes used, wherein the unit is the *neper* (after John Napier, the inventor of logarithms). Voltage ratio (nepers) = $\log_e (V_2/V_1)$.

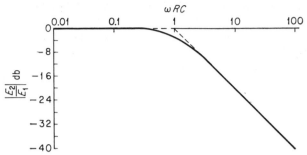

FIG. 7.30. Figure 7.28a redrawn on logarithmic coordinates.

using also a logarithmic frequency scale.   It is noted that in this plot the
amplitude response except near $\omega = 1/RC$ is represented by straight-line
segments.   This property of logarithmic plots enables us to approximate
readily many amplitude-response curves.

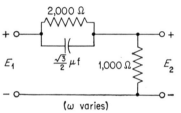

FIG. 7.31. Circuit for Example
7.6.

Another way of presenting frequency
responses is in the form of gain loci or
polar plots of complex gain.   These are
quite analogous to the impedance loci
developed in Sec. 6.5.   Often, too, these
plots are circles, as in the following
example.

Example 7.6.   Determine the maximum difference in phase between $E_2(j\omega)$ and $E_1(j\omega)$ in the
circuit shown in Fig. 7.31, as ω varies from zero to infinity.

Solution.   The gain is

$$\text{Gain } (j\omega) = \frac{E_2(j\omega)}{E_1(j\omega)} = \frac{1000}{1000 + \dfrac{2000}{1 + j\omega 2000 \dfrac{\sqrt{3}}{2} 10^{-6}}}.$$

This equation does not have the form of Eq. (6.28) (although it may be reduced to
that form), and so it is easier to deal with the ratio E_1/E_2.   (This is the reciprocal of
the forward transfer function; it is not the same as the backward transfer function,
which is also designated E_1/E_2):

$$\frac{E_1(j\omega)}{E_2(j\omega)} = 1 + \frac{2}{1 + j\omega 10^{-3} \sqrt{3}}.$$

The second term of the right-hand member of this equation may be written, in accordance with Eqs. (6.31) and (6.32), as

$$1 + 1\epsilon^{-j2\theta}$$

where

$$\theta = \arctan \left(10^{-3} \sqrt{3} \frac{\omega}{1} \right)$$

and since $0 \leqq \omega \leqq \infty$, we have $0 \leqq \theta \leqq 90°$ or $-180° \leqq -2\theta \leqq 0$. Thus

$$\frac{1}{\text{Gain}} = \frac{E_1}{E_2} = 1 + 1 + 1\epsilon^{-j2\theta} = 2 + \epsilon^{-j2\theta}, \quad -180° \leqq -2\theta \leqq 0.$$

This expression, representing a circle with center (2,0) and radius 1, is plotted in Fig. 7.32. From this figure, it is clear that the maximum phase shift occurs for 2θ such that $\overline{BA}$ is normal to the line $\overline{OA}$ which is drawn from the origin tangent to the

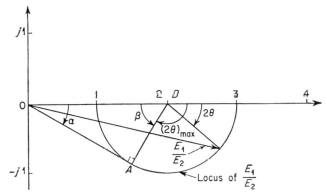

FIG. 7.32. Locus of E_1/E_2 for circuit of Fig. 7.31.

circle. Since $\overline{BA} = 1$, $\overline{OB} = 2$, then $\overline{OB} = \sqrt{3}$ and $\alpha = 30°$. Consequently $\beta = 60°$ and $2\theta_{\text{max}} = 120°$. Thus, $\theta_{\text{max}} = 60°$, and the frequency for maximum phase shift is given by

$$60° = \arctan 10^{-3} \sqrt{3}\, \omega,$$

or

$$\omega = 10^3.$$

Observe that the maximum phase shift is $\alpha = 30°$ and not θ_{max}.

This example was discussed in more detail than would have been necessary if the method were familiar. The alternative method is to differentiate the expression for phase angle and set the derivative equal to zero to find α.

Although the gain loci of most two-ports do not conveniently turn out to be circles, plots of the loci are used frequently in the design of feedback amplifiers and servomechanisms, in the form of *Nyquist diagrams*.

The extension of frequency-response techniques to the s plane will be reserved until Chap. 10.

7.12. Filters. One of the more important applications of the theory of two-ports is the design of filters. A filter is a two-port whose frequency response shows discrimination against certain frequencies, with some bands of frequencies not being passed, or at least being highly attenuated, and with some bands being passed without significant attenuation. The attenuated bands are termed *attenuation bands* or *stop bands*, and the others are *passbands*. Filters are used to discriminate among various frequencies in such applications as carrier telephony (where several conversations are carried on one pair of lines) or frequently to compensate for nonuniform frequency response of telephone lines or transmission circuits.

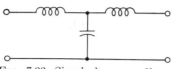

FIG. 7.33. Simple low-pass filter (prototype filter section).

The design of filters is a highly specialized subject, and so we shall not consider it in detail but shall instead give a few examples and indicate some of the design considerations involved.

One of the simplest forms of filter is the low-pass filter shown in Fig. 7.33. This rudimentary filter is also called a *filter section*, since several may be connected to achieve the over-all filter characteristic desired. The low-pass filter, as the name implies, passes low frequencies and attenuates high frequencies. It does this because the inductors offer a high impedance to high frequencies but low impedance to low frequencies, whereas the capacitor offers a high shunt admittance to high frequencies and a low admittance to low frequencies. Other basic (or *prototype*) filters are the high-pass and the band-elimination filters (Fig. 7.34).

These particular filters are called constant-k filters, because the product of the impedance of a series arm and the shunt arm is a constant. As might be imagined, this does not represent a very sophisticated approach to filter design, and more elaborate prototype filters exist.

In order to obtain a desired frequency-response characteristic, it is usually necessary to connect many filter sections in cascade. This would be a difficult procedure were not the method of image parameters available. Each filter section is arranged so that it "sees" its image impedance in the adjacent sections.

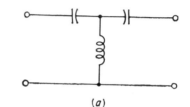

(a)

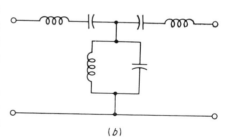

(b)

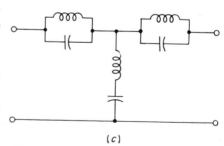

(c)

FIG. 7.34. Prototype filter sections. (a) High-pass; (b) bandpass; (c) band-elimination.

The first section is designed so that its input image impedance is the impedance of the source, and the last section so that its output image impedance is that of the load (Fig. 7.35). Now, when a network is terminated in its image impedance, its mismatch ratio is given by $\epsilon^{-\theta}$. Hence if the mismatch ratios of the various sections of a filter are $\epsilon^{-\theta_1}, \epsilon^{-\theta_2}, \ldots, \epsilon^{-\theta_n}$, the mismatch ratio of the entire filter is $\epsilon^{-(\theta_1 + \theta_2 + \cdots + \theta_n)}$. Therefore, to design a filter, we calculate, from the desired frequency response, the mismatch ratio (as a function of frequency). The mismatch ratio is divided into several convenient components, each of which may be provided by a single filter section. This is, of course, much easier said than done, but the details of doing it are beyond the scope of this book.

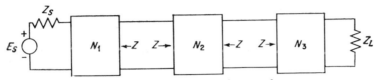

FIG. 7.35. Filter sections in cascade.

7.13. Passivity and Reciprocity in Two-terminal-pair Networks. In previous discussions we have seen that a network is passive if it contains no sources. That this is an inadequate definition is seen when we consider the equivalent circuits developed in Sec. 7.6. Intuitively we feel that a passive network is one which contains only resistance, capacitance, and inductance. However, by using the forms of equivalent circuits of Sec. 7.6, we can replace an RLC circuit by one containing active elements. Are we to call this an active network? In some sense, of course, we can, but it appears that a broader point of view is to consider as passive those networks which are equivalent to a passive network. This we shall do. It is often very difficult to show the equivalence of a network containing sources to one which contains no sources, in order to demonstrate the passivity of the original network. It is desirable, therefore, to have a definition of passivity which is easier to apply. Such is the following: A network is *passive* if the total power into it is nonnegative for all frequencies ω and for all combinations of input voltages and/or currents; a network is *active* if it is nonpassive,

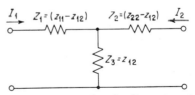

FIG. 7.36. T section, for discussion of passivity.

that is, if there is some combination of input voltages (currents) and frequency for which the total power input is negative.

This definition may seem unduly clumsy, but actually it is often simple to apply. To illustrate its application we shall consider the conditions under which the T network in Fig. 7.36 may be active.

The total power input to the network is equal to the sum of the power in each of the three impedances.

$$P_{in} = \text{Re}\,[V_{z1}I_1^* + V_{z2}I_2^* + V_{z3}(I_1 + I_2)^*]$$
$$= \text{Re}\,[I_1(z_{11} - z_{12})I_1^* + I_2(z_{22} - z_{12})I_2^* + (I_1 + I_2)z_{12}(I_1 + I_2)^*]$$
$$= \text{Re}\,[I_1I_1^*(z_{11} - z_{12}) + I_2I_2^*(z_{22} - z_{12}) + (I_1I_1^* + I_2I_2^* + I_1I_2^* + I_1^*I_2)z_{12}]$$
$$= \text{Re}\,[I_1I_1^*z_{11} + I_2I_2^*z_{22} + (I_1I_2^* + I_1^*I_2)z_{12}]. \tag{7.58}$$

Now, if $I_1 = |I_1|\,\underline{|\theta_1}$ and $I_2 = |I_2|\,\underline{|\theta_2}$, it is easy to show that

$$(I_1I_2^* + I_1^*I_2) = 2|I_1I_2|\,\cos\,(\theta_1 - \theta_2). \tag{7.59}$$

Therefore

$$P_{in} = |I_1|^2\,\text{Re}\,[z_{11}] + |I_2|^2\,\text{Re}\,[z_{22}] + 2|I_1I_2|\,\cos\,(\theta_1 - \theta_2)\,\text{Re}\,[z_{12}]. \tag{7.60}$$

Designating $\text{Re}\,[z_{11}]$ by r_{11}, $\text{Re}\,[z_{22}]$ by r_{22}, and $\text{Re}\,[z_{12}]$ by r_{12},

$$P_{in} = |I_1|^2r_{11} + |I_2|^2r_{22} + 2|I_1I_2|\,\cos\,(\theta_1 - \theta_2)r_{12}. \tag{7.60a}$$

Clearly, if r_{11} or r_{22} is negative, $P_{in} < 0$ for some values of I_1 and I_2. Merely making r_{12} negative does not guarantee that $P_{in} < 0$, for r_{12} may be positive or negative, depending upon how we assign our current references. Let us investigate the constraints on r_{12} which are required to make $P_{in} < 0$. Since the magnitudes of the I's are positive numbers, this can be done only by making the last term negative [either by setting $90° < (\theta_1 - \theta_2) < 270°$, or by taking r_{12} negative]. Also, the maximum magnitude of the last term is $2|I_1I_2r_{12}|$. Then

$$P_{in,\,min} = |I_1|^2r_{11} + |I_2|^2r_{22} - 2|I_1I_2r_{12}|. \tag{7.61}$$

Here $P_{in,\,min}$ is the "most negative" value of P_{in} as θ_1 and θ_2 are varied. If $P_{in,\,min}$ is negative for any set of values $|I_1|$, $|I_2|$, then it is negative for any other set obtained by multiplying both values by the same constant. Thus, we may simplify by setting $|I_1| = 1$,

$$P'_{in} = r_{11} + |I_2|^2r_{22} - 2|I_2r_{12}|. \tag{7.61a}$$

We shall determine what values of $|I_2|$ make P'_{in} negative by finding what values make P'_{in} equal to zero. If there are two such values it follows that values of $|I_2|$ between these values† make P_{in} negative. In order that the quadratic equation

$$r_{22}|I_2|^2 - 2|I_2|\,|r_{12}| + r_{11} = 0 \tag{7.62}$$

in $|I_2|$ have real roots, we must have

$$r_{11}r_{22} - r_{12}{}^2 < 0. \tag{7.63}$$

Neglecting the trivial cases r_{11} or r_{22} negative modifies the foregoing expression to

$$0 \leq r_{11}r_{22} < r_{12}{}^2. \tag{7.64}$$

† The case of $|I_2|$ outside these values is trivial, corresponding to r_{22} negative.

This requires either $|r_{11}| < |r_{12}|$ or $|r_{22}| < |r_{12}|$ or both, which requires that one or the other arm of the T network contain a negative resistance.

The definition of passivity stated above is quite useful, because it may be used with networks having any number of terminal pairs and with both reciprocal and nonreciprocal networks.

In order to realize an active circuit such as that discussed above, some form of electron device may be used. Because electron devices are used in most active networks, there is a common but erroneous tendency to consider all networks containing electron devices as active. This is not true, as can be seen from the circuit in Fig. 7.37 (which can be realized with a single vacuum tube). The input power at terminals 1 is V_1^2/R; the output power from terminals 2, with matched load (maximum power output), is $\frac{1}{2}(4V_1^2/2R)$ or V_1^2/R.

Thus the total input power is zero or positive. (A voltage source at terminals 2 only increases the input power.) Here is a network which is passive but which contains active elements.

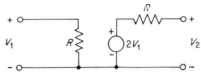

FIG. 7.37. Passive network containing an active element.

The circuit, however, is not reciprocal, for $r_{12} \neq r_{21}$. (We recall that a reciprocal network is one which satisfies the reciprocity theorem, that is, $z_{ij} = z_{ji}$.) There is a common tendency to confuse nonreciprocal networks with active networks, because most active networks are also nonreciprocal. However, the fundamental or prototype nonreciprocal network is passive; it is called a *gyrator*. The gyrator is denoted by the symbol in Fig. 7.38.

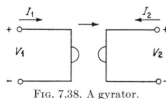

FIG. 7.38. A gyrator.

The gyrator is a network whose admittance parameters are the following:

$$\begin{pmatrix} y_{11} & y_{12} \\ y_{21} & y_{22} \end{pmatrix} = \begin{pmatrix} 0 & Y \\ -Y & 0 \end{pmatrix}. \quad (7.65)$$

This condensed, or matrix, notation means merely that corresponding terms in each array are equal (see Chap. 11). That is [recall the definition of admittance parameters, Eq. (7.3)],

$$\begin{aligned} I_1 &= YE_2 \\ I_2 &= -YE_1. \end{aligned} \quad (7.66)$$

The power to the gyrator is

$$\begin{aligned} P_{\text{in}} &= \text{Re}\,[E_1 I_1^* + E_2 I_2^*] \\ &= \text{Re}\,[E_1 E_2^* Y^* - E_2 E_1^* Y^*] \\ &= \text{Re}\,[Y^*(E_1 E_2^* - E_2 E_1^*)] = 0. \end{aligned}$$

The gyrator is a useful device in network theory. It can be shown, for example, that a nonreciprocal network can be resolved into a reciprocal network plus a gyrator.

At low and moderate frequencies, to the authors' knowledge, no one has yet succeeded in constructing a gyrator without the use of electron devices. However, at microwave frequencies gyrators are built which contain no active elements.

Other methods of characterizing gyrators exist besides the admittance parameters of Eq. (7.65). Most common are the impedance parameters

$$\begin{pmatrix} z_{11} & z_{12} \\ z_{21} & z_{22} \end{pmatrix} = \begin{pmatrix} 0 & -Y^{-1} \\ Y^{-1} & 0 \end{pmatrix}. \tag{7.67}$$

EXERCISES

7.1. Determine the impedance parameters z_{11}, z_{12}, z_{21}, and z_{22} of the network shown in Fig. 7.39.

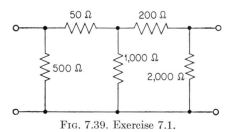

FIG. 7.39. Exercise 7.1.

7.2. Determine the admittance parameters of the network of Exercise 7.1.
7.3. Find the $ABCD$ constants for the network of Exercise 7.1.
7.4. Find the hybrid (h) parameters for the network of Exercise 7.1.
7.5. The discussion of impedance and admittance parameters given in Sec. 7.2 was based on a loop analysis of the circuit. Develop an analogous analysis based on node

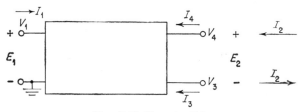

FIG. 7.40. Exercise 7.5.

analysis. [HINT: Consider the circuit shown in Fig. 7.40, and note that $E_1 = V_1$, $E_2 = V_4 - V_3$, $I_2 = I_4$, $I_2 = -I_3$.
7.6. Show that the circuits illustrated in Fig. 7.41 are equivalent circuits for any two-port,

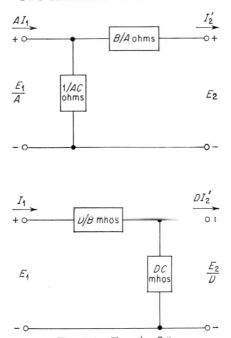

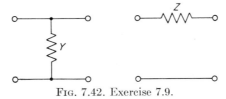

Fig. 7.41. Exercise 7.6.

7.7. Determine the $ABCD$ parameters of the symmetrical lattice network.

7.8. Solve Exercise 7.2 by direct solution of the node equations.

7.9. (a) Determine the $ABCD$ parameters of the simple networks shown in Fig. 7.42.

(b) Using the results of part (a) and repeated applications of the results of Example 7.1, determine the $ABCD$ parameters of a T network.

Fig. 7.42. Exercise 7.9.

7.10. (a) Express the vector power $P_2 + jQ_2$ at the receiving end of a transmission line in terms of the sending-end voltage, the receiving-end voltage, and the $ABCD$ parameters of the line.

(b) Repeat for the sending-end power in terms of the sending-end voltage, the receiving-end voltage, and the $ABCD$ parameters.

$$Ans. \quad P_2 + jQ_2 = \frac{D}{B}|E_1|^2 - \frac{E_2 E_1^*}{B}.$$

7.11. The results of Exercise 7.10 are often applied to the construction of a power circle diagram. This is a locus in the P-Q plane showing vector power as the relative phase of the voltages is varied.

(a) Show that the sending-end power locus is a circle if E_1 is fixed and E_2 is fixed in magnitude but varies in phase relative to E_1.

(b) Consider a power-transmission line having the following parameters:

$$A = D = 0.967\underline{|2.9°}$$
$$B = 49.2\underline{|81.4°}.$$

Construct a power circle diagram for $P_1 + jQ_1$ using $|E_1| = 220$ kv. (A suggested scale is 5 kva/cm.) Show circles for $E_2 = 150, 175, 200, 225,$ and 250 kv; show lines for angles of lag of $-15, 0, 15, 30, 45, 60,$ and 90°.

(c) What is the maximum real power delivered when $|E_2| = 220$ kv?

(d) What is the power delivered when the power factor is unity?

(e) What is the complex power delivered when $|E_2| = 250$ kv and E_2 lags E_1 by 45°?

7.12. (a) Establish the relationship between the parameters of the T network of Fig. 7.6 and the π network of Fig. 7.7.

(b) Find the π network equivalent to the T network illustrated in Fig. 7.43. Explain the anomaly. [HINT: Use Thévenin's theorem.]

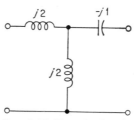

FIG. 7.43. Exercise 7.12b.

7.13. Can the circuit shown in Fig. 7.44 be used, at a given frequency, as the equivalent circuit of any two-port? If so, develop expressions for Z_1, Z_2, and Z_3 in terms of z_{11}, z_{12}, etc.

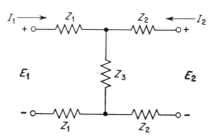

FIG. 7.44. Exercise 7.13.

7.14. Relate the parameters of the symmetrical T to the symmetrical lattice. (See Fig. 7.45.)

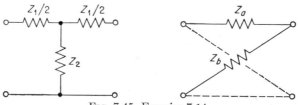

FIG. 7.45. Exercise 7.14.

7.15. Prove the statement made in the footnote on page 185.

7.16. Determine the $ABCD$ constants of an ideal transformer.

7.17. Determine the impedance parameters of the network in Fig. 7.46.

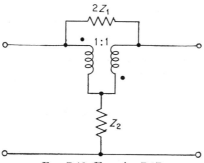

Fig. 7.46. Exercise 7.17.

7.18. Find the $ABCD$ constants of the network in Fig. 7.47, using $\omega = 1000$ radians/sec.

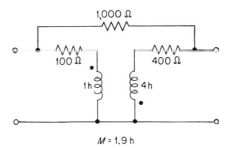

Fig. 7.47. Exercise 7.18.

7.19. The network shown in Fig. 7.48 is electrically symmetrical. The lattice network also shown is equivalent to it at all frequencies. Determine the configuration of the impedances Z_a and Z_b and give the values of their various circuit elements in terms of L and C.

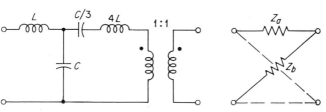

Fig. 7.48. Exercise 7.19.

7.20. Find the magnitude of the voltage across the 8000-ohm resistor in the circuit shown in Fig. 7.49.

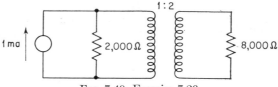

FIG. 7.49. Exercise 7.20.

7.21. (*a*) Find the *ABCD* constants of the network drawn in Fig. 7.50.
(*b*) Under what conditions is this equivalent to a lattice?

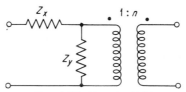

FIG. 7.50. Exercise 7.21.

7.22. A real transformer has the following parameters: 500 kva, $R_1 = 19.5$ Ω, $R_2 = 0.055$ ohm, $j\omega L_{11} = j39.5$ ohms, $j\omega L_{22} = j0.120$ ohms. Voltage ratio = 42,000 volts/2400 volts, $R_m = 840,000$ ohms, $j\omega L_m = j152,000$ Ω. Draw the phasor diagram for this transformer operating at full load at 80 per cent power factor lagging. Assume that the load terminal voltage is 2400 volts.

7.23. (*a*) Show that, if an ideal transformer is connected between a generator and a load, the transformer ratio for maximum load voltage is not the largest practical ratio of secondary to primary turns but is the same ratio as that for maximum power transfer.

(*b*) Show that the transformer ratio for maximum load current is not the largest practical ratio of primary to secondary turns but is the same ratio as that for maximum power transfer.

(*c*) Explain qualitatively the foregoing, often misunderstood, results.

7.24. Determine the ratio E_2/E_1 as a function of $j\omega$ for the network shown in Fig. 7.51.

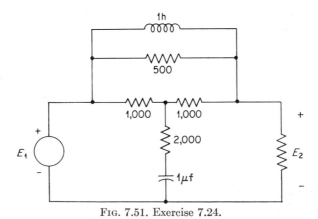

FIG. 7.51. Exercise 7.24.

7.25. Construct a circle diagram for the gain E_2/E_1 of the circuit shown in Fig. 7.52 as a function of $j\omega$. Indicate a rough frequency scale on the circle and the half-power points.

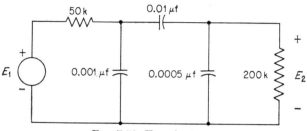

FIG. 7.52. Exercise 7.25.

7.26. Express the following power ratios in decibels:

(a) 1,000,000

(b) 10^3

(c) 2.0

(d) 15

(e) 30

(f) 95

(g) $\sqrt{2}$

(h) 10^{-6}

(i) 1.1

(j) 0.12

7.27. Express the following voltage ratios in decibels:

(a) 1

(b) 100

(c) 1000

(d) 10^6

(e) 10^7

(f) 1.1

(g) $\sqrt{3}$

(h) 2.3

(i) 0.12

(j) 3.5

7.28. Prove Eq. (7.59).

7.29. Show how a gyrator and a reciprocal two-port network may be combined to yield a general nonreciprocal two-port network.

CHAPTER 8

ENERGY DISTRIBUTION AND POLYPHASE CIRCUITS

In previous chapters we have studied the basic techniques of circuit analysis and their application to various general classes of problems. In most of these classes of problems, we considered implicitly circuits in which the frequency of the forcing function might vary. Also, although we discussed the calculation of power and energy in circuits, we were not specifically concerned with circuits the principal purpose of which was to transport electrical energy from one point to another. However, one of the principal fields of electrical engineering, in terms of economic investment, is the generation and distribution of electrical energy. In these circuits the study of power relations is in some measure of more direct concern than in communication circuits. On the other hand, frequency-response calculations as such are of less importance because such circuits operate at a fixed frequency and frequency-response calculations find a use only in the somewhat advanced phase of power-system-stability analysis.

In this chapter we focus our attention on the power transmitted by energy-distribution circuits and show how this emphasis leads to the development of polyphase circuits. We shall then consider some simplified methods of analyzing certain classes of polyphase circuits.

8.1. Simple Energy-distribution Systems. Suppose that it is desired to transmit energy from a source (generator) S to a load L. Let us set as constraints on this problem that the load be that of an average home and that the distance over which the energy is transmitted be moderate, say a few hundred feet. Let us also assume that the minimum size of the wire used is fixed by mechanical considerations. We shall now consider the means which might be used to transmit this energy with reasonable efficiency.

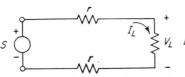

Fig. 8.1. Simple energy-distribution system.

The most obvious approach is to connect the source to the load by two wires. This situation is shown in Fig. 8.1, in which the resistance of each wire is represented by r. The load power is $I_L V_L \cos \theta$, and the line loss is

$2I_L^2 r$. Thus the efficiency of transmission, η_T, is given by

$$\eta_T = \frac{I_L V_L \cos \theta}{I_L V_L \cos \theta + 2I_L^2 r}. \tag{8.1}$$

It is clear that efficiency is highest when the voltage is large and the current small. Efficiency also increases when r is small, but the savings in energy are eventually offset by the increased cost of the wire.† There are limits, however, on the extent to which the voltage on home electrical circuits may be raised. Most household appliances operate at 120 volts, and although conceivably every light and appliance in a home could be placed in series, this is not practical both because an open circuit would render all inoperative and because voltage across individual elements would vary too much. Also, the high voltage is quite dangerous. A practical compromise is the three-wire circuit of Fig. 8.2. Here the load is split into two approximately equal parts and a third wire, r_1,

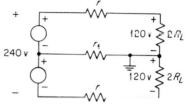

FIG. 8.2. Three-wire distribution system.

is connected from source to load (we are assuming that we have complete freedom in specifying the source). This is a practical scheme and extensively used, as it usually is possible to divide the load in such a fashion. A load divided into equal impedances is called a *balanced* load. The third wire improves regulation, which would otherwise be quite poor if the load became unbalanced, and also permits operation if one side of the load is, perchance, disconnected. Under balanced conditions, no current flows in the third wire, and there are no losses in that wire. Current flows, and losses increase rapidly, as the load becomes unbalanced. The third wire is also an important safety feature. It is grounded, so that the maximum voltage to ground can be no greater than 120 volts. (Were it not grounded, a short circuit of one outside wire to ground would raise the potential of the other to 240 volts. This way, only a fuse is blown.)

If we change the constraints on our problem, however, a different solution might be better. For example, some street lighting (constant-current systems) operate in series, at several thousand volts. (Automatic switches short-circuit defective lamps, so that one failure does not shut down the system.) If the distance over which the energy is to be transmitted is great or if the power is high, there is often economic justification for using transformers to raise the voltage at the sending end, transmit

† An additional constraint often affects the size of the wire, *regulation*. Regulation is defined as the percentage increase in load voltage as the load current varies from full load to zero, i.e., regulation $= (E_{\text{no load}} - E_{\text{full load}})/E_{\text{full load}}$. Good (low) regulation is required particularly on lighting circuits.

the energy at high voltage levels, and reduce the voltage at the receiving end with other transformers.   The limitations here are the cost of suitable insulators and also a high-voltage phenomenon known as corona loss. Some large power systems use voltages in excess of 500,000 volts for transmission.   Indeed, one of the principal reasons for the use of alternating current rather than direct current is the fact that the efficiencies of high-voltage transmission may be realized, even when the load requires low voltage, by the use of transformers.

8.2. Polyphase Circuits.   There is one factor not mentioned above which is important in the distribution of electrical energy, and that is the instantaneous power.   If we consider the circuit of Fig. 8.1, assuming for simplicity a resistive load, the instantaneous power p is

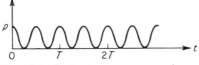

$$p = vi = \frac{2V^2}{R_L} \cos^2 2\pi ft. \quad (8.2)$$

FIG. 8.3. Instantaneous power in a simple distribution system.

The result is plotted in Fig. 8.3, where the fluctuating nature of the power is clearly seen.   In many applications this fluctuation is inconsequential— the thermal delay of electric heaters and most light bulbs, for example, effectively averages out the fluctuations.   More important, though, is the effect of fluctuating power on a-c motors.   Instantaneous developed torque is proportional to instantaneous power, so that the fluctuating power produces a fluctuating torque, which leads to vibration and other undesired effects.

The situation described is not obviated by the use of the three-wire system described, as is easily seen.   However, if we can split the load into three equal (*balanced*) impedances it is possible to deliver a constant total instantaneous power to the load.   This will be shown with the aid of Fig. 8.4.   We shall let the three voltage sources have the same magnitude and be shifted in phase from each other by 120° (Fig. 8.4*b*).   Thus

$$\begin{aligned}
E_1 &= E\underline{|0°} \\
E_2 &= E\underline{|240°} \\
E_3 &= E\underline{|120°}.
\end{aligned} \quad (8.3)$$

For simplicity we shall neglect the resistance of the wire.   Then the instantaneous total power input is

$$\begin{aligned}
p_{\text{in}} &= p_1 + p_2 + p_3 \\
&= \frac{2E^2}{3Z_L} \cos (\omega t - \theta) \cos \omega t + \frac{2E^2}{3Z_L} \cos (\omega t + 120 - \theta) \cos (\omega t + 120) \\
&\quad + \frac{2E^2}{3Z_L} \cos (\omega t + 240 - \theta) \cos (\omega t + 240). \quad (8.4)
\end{aligned}$$

(The factor 2 occurs because E is the rms, not peak, value of voltage.)

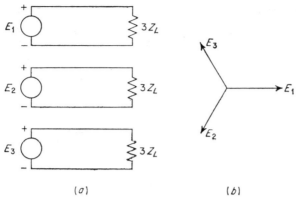

FIG. 8.4. Three-phase distributed system with balanced load. (a) Schematic diagram; (b) phasor diagram.

Expanding and collecting terms give

$$p_{\text{in}} = \frac{E^2}{3Z_L} \{3 \cos(-\theta) + \cos(2\omega t - \theta)[1 + \cos 240 + \cos 480]$$
$$- \sin(2\omega t - \theta)[\sin 240 + \sin 480]\}$$
$$= \frac{E^2}{Z_L} \cos(-\theta). \tag{8.5}$$

Thus the instantaneous power is constant.   Why this is so may be seen graphically in Fig. 8.5, which shows the instantaneous power delivered by each generator and also the total instantaneous power. The peaks in the power delivered by one generator "fill in" the dips in the power from the other generators.

It may seem that we have paid a rather high price for this constant power; six wires constitute a more complex distribution system than do three. However, the six wires are not necessary. A common return wire may be used, as in Fig. 8.6, thereby reducing the number of wires to four. (The particular layout of generators and impedances is used only for convenience and should not be interpreted literally.) The current which flows in the common or *neutral* lead, I_n, is given by (again neglecting the resist-

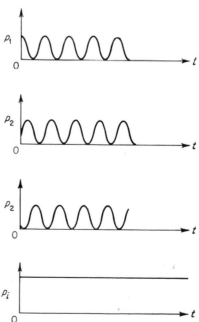

FIG. 8.5. Instantaneous power in a balanced three-phase system.

ances of the wires)

$$I_n = \frac{E\underline{|0}}{3Z_L} + \frac{E\underline{|120}}{3Z_L} + \frac{E\underline{|240}}{3Z_L} = 0. \tag{8.6}$$

Thus even the fourth wire is unnecessary to realize the advantages of this system.   The fourth wire is often retained, however, as it improves regulation in the case of unbalanced loads and also is used as a ground wire, as a safety precaution.

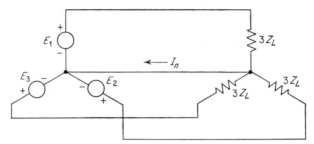

FIG. 8.6. Four-wire three-phase distribution system.

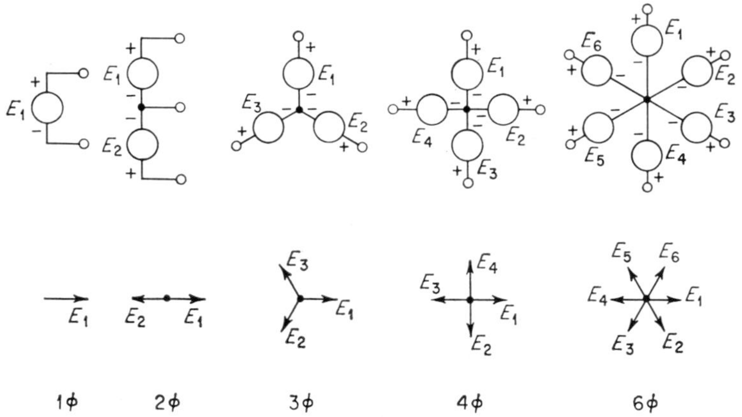

1ϕ 2ϕ 3ϕ 4ϕ 6ϕ

FIG. 8.7. Various polyphase systems.

One other advantage, which is not obvious, exists in this system.   This system permits the use of extremely simple and economical motors (induction motors) which have excellent starting-torque characteristics for the conversion of electrical energy into mechanical energy.

The system that we have considered is a simple example of a *polyphase* system.   An n-phase polyphase voltage source consists of n sources of equal magnitude, whose phases differ by $360°/n$, connected together. Some typical polyphase systems are shown in Fig. 8.7.   (The symbol ϕ is often used to denote "phase.")   This figure also shows the corresponding phasor diagrams.   The arrangement of generators shown is purely aesthetic. Although the schematic diagrams resemble the phasor diagrams, they are different diagrams and should not be confused.

We are already familiar with the single-phase system; the two-phase system is, strictly speaking, what we have already termed the single-phase three-wire system.   Generally, how-ever, the systems shown in Fig. 8.8 are known as two-phase systems, though the voltages are not sym-metrically disposed; in fact, however, that shown in Fig. 8.8a is half a four-phase system, and that in Fig. 8.8b is a four-phase system with the common lead omitted. The three-phase system, discussed above, is most common, as will be seen. Of other n-phase systems, only the six-phase system is often used, in appli-cations where large amounts of a-c power are to be converted to d-c power. Six-phase power is not usu-ally distributed but is obtained from three-phase power by means of the transformer scheme shown in Fig. 8.9.   Indeed, any number of phases may be obtained from any other number (greater than one) by suitable connection of transformers, but with the exception of the three- to six-phase conversion shown and of two- to three-phase conversion (see Exercise 8.16) these connections are only of academic interest.

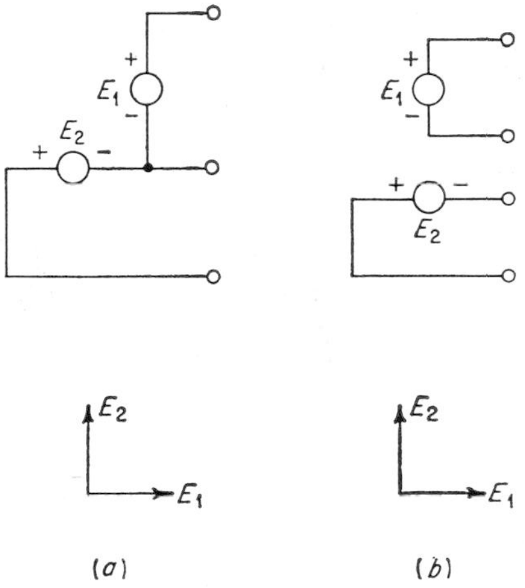

FIG. 8.8. So-called two-phase systems.

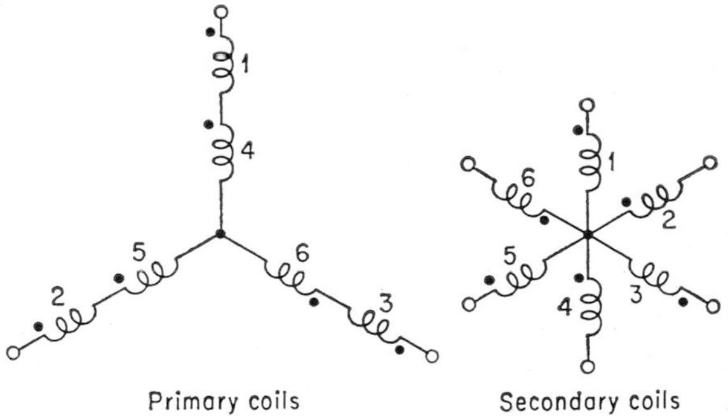

FIG. 8.9. Conversion of three-phase energy to six-phase energy by use of six trans-formers (three center-tapped transformers may also be used).

The particular arrangement of sources shown in Fig. 8.7, wherein all are connected to a single common point, is called a *star*, or in the case of three-phase connections, a *wye*- (Y-) connected system.   It is also possible to connect the sources in *mesh* [three-phase: delta (Δ)], as shown in Fig. 8.10.   (For $n \leqq 2$, the connections are trivial.)

There does not exist, as one might first suspect, a current circulating around the mesh, because the sum of the voltages in an n-phase system ($n > 1$) is zero, as is seen from an examination of Fig. 8.7.   We shall discuss the mesh connection, but only for the three-phase, or delta, case, in the next section.

8.3. Three-phase Systems.   All polyphase sources with $n \geqq 3$ (also including the so-called two-phase systems of Fig. 8.8) supply constant

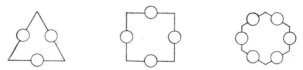

FIG. 8.10. Mesh connection of polyphase sources.

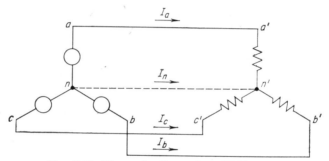

FIG. 8.11. Three-wire three-phase Y-Y system.

instantaneous power.   Why, then, are three-phase systems used almost exclusively?   The three-phase system is the simplest polyphase system, and it requires fewer wires, connections, switches, fuses, insulators, and the like than any other polyphase system and hence is more economical to install.   Other reasons for the superiority of three-phase systems over higher-order polyphase systems, based on efficiency of transmission, are often adduced.   These arguments, however, usually assume special and often unrealistic conditions and are generally invalid.

Any balanced polyphase system is equally superior to the single-phase system, from the point of view of line losses for a given weight of copper in wires, given load, and a given voltage to ground.   This is so because balanced polyphase systems do not require a neutral wire, and so there are no losses in the neutral.   A single-phase system requires a return wire, with attendant losses.

Let us now establish some definitions and conventions in order to facilitate discussion of three-phase circuits.   This will be done with the aid of Fig. 8.11, which shows the simple case of Y-connected generators and a

balanced Y-connected load.   (It may be remarked here that three separate generators are not required, nor used.   A three-phase generator, or
alternator, carries three windings on the same rotor, so that a single
machine generates the three-phase voltage.)   In describing polyphase
systems it is convenient to adopt a double-subscript notation.   We shall
use the convention that V_{ab} is the rise from a to b. I_{ab} is the current from
a to b.

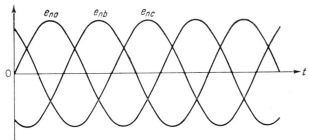

FIG. 8.12. Instantaneous voltages in a positive-sequence system.

We use the term *phase order* to denote the sequence in which the voltages reach their peak values.   Thus, phase order *abc* (called *positive
sequence*) means that e_{na} reaches its maximum first, followed by e_{nb} and
then by e_{nc} (Fig. 8.12).   Therefore, the phasor diagram for the three
source voltages has the form of Fig. 8.13a.   The inverse phase order
(*negative sequence*) *acb* implies that e_{na} reaches its peak first, followed by
e_{nc} and e_{nb}.   This leads to the phasor diagram Fig. 8.13b.   (There is a
tendency among beginners to think
that negative sequence implies a
clockwise, rather than counterclockwise, rotation of the phasors.   This
is incorrect.)

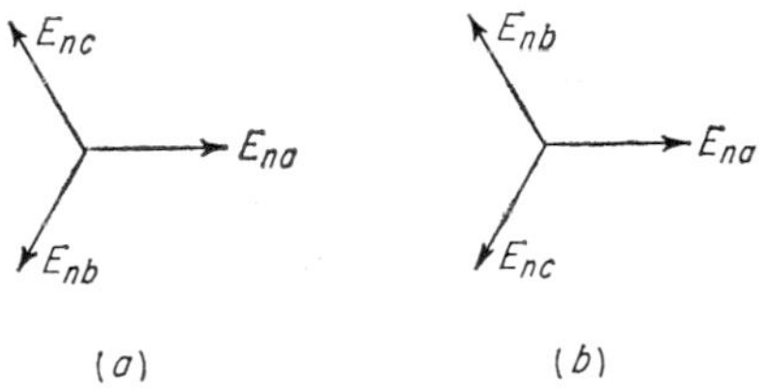

The voltages E_{na}, E_{nb}, E_{nc} are
called the *generated phase* voltages
and the voltages $V_{n'a'}$, $V_{n'b'}$, and $V_{n'c'}$
are called the *load voltages*.   The
voltages E_{ab}, E_{bc}, and E_{ca} are called
the *line-to-line*, or simply the *line*, voltages.   From Fig. 8.11 it is seen that

$$E_{ab} = E_{an} + E_{nb} = -E_{na} + E_{nb} \qquad (8.7.1)$$

(noticing that $-E_{na} = E_{an}$).   Similarly†

$$E_{bc} = E_{bn} + E_{nc} = -E_{nb} + E_{nc} \qquad (8.7.2)$$
$$E_{ca} = E_{cn} + E_{na} = -E_{nc} + E_{na}. \qquad (8.7.3)$$

† If we consider only the subscripts, it is a simple matter to check these equations,
for $bc = bn + nc$, etc.

FIG. 8.13. Phasor diagrams for (a)
positive-sequence system; (b) negative-
sequence system.

(a)

(b)

These relations are shown graphically in Fig. 8.14. From this figure it is also seen that if

$$E_{na} = E_Y \underline{|0}$$
$$E_{nb} = E_Y \underline{|-120}$$
$$E_{nc} = E_Y \underline{|+120}$$

(8.8)

then

$$E_{ab} = \sqrt{3}\, E_Y \underline{|-150}$$
$$E_{bc} = \sqrt{3}\, E_Y \underline{|+90}$$
$$E_{ca} = \sqrt{3}\, E_Y \underline{|-30}.$$

(8.9)

Observe that the fact that these voltages are shifted in phase does *not* imply a power factor other than unity. This will be reemphasized in subsequent examples.

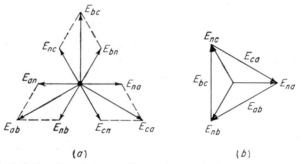

(a) (b)

FIG. 8.14. (a) Relationships between line-to-line and phase voltages; (b) alternative representation.

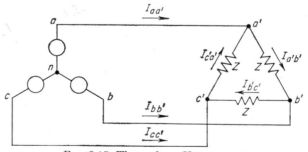

FIG. 8.15. Three-phase Y-Δ system.

The currents I_a, I_b, and I_c are both line and phase currents. (If we had a neutral conductor, NN', its current $I_{n'}$ would be called the neutral current. For balanced loads, $I_n = 0$.)

Let us now suppose that the load is a balanced Δ (Fig. 8.15). In this case the generator phase voltages are E_{na}, E_{nb}, and E_{nc}, and the generator line voltages are E_{ab}, E_{bc}, E_{ca}. Neglecting line drops for the time being, it follows from Eqs. (8.9) that

$$V_{a'b'} = E_{an} + E_{nb} = \sqrt{3}\ V_Y\underline{|-150}$$
$$V_{b'c'} = E_{bn} + E_{nc} = \sqrt{3}\ V_Y\underline{|+90} \qquad (8.10)$$
$$V_{c'a'} = E_{cn} + E_{na} = \sqrt{3}\ V_Y\underline{|-30}.$$

The phase currents in the load of Fig. 8.15 are $I_{a'b'}$, $I_{b'c'}$, and $I_{c'a'}$. As the load is balanced, the phase currents of the load each have the same relation to their respective phase voltages. This relation is

$$I_{a'b'} = -\frac{V_{a'b'}}{Z} = -\sqrt{3}\ \frac{V_Y\underline{|-150}}{Z\underline{|\theta}} = I_\Delta\underline{|30 - \theta}$$

$$I_{b'c'} = -\frac{V_{b'c'}}{Z} = I_\Delta\underline{|\ 90\ \ \theta} \qquad (8.11)$$

$$I_{c'a'} = -\frac{V_{c'a'}}{Z} = I_\Delta\underline{|150 - \theta}$$

where

$$I_\Delta = \sqrt{3}\ \frac{V_Y}{Z}. \qquad (8.12)$$

The phase currents are related to the line currents $I_{aa'}$, $I_{bb'}$, $I_{cc'}$ by†

$$I_{aa'} = I_{a'b'} - I_{c'a'}$$
$$I_{bb'} = I_{b'c'} - I_{a'b'} \qquad (8.13)$$
$$I_{cc'} = I_{c'a'} - I_{b'c'}.$$

These relations are evaluated graphically with the aid of Fig. 8.16 (drawn for an inductive load), which also shows the relationships between phase voltages and currents. The results are seen to be

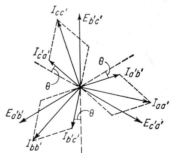

FIG. 8.16. Phasor diagram for Fig. 8.15.

$$I_{aa'} = \sqrt{3}\ I_\Delta\underline{|0 - \theta}$$
$$I_{bb'} = \sqrt{3}\ I_\Delta\underline{|-120 - \theta} \qquad (8.14)$$
$$I_{cc'} = \sqrt{3}\ I_\Delta\underline{|+120 - \theta}.$$

(The foregoing results should all be verified analytically by the student.) A comparison of Eqs. (8.14) with Eqs. (8.8) using the definition of I_Δ given in Eq. (8.12) shows that the line currents are given by the equation

$$I_{\text{line}} = \frac{3E_Y}{Z}. \qquad (8.15)$$

† Observe that the mnemonic scheme which was used for the subscripts on the voltages does not hold for those on the currents.

This is but the result which would have been obtained had we commenced the analysis by converting the Δ of impedances into a Y.

It should be carefully noted that phase difference between line and phase voltages and currents does not necessarily imply reactive loads. Only when there are phase shifts between corresponding voltages and currents† is the load reactive. It is to be stressed that the foregoing discussion applies only to balanced loads.

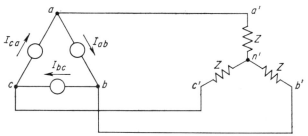

FIG. 8.17. Three-phase Δ-Y system.

We shall now consider simple relations which exist in a three-phase circuit containing a Δ-connected generator and a balanced Y-connected load (Fig. 8.17). The generator phase voltages are equal to the line voltages, E_{ab}, E_{bc}, E_{ca} (Fig. 8.18). The net voltage around the loop is

$$E_{ab} + E_{bc} + E_{ca} = E_\Delta \underline{|0} + E_\Delta \underline{|-120} + E_\Delta \underline{|120} = 0 \qquad (8.16)$$

so that there need be no circulating current around the Δ (there is, however, a current in each branch of the Δ). In this case, however, the impedance around the Δ of generators is zero, and so the current takes the indeterminate form $0/0$, as will be seen below.

The line currents are related to the generator phase currents by

$$I_{aa'} = I_{ca} - I_{ab}$$
$$I_{bb'} = I_{ab} - I_{bc} \qquad (8.17)$$
$$I_{cc'} = I_{bc} - I_{ca}.$$

FIG. 8.18. Generator voltages in Fig. 8.17.

It is seen by adding these three equations that they also satisfy the constraint that the sum of the line currents be zero. If an attempt is made to solve this set of equations for the generator phase currents, it is found that the solution is indeterminate. This is because we have not precluded the possibility of a current circulating in the Δ, which means that we may add the same arbitrary value to each phase current and still satisfy Eqs. (8.17). The difficulty may be resolved if we recognize that the line currents and phase currents form balanced three-phase systems of

† One must be quite careful in deciding which voltages and currents correspond.

currents. Thus we let

$$I_{aa'} = I_{\text{line}} \underline{|0 + \psi}$$
$$I_{bb'} = I_{\text{line}} \underline{|-120 + \psi} \qquad (8.18)$$
$$I_{cc'} = I_{\text{line}} \underline{|120 + \psi}$$

and

$$I_{ab} = I_{\Delta} \underline{|0 + \theta}$$
$$I_{bc} = I_{\Delta} \underline{|-120 + \theta} \qquad (8.19)$$
$$I_{ca} = I_{\Delta} \underline{|120 + \theta}.$$

(The phase angles ψ and θ are included for generality.) Then Eqs. (8.17) become

$$I_{\text{line}} \underline{|0 + \psi} = I_{\Delta} \underline{|120 + \theta} - I_{\Delta} \underline{|0 + \theta}$$
$$I_{\text{line}} \underline{|-120 + \psi} = I_{\Delta} \underline{|0 + \theta} - I_{\Delta} \underline{|-120 + \theta} \qquad (8.20)$$
$$I_{\text{line}} \underline{|120 + \psi} = I_{\Delta} \underline{|-120 + \theta} - I_{\Delta} \underline{|120 + \theta}.$$

These are essentially the same equation, differing only by being shifted in phase 120°. Taking the first of these, we may rewrite it as

$$I_{\text{line}} \underline{|0} = I_{\Delta} \underline{|120 + \theta - \psi} - I_{\Delta} \underline{|\theta - \psi}. \qquad (8.21)$$

Equating real and imaginary parts yields

$$I_{\text{line}} = I_{\Delta}[\cos (120 + \theta - \psi) - \cos (\theta - \psi)]$$
$$0 = I_{\Delta}[\sin (120 + \theta - \psi) - \sin (\theta - \psi)]. \qquad (8.22)$$

From the second equation, $\theta - \psi = 30°$, and so the first equation yields

$$I_{\text{line}} = I_{\Delta}(\cos 150° - \cos 30°) = -\sqrt{3}\, I_{\Delta}. \qquad (8.23)$$

The above results are utilized to plot Fig. 8.19 which is a graphical expression of Eqs. (8.17) to (8.19).

The phase voltages at the load are related to the line voltages by

$$V_{a'b'} = V_{a'n'} + V_{n'b'}$$
$$V_{b'c'} = V_{b'n'} + V_{n'c'} \qquad (8.24)$$
$$V_{c'a'} = V_{c'n'} + V_{n'a'}.$$

Again, the solution to this set of equations is indeterminate, because it also applies to the circuit shown in Fig. 8.20, where E is any voltage.

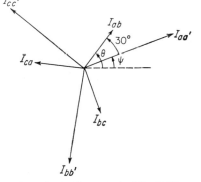

Fig. 8.19. Currents in Fig. 8.17.

However, if we recognize that the load phase voltages form a balanced three-phase system,

$$V_{n'a'} = V_Y \underline{|0 + \phi}$$
$$V_{n'b'} = V_Y \underline{|-120 + \phi} \qquad (8.25)$$
$$V_{n'c'} = V_Y \underline{|120 + \phi},$$

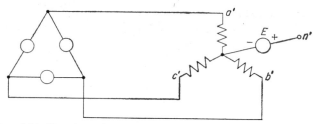

FIG. 8.20. Showing why solution of Eqs. (8.24) is indeterminate.

and recall that the line voltages are given by

$$V_{a'b'} = V_\Delta \underline{|0}$$
$$V_{b'c'} = V_\Delta \underline{|-120}$$
$$V_{c'a'} = V_\Delta \underline{|+120}$$

(8.26)

we may write Eqs. (8.24) as

$$V_\Delta \underline{|0} = -V_Y \underline{|\phi} + V_Y \underline{|-120 + \phi}$$
$$V_\Delta \underline{|-120} = -V_Y \underline{|-120 + \phi} + V_Y \underline{|120 + \phi}$$
$$V_\Delta \underline{|120} = -V_Y \underline{|120 + \phi} + V_Y \underline{|\phi}.$$

(8.27)

As was the case with currents, it is seen that all these are essentially the same equation.   Taking the first of these and equating real and imaginary parts gives

$$V_\Delta = V_Y[-\cos \phi + \cos (\phi - 120)]$$
$$0 = V_Y[-\sin \phi + \sin (\phi - 120)].$$

(8.28)

From the second equation, $\phi = 150°$, whence

$$V_\Delta = V_Y(-\cos 150 + \cos 30) = \sqrt{3}\, V_Y$$

(8.29)

or $V_Y = V_\Delta/\sqrt{3}$.   The relationships between the phase and line voltages may thus be shown graphically, as in Fig. 8.21, which also shows that the results agree with Eqs. (8.24).

In the preceding discussion we have not performed any actual analysis of three-phase circuits.   Rather we have only introduced definitions and pointed out some simple relationships between quantities measured on a phase basis and quantities measured on a line basis.   In the following sections we shall analyze various balanced three-phase circuits taking into account the line and generator impedances.

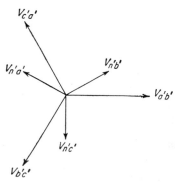

FIG. 8.21. Relationships among phase and line-to-line voltages in Fig. 8.17.

8.4. Analysis of Balanced Three-phase Systems.

The analysis of balanced three-phase systems is quite straightforward. The only sources of difficulty are the possibility of confusing line and phase quantities and the possibility of obtaining sets of equations whose solutions are indeterminate, as was the case in the previous section. The first difficulty may be

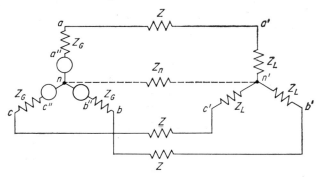

FIG. 8.22. Balanced three-phase Y-Y system with impedance in generators.

avoided by exercising care; the second will often require explicit use of the fact that in a balanced system all the various sets of currents and voltages are balanced.†

The first and simplest case is the balanced Y generator supplying a balanced load (Fig. 8.22). We now do not neglect the internal impedance of the generators‡ Z_G or the line impedance Z. This case is essentially the same as that considered in the previous section. Since there is no neutral current, points n and n' are at the same potential. Consequently, these two points may be connected by a (resistanceless) wire, and each phase may be analyzed separately, using the equivalent "per-phase" circuit of Fig. 8.23. For this circuit we have

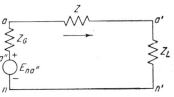

FIG. 8.23. Single-phase ("perphase") equivalent of Fig. 8.22.

$$E_{na''} = I_{aa'}(Z_G + Z + Z_L) \qquad (8.30)$$

or

$$I_{aa'} = \frac{E_{na''}}{Z_G + Z + Z_L} \qquad (8.31)$$

† We have not actually shown this. However, intuition indicates this to be so, and assuming this always leads to a result. This result can be shown, by direct substitution, to be a correct solution.

‡ Strictly speaking, this analysis applies only when the generators are separate for each phase. A real generator contains mutual inductance between the phases, which greatly complicates the analysis. Such a situation can be handled only by general circuit analysis or by the method of symmetrical components, to be mentioned later.

and

$$V_{n'a'} = I_{aa'}Z_L = E_{na''} \frac{Z_L}{Z_G + Z + Z_L}. \qquad (8.32)$$

Using these relationships we may construct the phasor diagram of Fig. 8.24a (with $E_{na''}$ as reference). Since the other phases differ from this phase only in that the generated voltage leads or lags $E_{na''}$ by 120°, it is seen that the phasor diagrams for the other phases are identical, except that they are shifted by 120°. Recognizing this, we may construct the complete phasor diagram, as shown in Fig. 8.24b. The line-to-line voltages may be found from Eqs. (8.9).

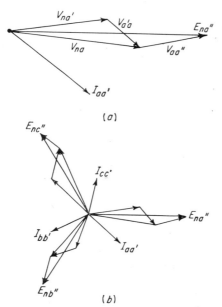

(a)

(b)

FIG. 8.24. (a) Phasor diagram for single phase of three-phase system; (b) complete three-phase diagram.

One simplifying assumption has been made in this analysis: There is no mutual inductance between the phases. When long transmission lines are used to transmit energy, it is found that these lines are inductively coupled. If this is the case, the analysis is more complicated than that considered here.

Less simple than the balanced Y to analyze is the balanced Δ. One may wonder why such a connection is used. When a power transformer is connected to a sinusoidal voltage source, it is found that the magnetizing current contains a high harmonic content, particularly the third harmonic. With a Y connection of transformers, this harmonic current must flow through the lines to the load, causing I^2R losses in both the line and the load, without generally doing useful work. If either the primary or secondary windings of a three-phase transformer bank is connected in Δ, the harmonic currents will circulate in the Δ windings, minimizing the losses. That the harmonic currents will circulate may be seen as follows. Let the fundamental components of the three generator currents be

$$
\begin{aligned}
I_{ab} &= I_\Delta \underline{|0 + \theta} \\
I_{bc} &= I_\Delta \underline{|-120 + \theta} \\
I_{ca} &= I_\Delta \underline{|120 + \theta}.
\end{aligned}
\qquad (8.19)
$$

Since we are to consider currents having two frequencies, we must write the currents as

$$i_{ab} = \sqrt{2}\, I_\Delta \cos(\omega t + \theta)$$
$$i_{bc} = \sqrt{2}\, I_\Delta \cos(\omega t - 120 + \theta) \qquad (8.33)$$
$$i_{ca} = \sqrt{2}\, I_\Delta \cos(\omega t + 120 + \theta).$$

Now, the third harmonic of a current of the form $I\cos(\omega t + \theta)$ is given by

$$I_3 \cos[3(\omega t + \theta) + \phi]$$

where the angle ϕ accounts for any displacement of the origin of the third harmonic relative to the fundamental.   Thus, the third harmonics of the currents of Eqs. (8.33) are

$$i_{ab3} = I_3 \cos[3(\omega t + \theta) + \phi]$$
$$i_{bc3} = I_3 \cos[3(\omega t - 120 + \theta) + \phi] \qquad (8.34)$$
$$i_{ca3} = I_3 \cos[3(\omega t + 120 + \theta) + \phi].$$

But since the term $3(120°)$ represents a full cycle it may be eliminated, and

$$i_{ab3} = I_3 \cos[3(\omega t + \theta) + \phi]$$
$$i_{bc3} = I_3 \cos[3(\omega t + \theta) + \phi] \qquad (8.34a)$$
$$i_{ca3} = I_3 \cos[3(\omega t + \theta) + \phi].$$

This set of relations shows that the third harmonic current in each branch of the Δ is the same, and hence the harmonic current merely

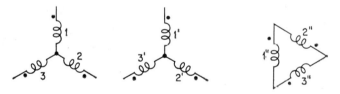

Primary coils   Secondary coils   Tertiary coils

Fig. 8.25. Three-phase Y-Y transformer, showing tertiary coils.

circulates, causing some losses, but less than if the harmonic currents traveled through the lines.

Sometimes transformers are connected with both their primary and their secondary windings in Y.   An additional *tertiary* winding is placed on each transformer, and the tertiary windings are connected in Δ, to carry the circulating harmonic current (see Fig. 8.25).

Returning to the analysis of the Δ-connected generators and load, let us consider Fig. 8.26.   This figure represents the general case of a balanced Δ-connected generator or a balanced Δ-connected load, including the effects of generator and line impedance.†   The general analysis of

† See second footnote on page 223.

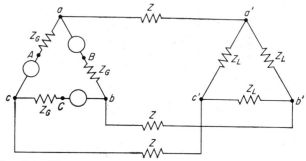

FIG. 8.26. Three-phase Δ-Δ system, with generator impedance.

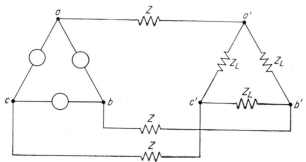

FIG. 8.27. Simplified three-phase Δ-Δ system, with impedanceless generators.

this circuit can be simplified considerably by taking the case where $Z_G = 0$. This is done in Fig. 8.27. The circuit may be analyzed most conveniently by starting at the load. Taking the voltage rise $V_{a'b'}$ as reference and writing its magnitude as V_Δ yield

$$I_{b'a'} = \frac{V_{a'b'}}{Z_L} = \frac{V_\Delta \underline{|0}}{Z_L} = I_\Delta \underline{|0 - \theta}$$

$$I_{c'b'} = \frac{V_{b'c'}}{Z_L} = \frac{V_\Delta \underline{|0 - 120}}{Z_L} = I_\Delta \underline{|-120 - \theta} \qquad (8.35)$$

$$I_{a'c'} = \frac{V_{c'a'}}{Z_L} = \frac{V_\Delta \underline{|120}}{Z_L} = I_\Delta \underline{|120 - \theta}$$

where

$$I_\Delta = \frac{V_\Delta}{Z_L}. \qquad (8.36)$$

Thus, the line currents are

$$I_{aa'} = I_{a'c'} - I_{b'a'} = \sqrt{3}\, I_\Delta \underline{|150 - \theta}$$

$$I_{bb'} = I_{b'a'} - I_{c'b'} = \sqrt{3}\, I_\Delta \underline{|30 - \theta} \qquad (8.37)$$

$$I_{cc'} = I_{c'b'} - I_{a'c'} = \sqrt{3}\, I_\Delta \underline{|-90 - \theta}.$$

The preceding sets of equations are shown graphically in Fig. 8.28.

The generator currents are related to the line currents by

$$I_{aa'} = I_{ca} - I_{ab}$$
$$I_{bb'} = I_{ab} - I_{bc} \qquad (8.38)$$
$$I_{cc'} = I_{ba} - I_{ca}.$$

These equations may be solved explicitly by invoking the fact that the generator currents form a balanced three-phase set, as was done in deriving Eqs. (8.18) and (8.25). However, we may eliminate much of the complication by solving them graphically, as in Fig. 8.29. Draw first the line currents, which are known, taking the direction of $I_{aa'}$ as the reference.† The proper values of I_{ab}, I_{bc}, and I_{ca} may be determined

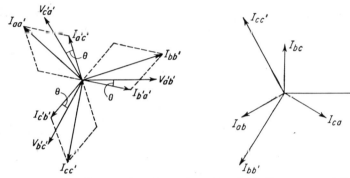

FIG. 8.28. Phasor diagram for Fig. 8.27.   FIG. 8.29. Generator and line currents in Fig. 8.27.

most conveniently by a heuristic process (i.e., by "educated guessing"). This leads to the results shown graphically in Fig. 8.29, from which

$$I_{ab} = \frac{I_{\text{line}}}{\sqrt{3}} \underline{|-150}$$

$$I_{bc} = \frac{I_{\text{line}}}{\sqrt{3}} \underline{|90} \qquad (8.39)$$

$$I_{ca} = \frac{I_{\text{line}}}{\sqrt{3}} \underline{|-30}\cdot$$

Comparing Fig. 8.29 with 8.28 (rotating Fig. 8.29 until the phasors $I_{aa'}$ in both diagrams are parallel), we see that

$$I_{ab} = I_{b'a'}$$
$$I_{bc} = I_{c'b'} \qquad (8.40)$$
$$I_{ca} = I_{a'c'}$$

which results are not unexpected in light of Fig. 8.27.

† This is done only for convenience. We know the actual phase of $I_{aa'}$, but since we are interested only in the phases of the generator current *relative* to the line current, the absolute angle of $I_{aa'}$ need not be considered.

Using some of the relationships derived above, it is a simple matter to relate the load currents directly to the source voltages. Referring to Fig. 8.27, we may sum the voltages around the loop $abb'a'a$:

$$E_{ab} - I_{bb'}Z - I_{b'a'}Z_L - I_{a'a}Z = 0. \tag{8.41}$$

But from Eqs. (8.37) or Fig. 8.28,

$$I_{bb'} = \sqrt{3}\, I_{b'a'}\underline{|30} \tag{8.42}$$

$$I_{aa'} = \sqrt{3}\, I_{b'a'}\underline{|150} \tag{8.43}$$

and so

$$V_{ab} = I_{b'a'}(Z_L + \sqrt{3}\, Z\underline{|30} - \sqrt{3}\, Z\underline{|150})$$
$$= I_{b'a'}(Z_L + 3Z), \tag{8.44}$$

whence

$$I_{b'a'} = \frac{E_{ab}}{Z_L + 3Z}. \tag{8.45.1}$$

Similarly,

$$I_{c'b'} = \frac{E_{bc}}{Z_L + 3Z} \tag{8.45.2}$$

$$I_{a'c'} = \frac{E_{ca}}{Z_L + 3Z}. \tag{8.45.3}$$

The preceding analysis may be generalized to the case where the generator impedance Z_G is not zero by noting that (see Fig. 8.26)

$$\begin{aligned} E_{ab} &= E_{aB} - I_{ab}Z_G \\ E_{bc} &= E_{bC} - I_{bc}Z_G \\ E_{ca} &= E_{cA} - I_{ca}Z_G. \end{aligned} \tag{8.46}$$

Recalling Eqs. (8.40), we see that these become

$$\begin{aligned} E_{ab} &= E_{aB} - I_{b'a'}Z_G \\ E_{bc} &= E_{bC} - I_{c'b'}Z_G \\ E_{ca} &= E_{cA} - I_{a'c'}Z_G. \end{aligned} \tag{8.47}$$

Combining these equations with Eqs. (8.45) shows that Eqs. (8.45) may be written

$$\begin{aligned} I_{b'a'} &= \frac{E_{aB}}{Z_L + Z_G + 3Z} \\ I_{c'b'} &= \frac{E_{bC}}{Z_L + Z_G + 3Z} \\ I_{a'c'} &= \frac{E_{cA}}{Z_L + Z_G + 3Z}. \end{aligned} \tag{8.48}$$

In order to analyze situations wherein the load is connected in Y and the generators in Δ, or vice versa, the simplest method of attack is to make a Y-Δ or Δ-Y transformation of the load. For a balanced load the relation between impedances is

$$Z_Y = \frac{Z_\Delta}{3}. \tag{8.49}$$

In this section we have developed many relationships which apply to balanced three-phase circuits. It is not expected that the reader commit them all to memory—there is no point to that. Instead, he should concentrate on understanding the derivations, making ample use of the phasor diagrams in the process. When the analysis is understood, almost any of the equations developed may be written merely by sketching and inspecting the appropriate diagram. Again, it should be emphasized that the exercise of care in the use of the double-subscript notation is essential in order to avoid mistakes.

8.5. Analysis of Unbalanced Three-phase Circuits. Unbalanced three-phase circuits are those in which either the impedances are unequal

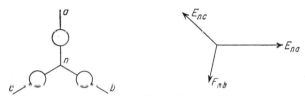

FIG. 8.30. Unbalanced three-phase voltage source.

or the sources are unbalanced, either in magnitude or in phase or both. When we analyze unbalanced three-phase circuits there no longer exist the symmetries which enable us to simplify greatly our analyses. Consequently, a more general method of attack must be employed. The most obvious approach which we may use is a straightforward analysis on a loop or node basis. This always gives correct results, of course, but is time-consuming in actual problems. In practical problems we are not usually concerned with the general analysis of unbalanced systems. Large systems usually are well balanced unless a *fault* occurs. A fault is a short circuit or an open circuit, and the problem which usually must be solved is the determination of currents and voltages which exist under fault conditions. As might be expected, this limiting of the class of problems treated permits great simplification in analysis.

The simplified method of analysis to be used is the method of *symmetrical components*. The method is based on the fact that an arbitrary set of unbalanced voltages can always be decomposed into three sets of balanced (or *symmetrical*) voltages or currents. The three sets of voltages are a positive-sequence set, a negative-sequence set, and a zero-sequence set. The positive-sequence set has phase order *abc*, the negative-sequence set has phase order *acb*, and all the components of the zero-sequence set are in phase. In elaboration of these definitions, let us

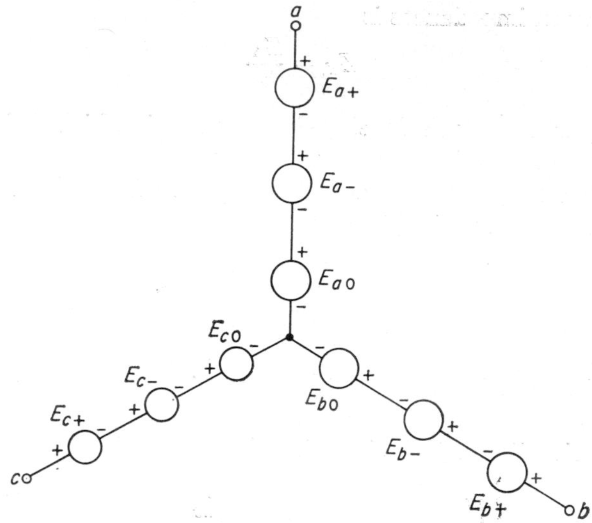

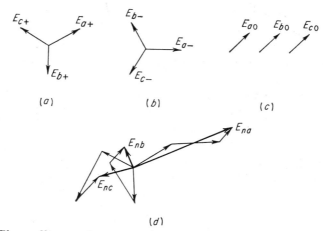

FIG. 8.31. Set of symmetrical component generators equivalent to an unbalanced three-phase source.

FIG. 8.32. Phasor diagrams for symmetrical components. (a) Positive-sequence set; (b) negative-sequence set; (c) zero-sequence set; (d) total voltages.

consider three single-phase generators connected in Y, producing an unbalanced set of voltages (Fig. 8.30). We have said that this is equivalent to the set of generators shown in Fig. 8.31. Figure 8.32 shows how the three sets of voltages add to produce the original set of unbalanced voltages. Observe that all the phasors rotate in the counterclockwise direction.

The method of symmetrical components is essentially a change of variables. Instead of specifying the original three magnitudes and three phase angles, we specify the magnitude and phase of the a component of each of three sets of components. By means of this transformation we reduce the solution of an unbalanced circuit to the solution of three balanced problems. In many cases this latter method involves less work than the original problem.

When the load is unbalanced it is found to present a different imped-ance to the positive-sequence components of voltage, the negative-sequence components, and the zero-sequence components. These we call the positive-, negative-, and zero-sequence components of impedance (although these are not directly analogous to the components of voltage, as the components of voltage are rotating phasors, whereas the imped-ance components are merely complex numbers).

The components of impedance are particularly easy to identify when the line is faulted so that one of the load impedances is zero or infinity. Accordingly, the method of symmetrical components is particularly useful in fault-current calculations.

The method is also quite useful in handling some of the more difficult problems associated with balanced systems, such as transmission lines which are inductively coupled or the inductive coupling of the windings in a generator.

Since the method of symmetrical components is largely a computa-tional technique, its principal advantage is that of reducing laborious calculations. To make effective use of this technique one must be very familiar with the subject and have occasion to make many calculations involving unbalanced three-phase circuits. As a rather extensive discus-sion would be required to give the reader the requisite familiarity, the interested reader is referred to the literature on symmetrical components for further discussion of this subject.[†]

8.6. Power in Three-phase Circuits. The calculation of power in balanced three-phase systems is a trivial extension of the calculation of power in single-phase systems. With single-phase circuits we had the relation

$$P = VI \cos \theta \qquad (8.50)$$

where $\cos \theta$ is the power factor of the circuit. Consequently, for a balanced Y load

$$P = 3V_Y I_{\text{line}} \cos \theta \qquad (8.51)$$

and for a balanced Δ load

$$P = 3V_\Delta I_\Delta \cos \theta \qquad (8.52)$$

where $\cos \theta$ is the phase angle between current and the voltage. These

† E. Clarke, "Circuit Analysis of A-C Power Systems," John Wiley & Sons, Inc., New York, 1943.

expressions may also take the form

$$P = \sqrt{3}\ V_\Delta I_{\text{line}} \cos \theta. \qquad (8.53)$$

Here, however, θ is not the angle between V_Δ and I_{line} but is the angle between V_Δ and the equivalent I_Δ, or between I_{line} and the equivalent V_Y. Thus, by exercising a moderate amount of care we may readily compute the power in balanced three-phase circuits.

When dealing with unbalanced loads, on the other hand, we have no such simple expression for the power, as the power dissipated in each phase is different. To find the power in an unbalanced load we need to determine the power in each phase separately and combine the three values to give the total power. Since the unbalanced load may be reduced to either a Y or a Δ, the total power is given by [see Eq. (4.72)]:

$$P = \text{Re}\ [V_1 I_1^* + V_2 I_2^* + V_3 I_3^*] \qquad (8.54)$$

where the V_i and I_i, $i = 1, 2, 3$, both represent corresponding quantities, either line voltages and Δ phase currents, or equivalent Y phase voltages and line currents.

It is seen that no simple expression exists for the power factor. Nonetheless in practical situations the power factor is an important characteristic of a load. Generators and transformers, and to some extent transmission lines, are rated not by the power they develop but by their volt-ampere (usually specified in kilovolt-amperes) rating—the product of rated voltage and rated current. This is because they usually operate at constant rated voltage and because the current is limited by internal I^2R losses, which do not depend on the phase of the current relative to the voltage. Thus, high efficiency of operation requires high power factors. Electric utility companies generally make penalty charges to wholesale users of electricity for low power factors. Accordingly, a definition of power factor is required which may be applied to unbalanced loads. If we examine the definition of power factor used with single-phase loads, we see that it is the ratio of real power to volt-amperes. This we may rather simply extend to three-phase systems by letting

$$\text{Power factor} = \frac{\text{total real power}}{\text{total volt-amperes}} \qquad (8.55)$$

or

$$\text{pf} = \frac{P}{\sqrt{P^2 + Q^2}} \qquad (8.56)$$

where Q, the reactive volt-amperes, is given by [see Eq. (4.71)]

$$Q = \text{Im}\ [V_1 I_1^* + V_2 I_2^* + V_3 I_3^*]. \qquad (8.57)$$

8.7. Measurements of Current, Voltage, and Power in A-C Circuits.
Hitherto, when discussing measurements, we have found it convenient to
postulate ideal (impedanceless) ammeters and ideal (admittanceless)
voltmeters.   Real ammeters do, however, have some impedance, and
real voltmeters some admittance, which quantities may or may not be
negligible.   In making actual measurements we may have to allow for
the voltage drop across ammeters and current through voltmeters.   In

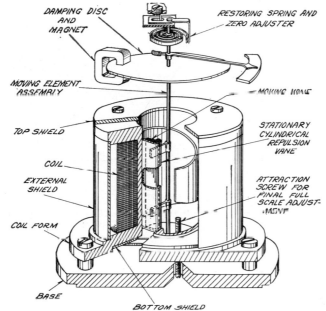

DAMPING DISC
AND
MAGNET

RESTORING SPRING AND
ZERO ADJUSTER

MOVING ELEMENT
ASSEMBLY

MOVING VANE

TOP SHIELD

STATIONARY
CYLINDRICAL
REPULSION
VANE

COIL

EXTERNAL
SHIELD

ATTRACTION
SCREW FOR
FINAL FULL
SCALE ADJUST-
MENT

COIL FORM

BASE

BOTTOM SHIELD

FIG. 8.33. Iron vane ammeter and its construction.   (*Courtesy of Westinghouse
Electric & Manufacturing Company.*)

making d-c measurements the matter of applying corrections to instrument readings is straightforward and usually is presented early in the
first laboratory course.   Usually only voltage and current are measured,
and the value of power is obtained from their product.

In making a-c measurements the situation is greatly complicated by
the fact that in general there are phase shifts between currents and voltages.   Thus, wattmeters are needed to measure power.   Also, the instruments used are usually less sensitive than corresponding d-c instruments,
so that the corrections which we need to apply are greater and are also
less straightforward.

Before discussing the methods of measurement we shall consider the
instruments used.   Ammeters and voltmeters used in power systems are
generally of the iron-vane type.   In this form of instrument (Fig. 8.33)
the current to be measured passes through a coil which sets up a magnetic

field.   Supported in the field by a shaft pivoted at each end is a vane of
soft iron, and the shaft is restrained in its rotation by a spring.   The vane
tends to align itself with the field, so that a torque is exerted on the shaft.
Thus, the shaft rotates until the restoring torque of the spring and the
torque due to the field are in equilibrium.   The amount of rotation
depends on the geometry of the coil and vane and on the current in the
coil.   The pointer which indicates shaft rotation, then, also gives a

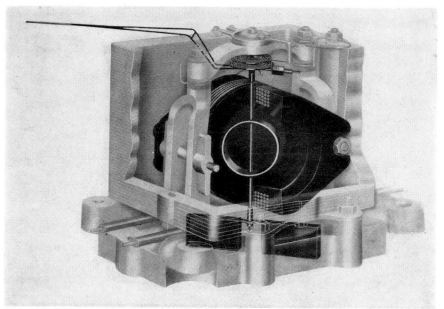

FIG. 8.34. Dynamometer wattmeter movement.   (*Courtesy of Weston Instruments,*
Division of Daystrom, Inc.)

measure of the current, and the scale may be calibrated in amperes.
The same instrument may be used for the measurement of voltage by
placing a resistor in series with the coil.   Generally this resistance is
much greater than the impedance of the coil, and so the current is given
essentially by

$$I = \frac{V}{R}. \tag{8.58}$$

Typically, the most sensitive moving-vane instruments require 10 ma for
full-scale deflection, so that the total resistance of a moving-vane voltmeter is only 100 ohms/volt of full scale reading (usually referred to as
merely "100 ohms/volt") compared with up to 20,000 ohms/volt for
d-c instruments.

Wattmeters are usually of the dynamometer type (Fig. 8.34).   A fixed
coil (the *current* coil) carries the line current and sets up a magnetic field
proportional to that current.   A smaller coil is arranged to rotate in the

fixed magnetic field (but is restrained by a spring from doing so). This coil (the *potential* coil), in series with a resistor, is placed across the lines and carries a current proportional to the line voltage. Thus, the instantaneous torque on the potential coil is proportional to the product of current and voltage,

$$t = kvi. \tag{8.59}$$

The potential coil is heavily damped, so that what is read is the average torque T, which is

$$T = \lim_{\tau \to \infty} \frac{k}{\tau} \int_0^\tau vi \, dt = \lim_{\tau \to \infty} \frac{k}{\tau} \int_0^\tau 2VI \cos \omega t \cos (\omega t + \theta) \, dt$$
$$= kVI \cos \theta. \tag{8.60}$$

Thus the torque, and hence the reading, is proportional to the average power.

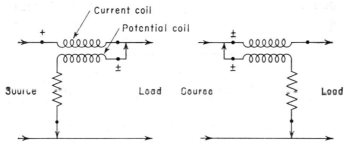

FIG. 8.35. Proper methods of connecting a wattmeter.

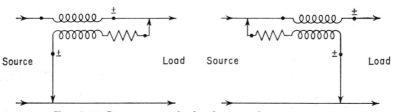

FIG. 8.36. Incorrect methods of connecting a wattmeter.

To permit flexibility in making connections, the terminals of both the current coil and the potential coil are brought out separately. Since it is possible to reverse the connections of one coil, producing a downscale reading, one terminal on each coil is identified by a dot or a $\pm$ sign. The proper connections of a wattmeter are shown in Fig. 8.35. It would appear that the connections shown in Fig. 8.36 would also be correct. However, these connections result in large differences of potential between the current and voltage coils, which leads to electrostatic forces between the coils and may result in incorrect readings. Also, there is the possibility of damaging the instrument by arcing.

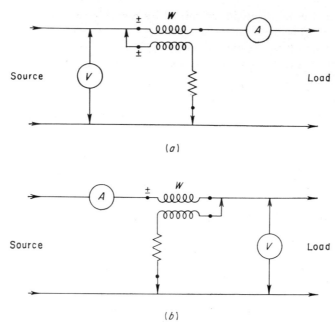

(a)

(b)

Fig. 8.37. Measurements of a-c current, voltage, and power. (a) Small errors, complex corrections; (b) larger errors, simpler corrections: A, ammeter; V, voltmeter.

The dynamometer principle is also applied to ammeters and voltmeters used as standard instruments. Here the coils are connected in series or in parallel.

Returning to the matter of instrument connections, there are two sensible ways in which an ammeter, a voltmeter, and a wattmeter may

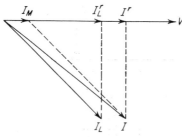

Fig. 8.38. Phasor diagram used in determining ammeter corrections.

be connected between a generator and a load. The method shown in Fig. 8.37a results in the smaller errors. However, corrections are very difficult to apply. The corrections shown in Fig. 8.37b result in larger errors, but corrections are fairly straightforward (although not as trivial as one might hope).

Let us take the voltage V across the load as reference. This is the voltage read by the voltmeter. Also, for concreteness, we consider an inductive load, drawing a current I_L (see Fig. 8.38). The ammeter does not measure the load current I_L but rather the total current I, where I is the sum of the load current I_L and the current drawn by the voltmeter and potential coil, I_M. This latter current is in phase with the voltage, because the potential coil and voltmeter act as pure resistance, and is given by

$$I_M = \frac{V}{R} \tag{8.61}$$

where R is the equivalent resistance of the voltmeter and potential coil in parallel.

To find the true value of I_L we shall find its in-phase and quadrature components, which we designate $I_L{}^r$ and $I_L{}^q$, and combine them.   Now

$$I_L{}^r = I^r - I_M. \tag{8.62}$$

But I^r, the in-phase component of I, is given by

$$I^r = \frac{W}{V}. \tag{8.63}$$

That is, the wattmeter reading W is equal to the product of the voltage and the in-phase component of current.   (Remember, the wattmeter also reads the power drawn by the voltmeter and potential coil.)   Thus Eq. (8.62) becomes

$$I_L{}^r = \frac{W}{V} - \frac{V}{R}. \tag{8.64}$$

Noting that $I_L{}^q = I^q$, we have

$$I_L{}^q = \sqrt{I^2 - (I^r)^2} = \sqrt{I^2 - \frac{W^2}{V^2}}. \tag{8.65}$$

Thus

$$I_L = \sqrt{(I_L{}^q)^2 + (I_L{}^r)^2} = \sqrt{I^2 - \frac{W^2}{V^2} + \left(\frac{W}{V} - \frac{V}{R}\right)^2}$$

$$= \sqrt{I^2 + \frac{V^2}{R^2} - \frac{2W}{R}}. \tag{8.66}$$

Since generally the corrections are small, we may make use of the relation

$$\sqrt{1 + \epsilon} \doteq 1 + \frac{\epsilon}{2}, \qquad |\epsilon| \ll 1$$

and write

$$I_L \doteq I\left(1 + \frac{V^2}{2I^2R^2} - \frac{W}{2R}\right). \tag{8.67}$$

Note that a wattmeter is required if we wish to correct the ammeter reading even though we may not be interested in measuring power.   The wattmeter is needed to indicate the phase angle of the load.   Wattmeter corrections can be made rather simply.   In addition to the load power, the wattmeter also reads the power drawn by the potential coil and the voltmeter (since the current through the current coil is not only the load

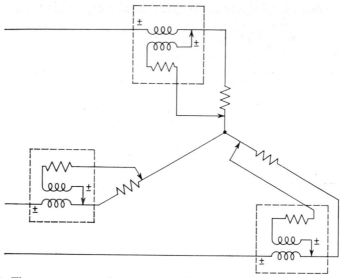

FIG. 8.39. Three wattmeters for measuring three-phase power in balanced Y load.

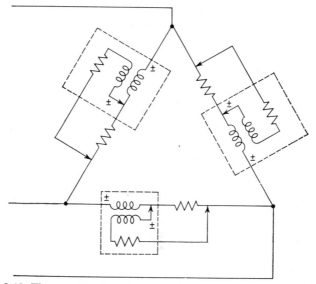

FIG. 8.40. Three wattmeters for measuring power in Δ-connected load.

current but also the instrument current). Thus, the actual load power P is given by

$$P = W - \frac{V^2}{R}.\qquad (8.68)$$

8.8. Measurement of Power in Three-phase Circuits. Power measurements in three-phase circuits are, fortunately, much easier to make than one might initially expect.   Let us consider first a three-phase balanced Y-connected load.   The power can be measured by connecting a wattmeter in each phase (see Fig. 8.39).   The total power is then the sum of the three wattmeter readings.   Since we know that the load is balanced, it is not necessary even to use three wattmeters; we need merely to measure the power in one phase and multiply by 3.

Similarly, for balanced Δ-connected loads, we may measure the power in each phase (see Fig. 8.40) and take the sum or merely measure the power in one phase and multiply by 3.

Often, however, the neutral of a Y-connected load is inaccessible, or we cannot break into the branches of a Δ.   If the load be balanced, we may

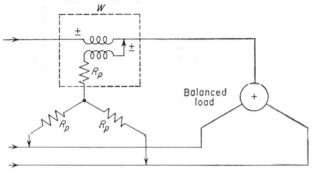

FIG. 8.41. Single wattmeter, with resistors, for measuring power in a balanced three-phase load.

analyze this case by considering the load, whether it be Y or Δ, as a Y, and by creating an artificial neutral.   This may be done by arranging two resistors, equal to the resistance of the wattmeter potential coil, to form, in conjunction with the wattmeter potential coil, a balanced Y (see Fig. 8.41).   It is to be stressed that this method works only with balanced loads.

Suppose now that the problem is to measure the power in an unbalanced load.   Clearly, the methods shown in Figs. 8.39 and 8.40 will be satisfactory.   However, it is quite common to have unbalanced loads in which the neutral of the Y or the individual branches of the Δ are inaccessible.   What procedure may be followed then?   We shall now show that the connection of Fig. 8.42 may be used, with the neutral point n' of the wattmeters connected to *any* point in the circuit.   For concreteness, we take the load to be an unbalanced Y.   We shall neglect the wattmeter corrections, for simplicity.

Now, the actual power delivered to the load is found by adding the power in each phase and is

$$P = \text{Re}\,[V_{na}I_a^* + V_{nb}I_b^* + V_{nc}I_c^*]. \qquad (8.69)$$

What is measured by the wattmeters is

$$P_w = \text{Re} \left[(V_{n'n} + V_{na}) I_a^* + (V_{n'n} + V_{nb}) I_b^* + (V_{n'n} + V_{nc}) I_c^* \right]$$
$$= \text{Re} \left[V_{n'n} (I_a^* + I_b^* + I_c^*) + V_{na} I_a^* + V_{nb} I_b^* + V_{nc} I_c^* \right]. \qquad (8.70)$$

However, $I_a + I_b + I_c = 0$, and this implies $I_a^* + I_b^* + I_c^* = 0$, so that
the power read by the wattmeters is

$$P_w = \text{Re} \left[V_{na} I_a^* + V_{nb} I_b^* + V_{nc} I_c^* \right] \qquad (8.70a)$$

which is the actual power delivered to the load. Observe that we have
not specified the potential of the point n'. The wattmeters need not be

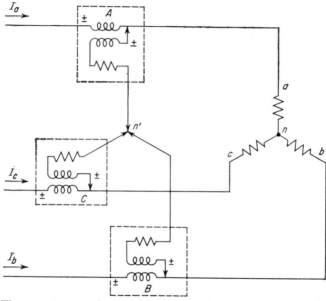

Fig. 8.42. Three wattmeters for measuring three-phase power, connected to an arbitrary neutral.

identical. In particular, we may connect the neutral n' to point c. In
that case, wattmeter C will always read zero, and so *only two wattmeters
are necessary to measure three-phase power*. (In general, $n - 1$ wattmeters are necessary to measure n-phase power, when no neutral wire is
used.)

In applying the two-wattmeter method of power measurement, it is
often found that one of the wattmeters will read negatively (downscale).
If the particular wattmeter used does not have a zero reading high on the
scale, it will be necessary to reverse the reading by reversing the terminals
of the current coil (*never* the voltage coil, for reasons explained in Sec. 8.6,
although that is usually easier).

The two-wattmeter method (Fig. 8.43) also may be used to indicate

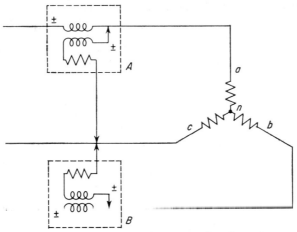

FIG. 8.43. Two-wattmeter method of measuring three-phase power.

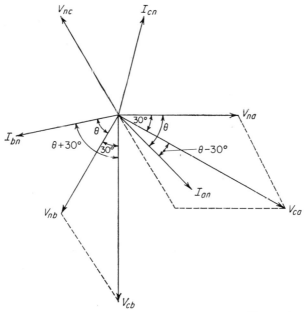

FIG. 8.44. Phasor diagram for two-wattmeter measurement, illustrating power factor angle θ.

the power factor of *balanced loads*. Referring to Fig. 8.44, which shows that phasor diagram for a balanced Y load, it is seen that the two wattmeters of Fig. 8.43 indicate values of

$$P_A = I_a V_{ca} \cos (\theta - 30°) \tag{8.71.1}$$
$$P_B = I_b V_{cb} \cos (\theta + 30°). \tag{8.71.2}$$

If we take the sum and difference of P_A and P_B and expand the expressions $\cos(\theta \pm 30)$, we may readily show that

$$\tan \theta = \sqrt{3}\, \frac{P_A - P_B}{P_A + P_B}. \tag{8.72}$$

This may be written

$$\theta = \arctan \sqrt{3}\, \frac{P_A/P_B - 1}{P_A/P_B + 1}. \tag{8.73}$$

The above relation is often presented in graphical form to facilitate the determination of power factor from wattmeter readings (see Exercise 8.17).

EXERCISES

8.1. Kelvin stated a law relating to the economics of power distribution as follows: The most economical cross-sectional area of a conductor for distributing electrical energy, when the operating voltage is prescribed, is that for which the annual cost of energy wasted is equal to the interest on that portion of the capital outlay which is proportional to the weight of conductor used.   Prove this law.

8.2. On a three-wire distribution system it is sometimes observed that when a load is removed some incandescent lights connected to the system increase in brightness whereas others diminish in intensity.   Explain this phenomenon by constructing a numerical example.

8.3. Show that the instantaneous power delivered by an n-phase system $(n \geqq 3)$ is constant.

8.4. In distributing d-c energy, the neutral wire in a three-wire system is sometimes obtained through the use of a balancer set, as illustrated in Fig. 8.45.   The main

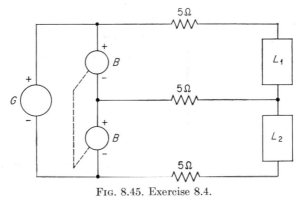

Fig. 8.45. Exercise 8.4.

generator G supplies most of the energy (all, when the load is balanced); the balancer set consists of two identical generators connected to the same shaft.   These machines run free when the load is balanced.   With an unbalanced load one machine operates as a motor and the other as a generator, which tends to maintain balanced load voltages.   For the purposes of this problem it is sufficient to consider the generators as being voltage sources of equal value.   The loads L_1 and L_2 draw 500 and 300 watts, respectively, when 150 volts is applied to them.   For a generator voltage of 220 volts determine (a) the voltage across each load; (b) the voltage drop in each transmission wire; (c) the current in each generator; (d) the over-all efficiency of transmission.

8.5. (a) Consider six generators, each having a voltage of 100 volts.   The phases of the six voltages are 0°, 60°, 120°, 180°, 240°, and 300°, respectively.   In how many ways may these six generators be connected to form a balanced three-phase Y? What are the phase and line voltages in each case?   Give answers in the form of vector diagrams.

(b) If the phases of the six voltages are 0°, 30°, 60°, 90°, 120°, and 150° and if the generators are connected to form a balanced three-phase Δ, what is the connection, and what must the coil voltages be to give 220 volts line to line?

8.6. For the circuit shown in Fig. 8.46, determine the various line currents and the voltage drops along the lines and across each element, and draw the phasor diagram showing the various currents and voltages

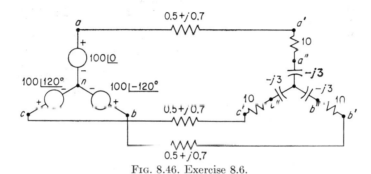

FIG. 8.46. Exercise 8.6.

8.7. Determine the currents in the Δ load for the circuit shown in Fig. 8.47.

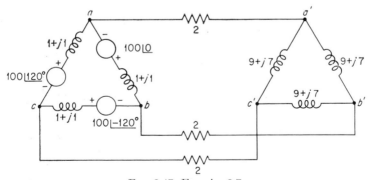

FIG. 8.47. Exercise 8.7.

8.8. A Δ-connected generator has one phase open, as shown in Fig. 8.48.   Determine the three line currents and the phase currents in the load.

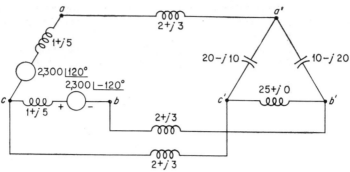

FIG. 8.48. Exercise 8.8.

8.9. A three-phase 2300-volt (line-to-line) feeder supplies a balanced three-phase lighting load of 108 kw at unity power factor and a balanced motor load of 500 kw at a power factor of 78 per cent.   Determine the current in the feeder, the power factor of the feeder, and the kilovolt-amperes supplied.

8.10. A balanced three-phase load is supplied with balanced voltages whose magnitudes are 208 volts, line to line.   The power is measured by two wattmeters whose current coils are connected in lines A and C and whose voltage circuits have a common connection to line B.   The current in line A lags the voltage drop from line A to B by 20°.   The line current is 10 amp.   What is the reading of each wattmeter and what is the total power?

8.11. What does a wattmeter read if it is connected to a balanced load as shown in Fig. 8.49?

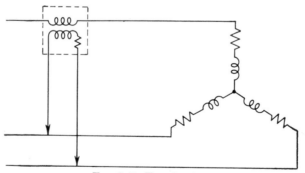

FIG. 8.49. Exercise 8.11.

8.12. Show that a "varmeter" (that is, a device to measure reactive power) may be constructed from a wattmeter by replacing the resistor in series with the potential coil by an inductor whose impedance is equal to the resistor replaced.   Show that a "two-varmeter" measurement may be used to determine reactive power in an unbalanced load.

8.13. Develop expressions for finding the symmetrical components equivalent to a set of unbalanced voltages.

8.14. A balanced three-phase load draws 2.5 kw and 8.66 kva.   What are the readings of two wattmeters connected to measure the total power?

8.15. Two wattmeters measuring power to a balanced three-phase load read 1500 and −450 watts.   How many volt-amperes does the load take and at what power factor?

8.16. Two identical transformers have their primary windings connected to a two-phase system, as shown in Fig. 8.50.   One secondary winding is connected to a center

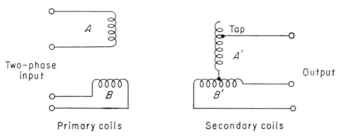

Two-phase input

Output

Primary coils   Secondary coils

Fig. 8.50. Exercise 8.16.

tap on the other.   The first secondary also has a tap.   At what position must this tap be connected so that the output of the transformers is balanced three-phase alternating current?   Show that, if three-phase power is applied to the secondary windings, then two-phase power will be available at the erstwhile primary windings. Assume ideal transformers.   (This arrangement of transformers is known as a Scott connection.)

8.17. Using Eq. (8.73) construct a chart showing power factor as a function of the ratio P_A/P_B.   Use a logarithmic scale for P_A/P_B, for a range of values from 0.1 to 10.

CHAPTER 9

FOURIER SERIES

In almost all of our previous analyses of electric circuits we assumed that the forcing function (current or voltage) was sinusoidal in nature. Thus, for example, when we wished to find the voltage at the output terminals of the circuit illustrated in Fig. 9.1, we explicitly assumed that $e_{in} = \sqrt{2}\, E_0 \sin \omega_0 t$.   That is, the voltage was assumed to be a constant-amplitude, constant-frequency sine wave.   Our steady-state analysis was predicated on such choices of forcing functions and enabled us, for example, to use such representations as Im $[\sqrt{2}\, E_0 \epsilon^{j\omega_0 t}] = \sqrt{2}\, E_0 \sin \omega_0 t$

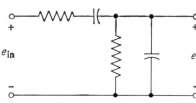

which, further, permits us to reduce the determination of the steady-state solution of linear differential equations with constant coefficients having sinusoidal forcing functions to calculations with complex numbers.

FIG. 9.1. Simple two-port network.

Since the solution of network problems is equivalent to the solution of appropriate differential equations and since solutions exist for differential equations having an arbitrary forcing function, we can solve the circuit equations with an arbitrary forcing function $f(t)$.   Thus from the theoretical point of view, we can encompass current and voltage sources with arbitrary waveforms.   However, we have seen that sinusoidal steady-state analysis was simpler than a direct assault on the differential equations and also lent itself to useful physical interpretations.   The question we would like to pose now is the following: Can the methods of steady-state analysis be extended to *nonsinusoidal* functions?   We shall give a relatively complete answer to this problem in the present chapter.

Suppose that the input voltage of a two-port such as that of Fig. 9.1 has a waveform as illustrated in Fig. 9.2.   What is the output voltage? Of course we could solve this problem by setting up the differential equation of the network and applying standard techniques of the theory of differential equations.   However, this waveform is composed of sinusoidal terms,

$$e_{in}(t) = \sin \omega_0 t + \tfrac{1}{3} \sin 3\omega_0 t + \tfrac{1}{5} \sin 5\omega_0 t. \tag{9.1}$$

Thus if the output voltage in Fig. 9.1 due to an input voltage $e_{in} = \sin \omega t$ is represented by $F(\omega t)$, then, because of the linearity of the circuit, the output due to the input of Eq. (9.1) is represented by

$$F(\omega_0 t) + \frac{1}{3}F(3\omega_0 t) + \frac{1}{5}F(5\omega_0 t). \qquad (9.2)$$

This simple result immediately raises the following question: Given an arbitrary periodic function, such as is illustrated in Fig. 9.3, is it possible

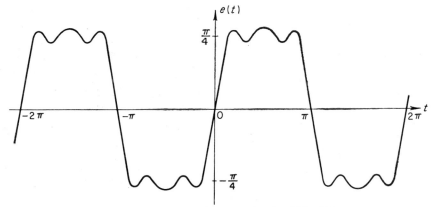

Fig. 9.2. Input waveform to circuit of Fig. 9.1.

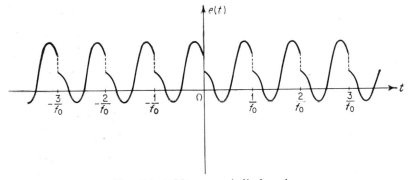

Fig. 9.3. Arbitrary periodic function.

to write it as the sum of sines and/or possibly cosines? The answer to this question is, in general, yes.   It will be one of the main tasks in the present chapter to develop this analysis.   We see therefore that if we can develop $e(t)$ into a sum of trigonometric functions then, because of the linearity of the circuit, the response to $e(t)$ can be found by superimposing the responses to all the components of $e(t)$.   Thus we shall have used frequency-response techniques to find the response of a linear circuit to an arbitrary periodic waveform.   A development of an arbitrary periodic function in terms of sines and cosines is called a *Fourier series.*

Before embarking on the detailed analysis of Fourier series, let us mention the problem of finding the response to a *nonperiodic* function. Again, differential equations yield a solution. However, we can extend the method of Fourier series to the *Fourier integral*, which essentially allows us to apply frequency-analysis techniques to nonperiodic functions. The Fourier integral will be developed in Sec. 9.5 of the present chapter.

9.1. Fourier Series. Suppose now that we are given an arbitrary periodic function $e(t)$ of period $T = 1/f_0$ (see Fig. 9.3). Mathematically we say that $e(t)$ is a periodic function of period T if $e(t)$ is defined for all t and

$$e(t) = e(t + T) \qquad \text{for all } t. \tag{9.3}$$

Thus, for example, any two values of t which differ by an integral multiple of T are equal. We show that $e(t + 2T) = e(t)$ analytically by writing

$$e(t + 2T) = e((t + T) + T) = e(t + T) = e(t), \tag{9.4}$$

that is, by applying Eq. (9.3) first with t replaced by $t + T$ and then using the formula directly. One sees immediately that, in general,

$$
\begin{aligned}
\cdots e(t - nT) = e(t - (n - 1)T) = \cdots &= e(t - 2T) \\
= e(t - T) = e(t) &= e(t + T) \\
= e(t + 2T) = \cdots = e(t + nT) &= \cdots .
\end{aligned}
\tag{9.5}
$$

Of course all the statements of this paragraph are clear from a simple inspection of Fig. 9.3. However, it is convenient to formulate these trivial remarks in a mathematical form, as we have just done.

Let us now write $e(t)$ as

$$
\begin{aligned}
e(t) = \frac{a_0}{2} &+ a_1 \cos \omega_0 t + a_2 \cos 2\omega_0 t + \cdots \\
&+ b_1 \sin \omega_0 t + b_2 \sin 2\omega_0 t + \cdots ,
\end{aligned}
\tag{9.6}
$$

where $\omega_0 = 2\pi f_0 = 2\pi/T$. That is, we are supposing that $e(t)$ can be developed into a series of sines and cosines all of whose frequencies are integral multiples of the fundamental frequency ω_0. We use $a_0/2$ for mathematical convenience, as will be shown a little later. There is no necessity for having a b_0 term since $\sin 0t = 0$. Our problem is then to find explicit formulas for the a_n and b_n.

The reader will recall that when he developed a function of x, say $f(x)$, into the power series

$$f(x) = \alpha_0 + \alpha_1 x + \alpha_2 x^2 + \cdots$$

the coefficients $\alpha_0, \alpha_1, \alpha_2, \ldots$ were determined by differentiating $f(x)$. In Fourier series we shall integrate to determine the coefficients $a_0, a_1,$

$a_2, \ldots, b_1, b_2, \ldots$. Let us therefore integrate every term of the series of Eq. (9.6) over one full period T. There results

$$\int_0^T e(t) \, dt = \int_0^T \tfrac{1}{2}a_0 \, dt + a_1 \int_0^T \cos \omega_0 t \, dt + a_2 \int_0^T \cos 2\omega_0 t \, dt + \cdots$$

$$+ b_1 \int_0^T \sin \omega_0 t \, dt + b_2 \int_0^T \sin 2\omega_0 t \, dt + \cdots. \quad (9.7)$$

From well-known integrals in the calculus,

$$\int_0^T \cos n\omega_0 t \, dt = \frac{1}{n\omega_0} \int_0^{n\omega_0 T} \cos x \, dx = \frac{1}{n\omega_0} \int_0^{2\pi n} \cos x \, dx$$

$$= \frac{1}{n\omega_0} \sin x \Big|_0^{2\pi n} = 0, \qquad n = 1, 2, \ldots,$$

where we have made the change of variable $n\omega_0 t = x$ and recalled that $\omega_0 = 2\pi/T$. Similarly,

$$\int_0^T \sin n\omega_0 t \, dt = \frac{1}{n\omega_0} \int_0^{2\pi n} \sin x \, dx = 0, \qquad n = 1, 2, \ldots,$$

while

$$\int_0^T \tfrac{1}{2}a_0 \, dt = \frac{a_0 T}{2}. \quad (9.8)$$

Thus every term on the right-hand side of Eq. (9.7) except possibly $\int_0^T \tfrac{1}{2}a_0 \, dt$ is zero and

$$\int_0^T e(t) \, dt = \frac{a_0 T}{2}$$

or

$$a_0 = \frac{2}{T} \int_0^T e(t) \, dt. \quad (9.9)$$

We have therefore determined a_0.

In order to determine $a_1, a_2, \ldots$, and $b_1, b_2, \ldots$ we must first recall some equations from the calculus. The ones we have in mind are

$$\int_0^T \cos n\omega_0 t \cos m\omega_0 t \, dt = \begin{cases} T/2 & \text{if } n = m \\ 0 & \text{if } n \neq m \end{cases}$$

$$\int_0^T \sin n\omega_0 t \sin m\omega_0 t \, dt = \begin{cases} T/2 & \text{if } n = m \\ 0 & \text{if } n \neq m \end{cases} \quad (9.10)$$

$$\int_0^T \sin n\omega_0 t \cos m\omega_0 t \, dt = 0$$

where n and m are nonnegative integers not both zero. The conditions of Eqs. (9.10) are known as *orthogonality conditions*.† We shall prove the second one and leave the proof of the other two as exercises for the reader. From the trigonometric identity

$$\sin x \sin y = \tfrac{1}{2}[\cos (x - y) - \cos (x + y)]$$

with $x = n\omega_0 t$ and $y = m\omega_0 t$, the second of Eqs. (9.10) becomes

$$\int_0^T \sin n\omega_0 t \sin m\omega_0 t \, dt = \tfrac{1}{2} \int_0^T [\cos (n - m)\omega_0 t - \cos (n + m)\omega_0 t] \, dt$$

$$= \frac{1}{2} \left[\frac{\sin (n - m)\omega_0 t}{(n - m)\omega_0} - \frac{\sin (n + m)\omega_0 t}{(n + m)\omega_0} \right]\Bigg|_0^T.$$

This last expression is valid only if $n - m \neq 0$ and $n + m \neq 0$. But if n and m are nonnegative integers not both zero, $n + m$ can never be zero. Thus only the case $n = m$ need be treated separately. Hence if $n \neq m$,

$$\int_0^T \sin n\omega_0 t \sin m\omega_0 t \, dt = \frac{1}{2} \left[\frac{\sin (n - m)\omega_0 T}{(n - m)\omega_0} - \frac{\sin (n + m)\omega_0 T}{(n + m)\omega_0} \right] = 0$$

since $\omega_0 T = 2\pi$. If $n = m$,

$$\int_0^T \sin n\omega_0 t \sin m\omega_0 t \, dt = \int_0^T \sin^2 n\omega_0 t \, dt$$

$$= \tfrac{1}{2} \int_0^T (1 - \cos 2n\omega_0 t) \, dt = \frac{T}{2}.$$

The second of Eqs. (9.10) is thus established. The other two are similarly proved.

Armed with the orthogonality conditions of Eqs. (9.10) let us return to Eq. (9.6) which we write in compact form as

$$e(t) = \tfrac{1}{2}a_0 + \sum_{n=1}^{\infty} (a_n \cos n\omega_0 t + b_n \sin n\omega_0 t). \tag{9.12}$$

Suppose that we multiply Eq. (9.12) by $\cos m\omega_0 t$, where m is a positive

---

† In general, a set of functions $\{\phi_n(x)\}$ (finite or infinite) is said to be *orthogonal* over the interval $[a,b]$ with respect to the weighting function $r(x) > 0$ if

$$\int_a^b r(x)\phi_n(x)\phi_m(x) \, dx = 0, \qquad n \neq m$$

$$= A_n > 0, \qquad n = m.$$

If $A_n = 1$ for all n, we say that $\{\phi_n(x)\}$ is an *orthonormal* set of functions. There are many useful sets of orthogonal functions in applied mathematics. We mention the Bessel functions, Legendre polynomials, Hermite polynomials. (See, for example, K. S. Miller, "Engineering Mathematics," Rinehart & Company, Inc., New York, 1956, pp. 178, 326.)

integer, and *then* integrate from 0 to T. There results

$$\int_0^T e(t) \cos m\omega_0 t \, dt = \frac{a_0}{2} \int_0^T \cos m\omega_0 t \, dt$$

$$+ \sum_{n=1}^{\infty} \left[a_n \int_0^T \cos n\omega_0 t \cos m\omega_0 t \, dt \right.$$

$$\left. + b_n \int_0^T \sin n\omega_0 t \cos m\omega_0 t \, dt \right]. \quad (9.13)$$

By virtue of Eqs. (9.10),

$$\int_0^T \cos m\omega_0 t \, dt = 0$$

$$\int_0^T \cos n\omega_0 t \cos m\omega_0 t \, dt = 0, \qquad n \neq m$$

$$\int_0^T \sin n\omega_0 t \cos m\omega_0 t \, dt = 0.$$

Thus the only term on the right of Eq. (9.13) which does not necessarily vanish is that involving two cosine terms with $n = m$, and for that the value of the integral is $T/2$. Therefore

$$\int_0^T e(t) \cos m\omega_0 t \, dt = a_m \frac{T}{2}$$

and

$$a_m = \frac{2}{T} \int_0^T e(t) \cos m\omega_0 t \, dt, \qquad m = 1, 2, \ldots . \quad (9.14)$$

Now the above expression was shown to be valid for m positive. But if we let $m = 0$,

$$a_0 = \frac{2}{T} \int_0^T e(t) \cos 0t \, dt = \frac{2}{T} \int_0^T e(t) \, dt$$

which is also valid by virtue of Eq. (9.9). Thus

$$a_n = \frac{2}{T} \int_0^T e(t) \cos n\omega_0 t \, dt, \qquad n = 0, 1, 2, \ldots . \quad (9.15)$$

This is why we chose $a_0/2$ rather than a_0 in our original representation of Eq. (9.6). For now *all* the a_n including $n = 0$ are given by the *same* formula, namely, Eq. (9.15).

To deduce the b_n's we multiply Eq. (9.12) by $\sin m\omega_0 t$ and integrate from 0 to T,

$$\int_0^T e(t) \sin m\omega_0 t \, dt = \frac{a_0}{2} \int_0^T \sin m\omega_0 t \, dt$$

$$+ \sum_{n=1}^{\infty} \left[a_n \int_0^T \cos n\omega_0 t \sin m\omega_0 t \, dt \right.$$

$$\left. + b_n \int_0^T \sin n\omega_0 t \sin m\omega_0 t \, dt \right] \quad (9.16)$$

and, by virtue of the orthogonality conditions, every term on the right is zero except $\int_0^T \sin m\omega_0 t \sin m\omega_0 t \, dt$. Thus

$$\int_0^T e(t) \sin m\omega_0 t \, dt = b_m \int_0^T \sin^2 m\omega_0 t \, dt = \frac{b_m T}{2}$$

and

$$b_m = \frac{2}{T} \int_0^T e(t) \sin m\omega_0 t \, dt, \qquad m = 1, 2, \ldots .$$

We may summarize our results as follows: If $e(t)$ is a periodic function of period $T = 1/f_0$, that is, $e(t) = e(t + T)$, then $e(t)$ has a Fourier series expansion given by

$$e(t) = \frac{a_0}{2} + \sum_{n=1}^{\infty} (a_n \cos n\omega_0 t + b_n \sin n\omega_0 t) \qquad (9.17)$$

where the coefficients a_n and b_n are given by the expressions

$$a_n = \frac{2}{T} \int_0^T e(t) \cos n\omega_0 t \, dt, \qquad n = 0, 1, 2, \ldots , \qquad (9.18)$$

and

$$b_n = \frac{2}{T} \int_0^T e(t) \sin n\omega_0 t \, dt, \qquad n = 1, 2, \ldots . \qquad (9.19)$$

These results will be illustrated by means of a few examples.

Example 9.1. Let $e(t)$ be the periodic function of Fig. 9.4. Find its Fourier series expansion.

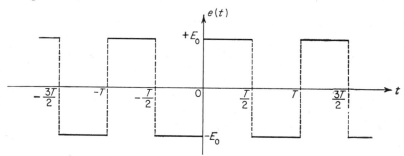

FIG. 9.4. Square wave (Example 9.1).

Solution. The expansion for $e(t)$ is given by Eq. (9.17). We must therefore compute the coefficients a_n and b_n by using Eqs. (9.18) and (9.19). Now since $e(t)$ is given graphically, we must first write the equation of $e(t)$ from 0 to T in mathematical form in order to apply these equations. This is simply done:

$$e(t) = E_0, \qquad 0 < t < T/2$$
$$e(t) = -E_0, \qquad T/2 < t < T.$$

Thus

$$a_n = \frac{2}{T} \int_0^{T/2} (E_0) \cos n\omega_0 t \, dt + \frac{2}{T} \int_{T/2}^{T} (-E_0) \cos n\omega_0 t \, dt$$

$$= \frac{2E_0}{T} \left[\frac{\sin n\omega_0 t}{n\omega_0} \right] \Big|_0^{T/2} - \frac{2E_0}{T} \left[\frac{\sin n\omega_0 t}{n\omega_0} \right] \Big|_{T/2}^{T}, \qquad n \neq 0.$$

The above expression is valid, of course, only if $n \neq 0$. For $n \neq 0$,

$$a_n = \frac{2E_0}{T} \left[\frac{\sin n\pi}{n\omega_0} - 0 \right] - \frac{2E_0}{T} \left[\frac{\sin 2n\pi}{n\omega_0} - \frac{\sin n\pi}{n\omega_0} \right] = 0$$

while if $n = 0$ we go back to the original formula to obtain

$$a_0 = \frac{2}{T} \int_0^{T/2} E_0 \, dt - \frac{2}{T} \int_{T/2}^{T} E_0 \, dt = 0.$$

Thus it turns out that *all* the a_n coefficients are zero.

Let us now determine the b_n's. From Eq. (9.19),

$$b_n = \frac{2}{T} \int_0^{T/2} E_0 \sin n\omega_0 t \, dt + \frac{2}{T} \int_{T/2}^{T} (-E_0) \sin n\omega_0 t \, dt$$

$$= \frac{2E_0}{T} \left[-\frac{\cos n\omega_0 t}{n\omega_0} \right] \Big|_0^{T/2} - \frac{2E_0}{T} \left[-\frac{\cos n\omega_0 t}{n\omega_0} \right] \Big|_{T/2}^{T}.$$

Since we are interested in b_n only for n *positive*, the above equation is valid for all values of n that we wish to consider. Thus

$$b_n = \frac{2E_0}{Tn\omega_0} [- \cos n\pi + 1] - \frac{2E_0}{Tn\omega_0} [- \cos 2n\pi + \cos n\pi]$$

But $\cos 2n\pi = +1$. Therefore

$$b_n = \frac{4E_0}{2n\pi} [1 - \cos n\pi].$$

Now $\cos n\pi$ is $+1$ if n is even and -1 if n is odd. Thus we may write compactly that

$$\cos n\pi = (-1)^n$$

and the expression for b_n becomes

$$b_n = \frac{2E_0}{n\pi} [1 - (-1)^n]$$

or

$$b_n = 0, \qquad n \text{ even}$$

$$b_n = \frac{4E_0}{n\pi}, \qquad n \text{ odd}.$$

Using these results and the fact that $a_n = 0$, $n = 0, 1, \ldots$, in Eq. (9.17) leads to†

$$e(t) = \frac{4E_0}{\pi} [\sin \omega_0 t + \tfrac{1}{3} \sin 3\omega_0 t + \tfrac{1}{5} \sin 5\omega_0 t + \cdots]$$

$$= \frac{4E_0}{\pi} \sum_{n=1,3,5,\ldots}^{\infty} \frac{1}{n} \sin n\omega_0 t.$$

---

† The notation $\displaystyle\sum_{n=1,3,5,\ldots}^{\infty}$ means that the index n runs from 1 to ∞ by odd integers only, as is explicitly written out in the first form of the expression for $e(t)$.

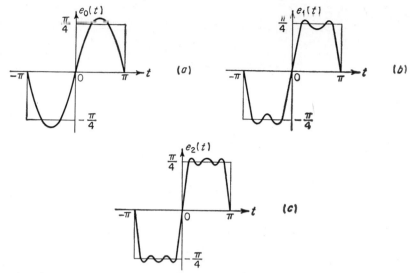

FIG. 9.5. Approximation to square wave by finite sum. (*a*) One term included; (*b*) two terms included; (*c*) three terms included.

We have thus expanded the square wave in terms of sinusoidal components and hence steady-state frequency analysis is applicable to each term individually. One would expect that if we considered the finite sum

$$e_N(t) = \frac{4E_0}{\pi} \sum_{n=1,3,5,\ldots}^{2N+1} \frac{1}{n} \sin n\omega_0 t,$$

where N is a large number, then $e_N(t)$ would closely approximate $e(t)$. This is true and is shown graphically in Fig. 9.5 where we have actually plotted $e_0(t)$, $e_1(t)$, and $e_2(t)$.

Example 9.2. Expand the saw-tooth wave illustrated in Fig. 9.6 into a Fourier series.

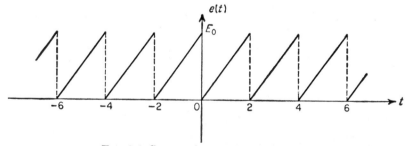

FIG. 9.6. Saw-tooth wave (Example 9.2).

Solution. We note first that the period T is 2 and the fundamental frequency ω_0 is $2\pi/T = \pi$. The coefficients of the Fourier series expansion are given by Eqs. (9.18) and (9.19); the analytic form of the periodic function is

$$e(t) = \frac{E_0}{2} t, \qquad 0 \leqq t < 2.$$

Thus

$$a_n = \frac{2}{T} \int_0^T e(t) \cos n\omega_0 t \, dt = \int_0^2 \left(\frac{E_0}{2} t\right) \cos n\pi t \, dt$$

$$= \frac{E_0}{2} \left[\frac{t \sin n\pi t}{n\pi} + \frac{\cos n\pi t}{n^2\pi^2}\right]\Big|_0^2, \quad n \neq 0$$

$$= \frac{E_0}{2} \left[\frac{\cos 2n\pi}{n^2\pi^2} - \frac{1}{n^2\pi^2}\right] = 0$$

since $\cos 2n\pi = +1$.   For $n = 0$,

$$a_0 = \frac{2}{T} \int_0^T e(t) \, dt = \int_0^2 \frac{E_0}{2} t \, dt = \frac{E_0 t^2}{4}\Big|_0^2 = E_0.$$

To determine the b_n we write

$$b_n = \frac{2}{T} \int_0^T e(t) \sin n\omega_0 t \, dt = \int_0^2 \left(\frac{E_0 t}{2}\right) \sin n\pi t \, dt$$

$$= \frac{E_0}{2} \left[-\frac{t \cos n\pi t}{n\pi} + \frac{\sin n\pi t}{n^2\pi^2}\right]\Big|_0^2$$

$$= \frac{E_0}{2} \left[-\frac{2 \cos 2n\pi}{n\pi}\right] = -\frac{E_0}{n\pi}.$$

Thus Eq. (9.17) yields

$$e(t) = \frac{E_0}{2} - \frac{E_0}{\pi} \sum_{n=1}^{\infty} \frac{1}{n} \sin n\pi t.$$

Example 9.3.   Find the Fourier series expansion of the full-wave-rectified sine wave illustrated in Fig. 9.7.

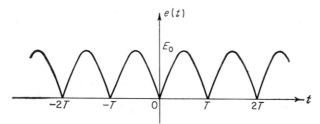

FIG. 9.7. Rectified sine wave (Example 9.3).

Solution.   Applying Eq. (9.18) yields

$$a_n = \frac{2}{T} \int_0^T \left(E_0 \sin \frac{\pi}{T} t\right) \cos \frac{2n\pi}{T} t \, dt$$

which may be written as

$$a_n = \frac{E_0}{T} \int_0^T \left[\sin \frac{\pi t(1 + 2n)}{T} + \sin \frac{\pi t(1 - 2n)}{T}\right] dt$$

by use of the trigonometric identity

$$\sin x \cos y = \tfrac{1}{2}[\sin (x + y) + \sin (x - y)]$$

with $x = \pi t/T$ and $y = 2n\pi t/T$. Evaluating the integral yields

$$a_n = \frac{E_0}{T}\left[-\frac{\cos\dfrac{\pi t(1 + 2n)}{T}}{\dfrac{\pi(1 + 2n)}{T}} - \frac{\cos\dfrac{\pi t(1 - 2n)}{T}}{\dfrac{\pi(1 - 2n)}{T}} \right]\Bigg|_0^T.$$

Since n assumes only integral values, there is no question of the denominators vanishing. Thus

$$a_n = E_0\left[-\frac{\cos\pi(1 + 2n)}{\pi(1 + 2n)} - \frac{\cos\pi(1 - 2n)}{\pi(1 - 2n)} + \frac{1}{\pi(1 + 2n)} + \frac{1}{\pi(1 - 2n)} \right].$$

Now

$$\cos\pi(1 + 2n) = -1 = \cos\pi(1 - 2n).$$

Thus

$$a_n = \frac{E_0}{\pi}\left[\frac{2}{1 + 2n} + \frac{2}{1 - 2n} \right] = \frac{4E_0}{\pi(1 - 4n^2)}, \qquad n = 0, 1, 2, \ldots.$$

To compute the b_n we refer to Eq. (9.19),

$$b_n = \frac{2}{T}\int_0^T \left(E_0\sin\frac{\pi}{T}t \right)\sin\frac{2n\pi}{T}t\,dt$$

$$= \frac{E_0}{T}\int_0^T \left[\cos\frac{\pi t(1 - 2n)}{T} - \cos\frac{\pi t(1 + 2n)}{T} \right]dt$$

by use of the appropriate trigonometric identity. Thus

$$b_n = E_0\left[\frac{\sin\dfrac{\pi t(1 - 2n)}{T}}{\pi(1 - 2n)} - \frac{\sin\dfrac{\pi t(1 + 2n)}{T}}{\pi(1 + 2n)} \right]\Bigg|_0^T = 0$$

and the Fourier series expansion of the rectified wave is

$$e(t) = \frac{2E_0}{\pi} + \frac{4E_0}{\pi}\sum_{n=1}^{\infty}\frac{\cos n\omega_0 t}{1 - 4n^2}, \qquad \omega_0 = \frac{2\pi}{T}.$$

9.2. Even and Odd Functions.

A function $f(x)$ which has the property that

$$f(x) = f(-x)$$

is called an *even* function. For example, $\cos x$, x^2, $\cosh x$, $\tan x^2$ are all even functions, since on replacing x by $-x$ we get the same function. A function $f(x)$ which has the property that

$$f(x) = -f(-x)$$

is called an *odd* function. For example, $\sin x$, x, x^3, $\sinh x$, $\tan x$ are all odd functions. Even and odd periodic functions merit detailed study since they occur frequently in problems in electric circuits. Their Fourier series also have a much simpler form than the general expressions Eqs. (9.17) to (9.19). Frequently, a function which is neither even nor odd can be made even or odd by shifting the axes. For example, if the t

axis of Fig. 9.6 is shifted up by the amount $E_0/2$, the function becomes an odd function. Even and odd functions are not as specialized as they might seem at first glance. In fact, we have the interesting result that any function $f(x)$ can be expressed as the sum of an even function and an odd function. For example, let

$$f(x) = \phi(x) + \psi(x)$$

where

$$\phi(x) = \frac{f(x) + f(-x)}{2}$$

and

$$\psi(x) = \frac{f(x) - f(-x)}{2}.$$

Then

$$\phi(-x) = \frac{f(-x) + f(x)}{2} = \phi(x)$$

and $\phi(x)$ is even, while

$$\psi(-x) = \frac{f(-x) - f(x)}{2} = -\psi(x)$$

and $\psi(x)$ is odd.

Suppose, now, that $e(t)$ is a periodic function of period T and is furthermore an even function. Let us find its Fourier series expansion. Certainly the formulas of Eqs. (9.17) to (9.19) hold; but since $e(t)$ is also *even*, certain simplifications can be achieved. First we note that

$$a_n = \frac{2}{T} \int_0^{T/2} e(t) \cos n\omega_0 t \, dt + \frac{2}{T} \int_{T/2}^{T} e(t) \cos n\omega_0 t \, dt. \tag{9.20}$$

In the second integral make the change of variable $x = T - t$. Then $\cos n\omega_0 t = \cos n\omega_0 (T - x) = \cos (2\pi n - n\omega_0 x) = \cos n\omega_0 x$ and

$$\frac{2}{T} \int_{T/2}^{T} e(t) \cos n\omega_0 t \, dt = -\frac{2}{T} \int_{T/2}^{0} e(T - x) \cos n\omega_0 x \, dx$$

$$= \frac{2}{T} \int_0^{T/2} e(-x) \cos n\omega_0 x \, dx = \frac{2}{T} \int_0^{T/2} e(x) \cos n\omega_0 x \, dx$$

since $e(T - x) = e(-x) = e(x)$. Thus Eq. (9.20) becomes

$$a_n = \frac{4}{T} \int_0^{T/2} e(t) \cos n\omega_0 t \, dt. \tag{9.21}$$

Thus if a function is *even*, we need only integrate over a *half* period and then double the result in order to compute the a_n. Now for an even function we may write b_n as

$$b_n = \frac{2}{T} \int_0^{T/2} e(t) \sin n\omega_0 t \, dt + \frac{2}{T} \int_{T/2}^{T} e(t) \sin n\omega_0 t \, dt$$

$$= \frac{2}{T} \int_0^{T/2} e(t) \sin n\omega_0 t \, dt + \frac{2}{T} \int_{T/2}^{0} e(x) \sin n\omega_0 x \, dx = 0$$

by again using the fact that $e(t)$ is even and making the substitution $x = T - t$. Thus, there are no sine components in an even periodic function. We therefore see that if $e(t)$ is periodic of period T and an even function, its Fourier series expansion is given by

$$e(t) = \tfrac{1}{2}a_0 + \sum_{n=1}^{\infty} a_n \cos n\omega_0 t$$

$$a_n = \frac{4}{T} \int_0^{T/2} e(t) \cos n\omega_0 t \, dt, \qquad n = 0, 1, 2, \ldots.$$

(9.22)

A similar argument establishes the fact that, if $e(t)$ is periodic of period T and an *odd* function, there are no cosine components and

$$e(t) = \sum_{n=1}^{\infty} b_n \sin n\omega_0 t$$

$$b_n = \frac{4}{T} \int_0^{T/2} e(t) \sin n\omega_0 t \, dt, \qquad n = 1, 2, \ldots.$$

(9.23)

We sometimes call $[0,T]$ the *full* Fourier interval and $[0,T/2]$ the *half* Fourier interval. Thus, if $e(t)$ is even or odd we need only integrate over a half Fourier interval in order to determine the coefficients.

With a knowledge of Eq. (9.22) we can see immediately that all the a_n coefficients of the Fourier series expansion for the square wave of Fig. 9.4 are zero, while from Eq. (9.23) we can see that all the b_n coefficients of the Fourier series expansion for the full-wave-rectified sine wave of Fig. 9.7 are zero.

Example 9.4. Determine the Fourier series expansion of the periodic function of Fig. 9.8.

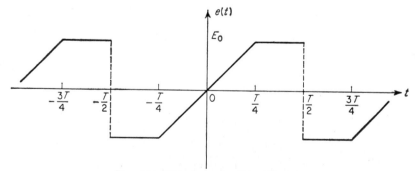

FIG. 9.8. Waveform for Example 9.4.

Solution. By inspection we see that this is an odd function. Thus

$$a_n = 0, \qquad n = 0, 1, 2, \ldots$$

and

$$b_n = \frac{4}{T} \int_0^{T/2} e(t) \, \sin \, n\omega_0 t \, dt$$

$$= \frac{4}{T} \int_0^{T/4} \left(\frac{4E_0}{T} t \right) \sin \, n\omega_0 t \, dt + \frac{4}{T} \int_{T/4}^{T/2} (E_0) \, \sin \, n\omega_0 t \, dt$$

$$= \frac{16E_0}{T^2} \left[-\frac{t \, \cos \, n\omega_0 t}{n\omega_0} + \frac{\sin \, n\omega_0 t}{n^2\omega_0^2} \right]\Big|_0^{T/4} + \frac{4E_0}{T} \left[-\frac{\cos \, n\omega_0 t}{n\omega_0} \right]\Big|_{T/4}^{T/2}$$

$$= \frac{16E_0}{T^2} \left[-\frac{\frac{T}{4} \cos \frac{n\pi}{2}}{n\omega_0} + \frac{\sin \frac{n\pi}{2}}{n^2\omega_0^2} \right] - \frac{4E_0}{T} \left[\frac{\cos \, n\pi}{n\omega_0} - \frac{\cos \frac{n\pi}{2}}{n\omega_0} \right]$$

$$= \frac{4E_0}{n^2\pi^2} \sin \frac{n\pi}{2} - \frac{2E_0}{n\pi} \cos \, n\pi.$$

Thus

$$b_n = -\frac{2E_0}{\pi n}, \qquad n \text{ even}$$

$$b_n = \frac{4E_0}{\pi^2 n^2} (-1)^{\frac{n-1}{2}} + \frac{2E_0}{\pi n}, \qquad n \text{ odd}$$

and

$$e(t) = \frac{4E_0}{\pi^2} \sum_{n=1,3,5,\ldots}^{\infty} \frac{(-1)^{(n-1)/2}}{n^2} \sin \, n\omega_0 t - \frac{2E_0}{\pi} \sum_{n=1}^{\infty} \frac{1}{n} (-1)^n \sin \, n\omega_0 t.$$

Note that, in general, if we write the Fourier series of Eq. (9.17) as

$$e(t) = \phi(t) + \psi(t)$$

where

$$\phi(t) = \tfrac{1}{2}a_0 + \sum_{n=1}^{\infty} a_n \cos \, n\omega_0 t$$

and

$$\psi(t) = \sum_{n=1}^{\infty} b_n \sin \, n\omega_0 t$$

then $\phi(t)$ is an even function and $\psi(t)$ is an odd function.

There are many special little formulas and side results that can be obtained by manipulating Fourier series. For some of these we refer the reader to texts which include a more extensive discussion of Fourier series.[†] One very useful result, however, that merits explicit mention is concerned with a change of interval. We have seen that

$$a_n = \frac{2}{T} \int_0^T e(t) \, \cos \, n\omega_0 t \, dt.$$

[†] See, for example, M. G. Salvadori and K. S. Miller, "The Mathematical Solution of Engineering Problems," Columbia University Press, New York, 1953, chap. 6, and K. S. Miller, "Partial Differential Equations in Engineering Problems," Prentice-Hall, Inc., Englewood Cliffs, N.J., 1953, chap. 2.

We assert that

$$a_n = \frac{2}{T} \int_\alpha^{\alpha+T} e(t) \cos n\omega_0 t \, dt \qquad (9.24)$$

where α is any real number. A similar formula holds for b_n. To prove Eq. (9.24) we write

$$c_n = \frac{2}{T} \int_\alpha^0 e(t) \cos n\omega_0 t \, dt + \frac{2}{T} \int_0^T e(t) \cos n\omega_0 t \, dt$$

$$+ \frac{2}{T} \int_T^{\alpha+T} e(t) \cos n\omega_0 t \, dt. \qquad (9.25)$$

Now if we let $x = T + t$ in the first integral on the right of Eq. (9.25) it becomes

$$\frac{2}{T} \int_\alpha^0 e(t) \cos n\omega_0 t \, dt = \frac{2}{T} \int_{T+\alpha}^T e(x - T) \cos n\omega_0 (x - T) \, dx$$

$$= - \frac{2}{T} \int_T^{T+\alpha} e(x) \cos n\omega_0 x \, dx$$

since $e(x - T) = e(x)$ by the periodicity of $e(t)$ and

$$\cos n\omega_0 (x - T) = \cos (n\omega_0 x - 2\pi n) = \cos n\omega_0 x.$$

Since the above integral is the negative of the third integral of Eq. (9.25),

$$c_n = \frac{2}{T} \int_0^T e(t) \cos n\omega_0 t \, dt = a_n$$

and we have established Eq. (9.24). Similarly,

$$b_n = \frac{2}{T} \int_\alpha^{\alpha+T} e(t) \sin n\omega_0 t \, dt.$$

9.3. Complex Fourier Series. Instead of using sines and cosines in determining the steady-state response, we sometimes find it convenient to use $\epsilon^{j\omega t}$ and then take real or imaginary parts to get the trigonometric functions. This follows from Euler's formula

$$\epsilon^{j\theta} = \cos \theta + j \sin \theta$$

developed in Chap. 3. The above formula also allows us to write sines and cosines in terms of complex exponentials, namely,

$$\cos \theta = \frac{\epsilon^{j\theta} + e^{-j\theta}}{2}$$

$$\sin \theta = \frac{\epsilon^{j\theta} - e^{-j\theta}}{2j}. \qquad (9.26)$$

Now if we wish to extend the use of complex exponentials to Fourier series, all we need to do is to replace the trigonometric functions of

Eqs. (9.17) to (9.19) by their complex exponential equivalents. What results is called the *complex Fourier series* and will be developed below. Besides the use already mentioned, the complex Fourier series is the starting point for developing the Fourier integral (see Sec. 9.5) which in turn is the starting point for the development of the Laplace transform (see Chap. 10).

Let us proceed with the development of the complex Fourier series. If we substitute Eqs. (9.26) into Eq. (9.17) there results

$$e(t) = \frac{1}{2} a_0 + \sum_{n=1}^{\infty} \left[a_n \left(\frac{\epsilon^{jn\omega_0 t} + \epsilon^{-jn\omega_0 t}}{2} \right) + b_n \left(\frac{\epsilon^{jn\omega_0 t} - \epsilon^{-jn\omega_0 t}}{2j} \right) \right]. \quad (9.27)$$

Collecting coefficients of positive and negative exponentials gives

$$e(t) = \tfrac{1}{2} a_0 + \tfrac{1}{2} \sum_{n=1}^{\infty} [(a_n - jb_n)\epsilon^{jn\omega_0 t} + (a_n + jb_n)\epsilon^{-jn\omega_0 t}]. \quad (9.28)$$

Now introduce the notation

$$c_n = a_n - jb_n.$$

Note that c_n is a complex number and its complex conjugate c_n^* is

$$c_n^* = a_n + jb_n.$$

In this notation Eq. (9.28) becomes

$$e(t) = \tfrac{1}{2} a_0 + \tfrac{1}{2} \sum_{n=1}^{\infty} c_n \epsilon^{jn\omega_0 t} + \tfrac{1}{2} \sum_{n=1}^{\infty} c_n^* \epsilon^{-jn\omega_0 t}. \quad (9.29)$$

To express the coefficients c_n in terms of complex exponentials we use Eqs. (9.18) and (9.19) to write

$$c_n = a_n - jb_n = \frac{2}{T} \int_0^T e(t) \cos n\omega_0 t \, dt - j \frac{2}{T} \int_0^T e(t) \sin n\omega_0 t \, dt$$

$$= \frac{2}{T} \int_0^T e(t) [\cos n\omega_0 t - j \sin n\omega_0 t] \, dt$$

$$= \frac{2}{T} \int_0^T e(t) \epsilon^{-jn\omega_0 t} \, dt. \quad (9.30)$$

Also

$$c_n^* = a_n + jb_n = \frac{2}{T} \int_0^T e(t) [\cos n\omega_0 t + j \sin n\omega_0 t] \, dt$$

$$= \frac{2}{T} \int_0^T e(t) \epsilon^{jn\omega_0 t} \, dt$$

$$= c_{-n}.$$

Equation (9.29) may now be written as

$$e(t) = \tfrac{1}{2}a_0 + \tfrac{1}{2}\sum_{n=1}^{\infty} c_n \epsilon^{jn\omega_0 t} + \tfrac{1}{2}\sum_{n=1}^{\infty} c_{-n}\epsilon^{-jn\omega_0 t}. \tag{9.31}$$

If we let $n = -m$ in the second sum of Eq. (9.31) it becomes

$$\tfrac{1}{2}\sum_{n=1}^{\infty} c_{-n}\epsilon^{-jn\omega_0 t} = \tfrac{1}{2}\sum_{m=-1}^{-\infty} c_m\epsilon^{jm\omega_0 t} = \tfrac{1}{2}\sum_{m=-\infty}^{-1} c_m\epsilon^{jm\omega_0 t}.$$

Since m is a dummy index of summation we may use the last result to write Eq. (9.31) as

$$e(t) = \tfrac{1}{2}a_0 + \tfrac{1}{2}\sum_{\substack{n=-\infty \\ n\neq 0}}^{\infty} c_n\epsilon^{jn\omega_0 t}. \tag{9.32}$$

But

$$a_0 = \frac{2}{T}\int_0^T e(t)\,dt$$

and extending Eq. (9.30) to include the case $n = 0$ gives

$$c_0 = \frac{2}{T}\int_0^T e(t)\epsilon^0\,dt = \frac{2}{T}\int_0^T e(t)\,dt = a_0.$$

Thus

$$\frac{a_0}{2} = \frac{c_0}{2} = \frac{c_0}{2}\,\epsilon^{j0\omega_0 t}$$

which allows us to write Eq. (9.32) as

$$e(t) = \tfrac{1}{2}\sum_{n=-\infty}^{\infty} c_n\epsilon^{jn\omega_0 t}.$$

Thus, in summary, if $e(t)$ is periodic of period T, it has the complex Fourier series expansion

$$e(t) = \tfrac{1}{2}\sum_{n=-\infty}^{\infty} c_n\epsilon^{jn\omega_0 t} \tag{9.33}$$

where

$$c_n = \frac{2}{T}\int_0^T e(t)\epsilon^{-jn\omega_0 t}\,dt, \qquad n = 0,\ \pm 1,\ \pm 2,\ \ldots. \tag{9.34}$$

The same argument that was used to establish Eq. (9.24) also proves that

$$c_n = \frac{2}{T}\int_\alpha^{\alpha+T} e(t)\epsilon^{-jn\omega_0 t}\,dt, \qquad n = 0,\ \pm 1,\ \pm 2,\ \ldots,$$

where α is any real number.

Of course Eqs. (9.33) and (9.34) are more compact than Eqs. (9.17) to (9.19). However, Eq. (9.34) makes no distinction between even and odd functions. That is, if $e(t)$ is even or odd we cannot deduce that half the c_n are zero. But, since $c_n = a_n - jb_n$ we can deduce that, if $e(t)$ is even, c_n is a real number, whereas if $e(t)$ is odd, c_n is a pure imaginary; and if $e(t)$ is neither even nor odd, c_n is a complex number. As in the case of the trigonometric function expansion, we can divide $e(t)$ into even and odd functions.

Example 9.5. Find the complex Fourier series expansion of the square wave of Fig. 9.4.

Solution. Since this is an odd function, the coefficients c_n will all be pure imaginary. We have from Eq. (9.34)

$$c_n = \frac{2}{T} \int_0^{T/2} (E_0) \epsilon^{-jn\omega_0 t}\, dt + \frac{2}{T} \int_{T/2}^{T} (-E_0)\epsilon^{-jn\omega_0 t} dt$$

$$= \frac{2E_0}{T} \left[\frac{\epsilon^{-jn\omega_0 t}}{-jn\omega_0} \right] \Big|_0^{T/2} - \frac{2E_0}{T} \left[\frac{\epsilon^{-jn\omega_0 t}}{-jn\omega_0} \right] \Big|_{T/2}^{T}, \qquad n \neq 0$$

$$= \frac{2E_0}{jn\omega_0 T} [1 - \epsilon^{-jn\omega_0 T/2}] + \frac{2E_0}{jn\omega_0 T} [\epsilon^{-jn\omega_0 T} - \epsilon^{-jn\omega_0 T/2}].$$

But $\epsilon^{-jn\omega_0 T} = \epsilon^{-jn2\pi} = \cos 2n\pi - j \sin 2n\pi = +1$ and $\epsilon^{-jn\omega_0 T/2} = \cos n\pi - j \sin n\pi = (-1)^n$. Thus

$$c_n = \frac{4E_0}{jn2\pi} [1 - (-1)^n], \qquad n \neq 0$$

$$= \frac{4E_0}{jn\pi}, \qquad n \text{ odd}$$

$$= 0, \qquad n \text{ even.}$$

It remains but to investigate the case $n = 0$. For this case Eq. (9.34) yields

$$c_0 = \frac{2}{T} \int_0^T e(t)\, dt = 0.$$

Hence Eq. (9.33) yields

$$e(t) = \frac{1}{2} \frac{4E_0}{j\pi} \sum_{\substack{n = -\infty \\ n \text{ odd}}}^{\infty} \frac{1}{n} \epsilon^{jn\omega_0 t}$$

$$= -j \frac{2E_0}{\pi} \sum_{\substack{n = -\infty \\ n \text{ odd}}}^{\infty} \frac{1}{n} \epsilon^{jn\omega_0 t}$$

as the complex Fourier series expansion of the square wave.

9.4. Numerical Analysis of Periodic Functions. In previous sections we have assumed that the periodic function we wished to analyze was given by a simple analytical expression or an unambiguous graph. Occasionally we meet problems in which the integrals cannot be evaluated in closed form. We then must resort to numerical methods. Again we may have an experimental record such as the output of an a-c machine

or the waveform on an oscilloscope.   This experimental data must then
be approximated analytically and standard techniques of Fourier series
applied, or else the wave must be analyzed by means of numerical procedures.   It is the purpose of the present section to mention some elementary types of numerical analysis applicable to such problems.

If $e(t)$ is a periodic function, then its Fourier series expansion is given
by

$$e(t) = \tfrac{1}{2}a_0 + \sum_{n=1}^{\infty} (a_n \cos n\omega_0 t + b_n \sin n\omega_0 t). \qquad (9.17)$$

As we have seen earlier, a good approximation to $e(t)$ may be obtained by
taking not an *infinite* number of terms but a large *finite* number of terms.
We write

$$e_N(t) = \tfrac{1}{2}a_0 + \sum_{n=1}^{N} (a_n \cos n\omega_0 t + b_n \sin n\omega_0 t). \qquad (9.35)$$

In general, the larger N, the better the approximation of $e_N(t)$ to $e(t)$.
Thus there are only a *finite* number of coefficients a_0, a_1, . . . , a_N, b_1,
. . . , b_N to be evaluated:

$$
\begin{aligned}
a_n &= \frac{2}{T} \int_0^T e(t) \cos n\omega_0 t \, dt, & n &= 0, 1, 2, \ldots, N \\
b_n &= \frac{2}{T} \int_0^T e(t) \sin n\omega_0 t \, dt, & n &= 1, 2, \ldots, N.
\end{aligned}
\qquad (9.36)
$$

If $e(t)$ is given by a complicated analytic form, these coefficients may be
approximated by methods of numerical integration exemplified by the
trapezoidal rule or Simpson's rule.†   We shall not consider this point
further.

Consider now the more interesting and practical situation where $e(t)$ is
obtained graphically or in tabular form from some experimental data.
In principle we may solve our problem as follows: Choose an integer N
which we feel is so large that harmonics of frequencies greater than $N\omega_0$
have a negligible effect on the waveform.   Now take any $2N + 1$ points
$t_k (k = 1, 2, \ldots, 2N + 1)$ in some period $[0,T]$.   From the graph we
can numerically evaluate $e(t_k)$.   Then

$$e(t_k) = \tfrac{1}{2}a_0 + \sum_{n=1}^{N} (a_n \cos n\omega_0 t_k + b_n \sin n\omega_0 t_k),$$

$$k = 1, 2, \ldots, 2N + 1 \quad (9.37)$$

becomes a system of $2N + 1$ *linear algebraic* equations on the $2N + 1$

† See, for example, K. S. Miller, "Engineering Mathematics," Rinehart & Company, Inc., New York, 1956, chap. 2.

unknowns a_0, a_1, . . . , a_N, b_1, . . . , b_N. The solution of these algebraic equations will yield the approximate values of the Fourier coefficients a_n and b_n.

As might be imagined, it is generally most convenient to take the points t_k evenly spaced. Furthermore, it is found after carrying through a few problems involving numerical evaluation of Fourier series that much of the work is repetitive. Because of this, several forms of worksheet have been developed to facilitate the mechanics of computation. The method of their use is mechanical, and the underlying mathematics is trivial. Typical schemes of varying degrees of complexity are explained in many textbooks.†

9.5. The Fourier Integral. The function illustrated in Fig. 9.9 is an even periodic function of period T. By the methods of Sec. 9.3 we easily

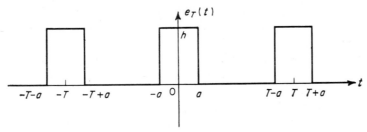

FIG. 9.9. Train of finite pulses.

determine that its complex Fourier series is

$$e_T(t) = \frac{2h}{T} \sum_{n=-\infty}^{\infty} \frac{\sin n\omega_0 a}{n\omega_0} e^{jn\omega_0 t}.$$

The set of Fourier coefficients,

$$c_n = \frac{4h}{T} \frac{\sin n\omega_0 a}{n\omega_0}, \qquad n = 0, \pm 1, \pm 2, \ldots , \qquad (9.38)$$

is called the *spectrum* of $e_T(t)$ and indicates the magnitude of the harmonics present in $e_T(t)$. Thus if we merely gave the coefficients of Eq. (9.38) with the understanding that we are dealing with a complex Fourier series, our function $e_T(t)$ would be completely determined. Since the coefficients in this example are real, we can actually plot them, as in Fig. 9.10, to give a pictorial representation of the spectrum. (In general, if c_n is complex we cannot give as simple a graphical picture of the spectrum.)

† See, for example, Salvadori and Miller, *op. cit.*, and K. S. Miller and J. B. Walsh, "Trigonometry," Harper & Brothers, New York, 1961, chap. 14.

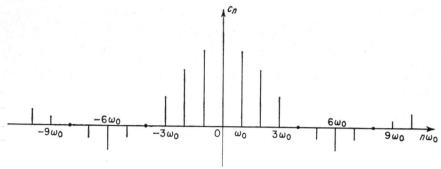

FIG. 9.10. Spectrum of wave of Fig. 9.9.

Now suppose that we hold h and a fixed and let T approach infinity. Physically, from an examination of Fig. 9.9, we see that the train of pulses becomes a single pulse, as illustrated in Fig. 9.11 (that is, a non-periodic function). Also from an examination of Fig. 9.10 we see that the lines of spectrum become closer and closer together since $\omega_0 = 2\pi/T$.

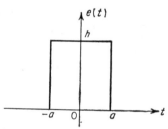

FIG. 9.11. Single pulse which results when T in Fig. 9.9 approaches infinity.

It is clear that the envelope of the discrete lines of Fig. 9.10 has the form of the continuous function $K(\sin \omega)/\omega$, where K is a constant. The question we would like to pose is: Does this envelope function have physical significance? Our answer is yes, and the results will be embodied in our derivation of the Fourier integral below.

The Fourier integral is a means of extending the frequency analysis so conveniently employed for periodic functions to the case of *nonperiodic* functions. Consider the nonperiodic function illustrated in Fig. 9.12. Clearly we cannot find its Fourier series since the function is not periodic. However, let us consider the following artifice. Define a

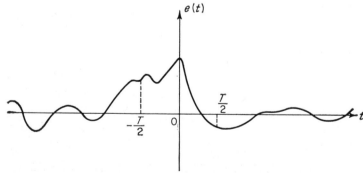

FIG. 9.12. Nonperiodic function.

function $e_T(t)$ by

$$e_T(t) = e(t), \qquad -T/2 \leqq t < T/2$$
$$e(t + T) = e_T(t).$$

Then $e_T(t)$ becomes a periodic function of period T which is identical with $e(t)$ in the interval $(-T/2, T/2)$. (See Fig. 9.13.) It appears plausible that, as T becomes very large, $e_T(t)$ will approach $e(t)$, that is, the non-periodic function of Fig. 9.12. We shall therefore find the Fourier *series*

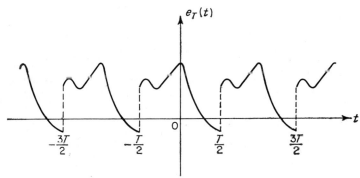

FIG. 9.13. Periodic function based on function of Fig, 9,12,

of $e_T(t)$ and let T approach infinity. The result will be the *Fourier integral* of $e(t)$. To do this in the most expedient manner, let us write Eqs. (9.33) and (9.34) in the form

$$e_T(t) = \frac{1}{T} \sum_{n=-\infty}^{\infty} E(j\omega_n)\epsilon^{j\omega_n t}$$

$$E(j\omega_n) = \int_{-T/2}^{T/2} e_T(t)\epsilon^{-j\omega_n t}\, dt, \qquad n = 0,\ \pm 1,\ \pm 2,\ \ldots\ , \tag{9.39}$$

where we have set

$$E(j\omega_n) = \frac{T}{2}\, c_n$$

and defined ω_n as

$$\omega_n = n\omega_0.$$

Since $e_T(t) = e(t)$ for t between $-T/2$ and $T/2$ we may write $E(j\omega_n)$ as

$$E(j\omega_n) = \int_{-T/2}^{T/2} e(t)\epsilon^{-j\omega_n t}\, dt. \tag{9.40}$$

If we let

$$\Delta\omega_n = \omega_n - \omega_{n-1} = n\omega_0 - (n-1)\omega_0 = \omega_0 = \frac{2\pi}{T}$$

then $e_T(t)$ of Eqs. (9.39) may be written

$$e_T(t) = \frac{1}{2\pi} \sum_{n=-\infty}^{\infty} E(j\omega_n)\epsilon^{j\omega_n t} \, \Delta\omega_n. \qquad (9.41)$$

Now as T approaches infinity, ω_0 approaches zero, and so ω_n tends to the continuous variable ω and

$$E(j\omega) = \lim_{T\to\infty} E(j\omega_n) = \lim_{T\to\infty} \int_{-T/2}^{T/2} e(t)\epsilon^{-j\omega_n t}\, dt = \int_{-\infty}^{\infty} e(t)\epsilon^{-j\omega t}\, dt$$

while the infinite sum of Eq. (9.41) approaches

$$\frac{1}{2\pi} \int_{-\infty}^{\infty} E(j\omega)e^{j\omega t}\, d\omega. \qquad (9.42)$$

To make this last limiting process appear more plausible, consider the definition of the infinite integral of Eq. (9.42). It is defined as

$$\frac{1}{2\pi} \lim_{A\to\infty} \int_{-A}^{A} E(j\omega)\epsilon^{j\omega t}\, d\omega$$

and $\int_{-A}^{A} E(j\omega)\epsilon^{j\omega t}\, d\omega$, in turn, is defined as the limit of the sum

$$\sum_{i=1}^{n} E(j\omega_i)\epsilon^{j\omega_i t}(\omega_{i+1} - \omega_i).$$

For a precise mathematical statement of the results, see Sec. 9.6.

Thus, in summary, if $e(t)$ is a nonperiodic function its "Fourier series" is given by

$$e(t) = \frac{1}{2\pi} \int_{-\infty}^{\infty} E(j\omega)\epsilon^{j\omega t}\, d\omega \qquad (9.43)$$

and its spectrum is given by

$$E(j\omega) = \int_{-\infty}^{\infty} e(t)\epsilon^{-j\omega t}\, dt. \qquad (9.44)$$

The function $E(j\omega)$ is called the *Fourier transform* of $e(t)$, and $e(t)$ is called the *inverse* Fourier transform of $E(j\omega)$. We sometimes write

$$E(j\omega) = \mathfrak{F}[e(t)] \qquad (9.45)$$

and

$$e(t) = \mathfrak{F}^{-1}[E(j\omega)].$$

The word *transform* is used since it transforms a function of *time*, $e(t)$, into a function of *frequency*, $E(j\omega)$. Note the symmetry of Eqs. (9.43) and (9.44), especially when written in the form

$$E(j\omega) = \int_{-\infty}^{\infty} e(t)\epsilon^{-j\omega t}\, dt$$

$$e(t) = \int_{-\infty}^{\infty} E(j\omega)\epsilon^{j\omega t}\, df \qquad (9.46)$$

where $\omega = 2\pi f$.

For example, the Fourier transform of the nonperiodic function of Fig. 9.11 is simply

$$E(j\omega) = \int_{-a}^{a} h\epsilon^{-j\omega t}\, dt = 2ha\, \frac{\sin \omega a}{\omega a}$$

and is plotted in Fig. 9.14. Thus $E(j\omega)$ is simply the envelope of Fig. 9.10.

Since we have a *continuous* spectrum, we cannot speak of the harmonic content at any particular frequency (since it is zero) as we could in the discrete case. However, we can speak of the harmonic content in a frequency *band*. The Fourier integral is an admirable tool for use in inves-

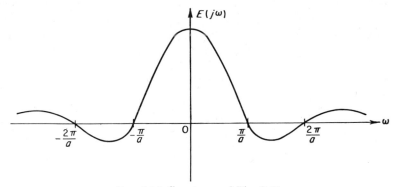

FIG. 9.14. Spectrum of Fig. 9.11.

tigating certain advanced problems in circuit theory, for example, the study of power spectra, correlation functions, and noise; the determination of the impulsive response of a network; the representation of the system function, etc. However, we cannot go into such topics in an elementary textbook.‡ Thus we shall leave the Fourier transform at this point but return to it in the next chapter to use it as a starting point in the development of the Laplace transform.

9.6. Mathematical Conditions on Fourier Expansions. The alert reader may have wondered whether *every* periodic function has a Fourier series expansion and what happens to the Fourier series at points of discontinuity. In the theory of Fourier analysis there are literally hundreds of theorems giving precise conditions under which a Fourier series or integral converges. We shall state two such theorems, one for Fourier series and one for Fourier integrals, which yield sufficient conditions under which the series or integral converges. ‡

† See, for example, K. S. Miller, "Engineering Mathematics," Rinehart & Company, Inc., New York, 1956.

‡ Proofs of these theorems in the form stated may be found in Miller, *op. cit.*, Appendix 3.

Theorem 1.   Let $e(t)$ be a periodic function of period T which is integrable in the interval $(0,T)$.   Then at every point $t = \xi$, where $e(t)$ has a right- and left-hand derivative, the Fourier series

$$\tfrac{1}{2} \sum_{n=-\infty}^{\infty} c_n \epsilon^{jn\omega_0\xi}$$

converges to

$$\tfrac{1}{2}[e(\xi+) + e(\xi-)]$$

where

$$c_n = \frac{2}{T} \int_0^T e(t)\epsilon^{-jn\omega_0 t}\, dt.$$

Theorem 2.   Let $e(t)$ be integrable in every finite subinterval of $(-\infty,\infty)$ and let $\int_{-\infty}^{\infty} |e(t)|\, dt$ exist.   Then

$$E(j\omega) = \int_{-\infty}^{\infty} e(t)\epsilon^{-j\omega t}\, dt$$

exists and at every point, $t = \xi$, where $e(t)$ has a right- and left-hand derivative,

$$\tfrac{1}{2}[e(\xi+) + e(\xi-)] = \frac{1}{2\pi} \int_{-\infty}^{\infty} E(j\omega)\epsilon^{j\omega\xi}\, d\omega.$$

It remains but to explain the term "right- and left-hand derivative" and $e(\xi+)$, $e(\xi-)$.   By $e(\xi+)$ we mean

$$e(\xi+) = \lim_{\substack{t\to\xi \\ t>\xi}} e(t)$$

and by $e(\xi-)$ we mean

$$e(\xi-) = \lim_{\substack{t\to\xi \\ t<\xi}} e(t).$$

For example, in Fig. 9.15, $e(\xi+) = 4$ and $e(\xi-) = 2$.   If t happens to be a point of continuity (such as ξ') then $e(\xi'+) = e(\xi'-) = e(\xi')$.   Thus $e(t+)$ and $e(t-)$ may exist without $e(t)$ being continuous.   The

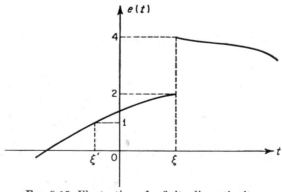

FIG. 9.15. Illustration of a finite discontinuity.

right-hand derivative at the point $t = \xi$ is defined as

$$\lim_{\substack{h \to 0 \\ h>0}} \frac{e(\xi + h) - e(\xi+)}{h}$$

and the left-hand derivative as

$$\lim_{\substack{h \to 0 \\ h<0}} \frac{e(\xi + h) - e(\xi-)}{h}.$$

Note that the right- and left-hand derivatives may exist even if the function is not continuous.

Now if we look at the various functions we have considered in the examples of this chapter (see Figs. 9.2, 9.3, 9.4, 9.6, 9.7, 9.8, 9.9, 9.11, 9.12, 9.13) we see that *all* of them have right- and left-hand derivatives at every point. Thus, for example, the square wave of Fig. 9.4 converges to zero at $t = \pm nT/2$, $n = 0, 1, 2, \ldots$; the saw-tooth wave of Fig. 9.6 converges to $E_0/2$ at $t = 0, \pm 2, \pm 4, \ldots$; while the full-wave-rectified sine wave of Fig. 9.7 converges to $|\sin \pi t/T|$ at every t (since this function is continuous for all t). We can therefore say without fear of contradiction that *any* periodic function the reader is likely to encounter in circuit analysis *has* a Fourier series expansion. We would like to make one final comment. A periodic function does *not* have a Fourier *transform* since the condition $\int_{-\infty}^{\infty} |e(t)| \, dt < \infty$ will not be met.

EXERCISES

9.1. Determine the constants a_0, a_1, a_2, b_1, b_2, c_2 so that the functions of $f_0(x)$, $f_1(x)$, $f_2(x)$ become orthonormal in the interval $[0,1]$.

$$f_0(x) = a_0$$
$$f_1(x) = a_1 + b_1 x$$
$$f_2(x) = a_2 + b_2 x + c_2 x^2.$$

9.2. The *Legendre polynomials* $P_n(x)$, $n = 0, 1, 2, \ldots$, satisfy the differential equation

$$\frac{d}{dx}\left[(1 - x^2) \frac{d}{dx} P_n(x) \right] + n(n + 1)P_n(x) = 0, \qquad n = 0, 1, 2, \ldots.$$

Prove that they are orthogonal in the interval $[-1,1]$.

9.3. The following functions are periodic of indicated period T and are defined in an interval of length T as follows:

(a) $f(x) = x, \quad 0 \le x < 1$
$f(x) = 1, \quad 1 \le x < 2 \qquad T = 2.$
(b) $f(x) = |\cos x|, \quad 0 \le x < \pi \qquad T = \pi.$
(c) $f(x) = x^3, \quad -1 \le x < 1 \qquad T = 2.$
(d) $f(x) = 16 - x^2, \quad -4 \le x < 4 \qquad T = 8.$
(e) $f(x) = e^x, \quad 1 \le x < 7 \qquad T = 6.$

Expand these functions in Fourier series.

9.4. Expand the functions indicated in Fig. 9.16 into Fourier series.

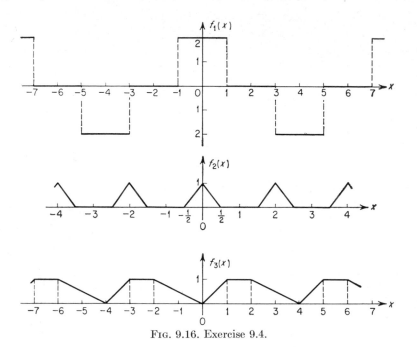

FIG. 9.16. Exercise 9.4.

9.5. The following functions are defined in a *half* Fourier interval. Define them in the *full* Fourier interval so that they become even functions and obtain their Fourier series expansions in terms of cosines alone.

(a) $f(x) = x,$ $0 < x < \pi.$
(b) $f(x) = x,$ $0 \leqq x < 1.$
     $f(x) = 1,$ $1 \leqq x < 2.$
(c) $f(x) = e^x,$ $0 < x < 2.$
(d) $f(x) = x^2,$ $0 < x < 3.$
(e) $f(x) = \sin x,$ $0 < x < \pi/2.$

9.6. Repeat Exercise 9.5, but extend the functions in the full Fourier interval so that they become odd functions and obtain their Fourier series expansions in terms of sines alone.
9.7. Assuming that we are free to choose either even or odd prolongations, which extension is to be preferred in each of the examples of the above two exercises?
9.8. Expand the functions of Exercises 9.5 and 9.6 into complex Fourier series.
9.9. If $f(x)$ is periodic of period T its Fourier series expansion is

$$f(x) = \tfrac{1}{2}a_0 + \sum_{n=1}^{\infty} \left(a_n \cos \frac{2n\pi}{T} x + b_n \sin \frac{2n\pi}{T} x \right)$$

where

$$a_n = \frac{2}{T} \int_{-T/2}^{T/2} f(x) \cos \frac{2n\pi}{T} x \, dx, \qquad b_n = \frac{2}{T} \int_{-T/2}^{T/2} f(x) \sin \frac{2n\pi}{T} x \, dx.$$

Show that $f(x)$ may also be written as

$$f(x) = \tfrac{1}{2}a_0 + \sum_{n=1}^{\infty} c_n \cos \left(\frac{2n\pi}{T} x + \phi_n \right)$$

where

$$c_n = \sqrt{a_n^2 + b_n^2}, \qquad \phi_n = \arctan \frac{-b_n}{a_n}.$$

This is called the *phase-angle form* of the Fourier series.

If $f(x)$ is periodic of period 2 and

$$
\begin{aligned}
f(x) &= 0, & 0 \leq x < 1 \\
f(x) &= -1 + x, & 1 \leq x < 2
\end{aligned}
$$

obtain its phase-angle-form Fourier series.

9.10. If the Fourier transform of $x(t)$ is $X(j\omega)$ show that $X(j\omega)\epsilon^{-j\omega\tau}$ is the Fourier transform of $x(t - \tau)$.

9.11. Assuming $\mathfrak{F}x'(t)$ exists and $\lim\limits_{t \to \pm\infty} x(t) = 0$, show that

$$\mathfrak{F}x'(t) = j\omega\mathfrak{F}x(t).$$

9.12. Find the Fourier transform of

(a) $f(t) = \begin{cases} \epsilon^{-\alpha t}, & t > 0 \\ 0, & t < 0 \end{cases} \quad \alpha > 0.$

(b) $\epsilon^{-\alpha|t|}, \qquad \alpha > 0.$

9.13. Find the function $x(t)$ whose Fourier transform is

$$X(j\omega) = \frac{\sin \omega}{\omega}$$

and show that at the points t where $x(t)$ is discontinuous, $\mathfrak{F}^{-1}X(j\omega)$ yields the average value of $x(t+)$ and $x(t-)$.

9.14. Starting with the function

$$
\begin{aligned}
x(t) &= 1 - |t|, & |t| < 1 \\
x(t) &= 0, & |t| > 1
\end{aligned}
$$

find its Fourier transform and then, using Theorem 2, prove that

$$\int_{-\infty}^{\infty} \left(\frac{\sin x}{x} \right)^2 dx = \pi.$$

9.15. Several waveforms are illustrated in Fig. 9.17. Write out the form of the Fourier series for each waveform. Do not evaluate the coefficients, but indicate, based on considerations of symmetry, which ones will be zero.

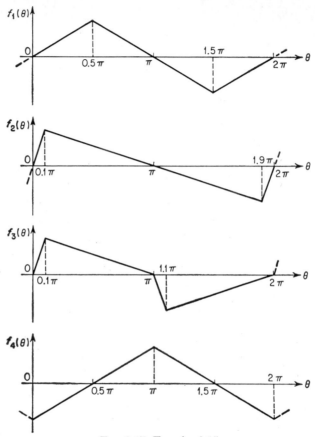

FIG. 9.17. Exercise 9.15.

9.16. The circuit shown in Fig. 9.18 is a full-wave rectifier. The diodes may be idealized as devices which present infinite resistance to the flow of current in one direction and zero resistance to the flow of current in the other direction. (The direction of easy current flow is indicated by the arrow.) Figure 9.18 also shows the current waveforms in each diode and the total current. Expand each of these currents in a Fourier series, and show that the series representing the total current is the sum of the series representing the individual currents.

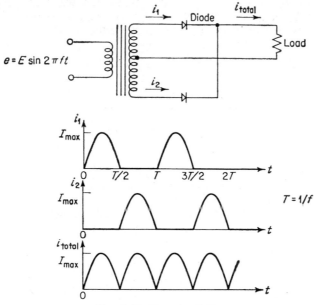

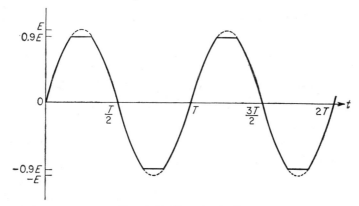

FIG. 9.18. Exercise 9.16.

9.17. One form of distortion which occurs in circuits employing electron devices is symmetrical clipping, whereby a sinusoidal signal is transformed to that shown in Fig. 9.19. Assume that the clipping occurs at 90 per cent of the peak value of the wave. Determine the Fourier expansion for the resultant waveform.

FIG. 9.19. Exercise 9.17.

Calculate directly, by integration, the average power developed by this wave in a 1-ohm resistor. Determine the power in a 1-ohm resistor of each of the Fourier components. How many components are necessary to account for 95 per cent of the power? Ninety-nine per cent?

9.18. One method of analyzing distortion in electronic circuits is to assume that the distorted waveform contains only a limited number of significant harmonics. Assume that a current waveform may be represented by

$$i = I_0 + I_1 \cos \omega t + I_2 \cos 2\omega t + I_3 \cos 3\omega t + I_4 \cos 4\omega t.$$

(*a*) Show that the coefficients are given by

$$I_0 = \tfrac{1}{6}(I_{\max} + 2I_{1/2} + 2I_{-1/2} + I_{\min})$$
$$I_1 = \tfrac{1}{3}(I_{\max} + I_{1/2} + I_{-1/2} - I_{\min})$$
$$I_2 = \tfrac{1}{4}(I_{\max} + I_{\min})$$
$$I_3 = \tfrac{1}{6}(I_{\max} - 2I_{1/2} + 2I_{-1/2} - I_{\min})$$
$$I_4 = \tfrac{1}{12}(I_{\max} - 4I_{1/2} - 4I_{-1/2} + I_{\min})$$

where $I_{\max}$ is the value of the current at $\omega t = 0$, $I_{1/2}$ at $\omega t = \pi/3$, $I_{-1/2}$ at $\omega t = 2\pi/3$, and $I_{\min}$ at $\omega t = \pi$. (See Fig. 9.20.)

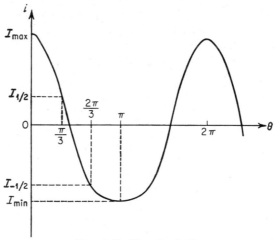

FIG. 9.20. Exercise 9.18.

(*b*) Determine the value of the coefficients in terms of $I_{\max}$ and $I_{\min}$ if the wave may be represented by

$$i = I_0 + I_1 \cos \omega t + I_2 \cos 2\omega t.$$

9.19. In the circuit shown in Fig. 9.21, $e = 10 \sin 50t + 5 \sin (100t - 30°)$. Find the instantaneous current and the voltage drops across R, L, and C. Draw the phasor diagram for each frequency.

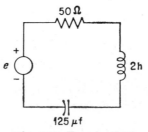

FIG. 9.21. Exercise 9.19.

CHAPTER 10

THE LAPLACE TRANSFORM AND TRANSIENT ANALYSIS

We originally obtained the equations characterizing networks as *differential equations*. In Chap. 3 we introduced the notion of *impedance function* and showed that if derivatives of i were replaced by si and integrals of i by i/s, the steady-state solution of the equilibrium equations could be reduced to *algebraic equations*. Later, in Chap. 4, complex numbers were introduced and the determination of steady-state currents and voltages in networks having sinusoidal forcing functions was reduced to the study of *complex numbers*. In Chap. 9 we extended these techniques to take care of periodic forcing functions by introducing the method of *Fourier series*, and finally we extended Fourier analysis to nonperiodic functions by introducing the *Fourier transform*.

In this chapter we briefly introduce the reader to the *Laplace transform*. This can be considered as a generalization or unification of all the above methods and techniques. In particular, we justify the replacing of derivatives of i by si and integrals by i/s in network equations (see the end of Sec. 3.2). Although the Laplace-transform method requires a further knowledge of mathematics, it provides a more penetrating insight into the significance of the relations among forcing functions, natural response, and forced response.

10.1. The Laplace Transform. The Fourier transform, introduced in Sec. 9.5 [see Eqs. (9.46)] is an admirable tool for many investigations.

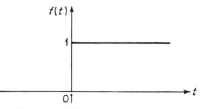

FIG. 10.1. The unit step function.

However, it does have some drawbacks. Suppose, for example, that $e(t)$ is defined as

$$e(t) = 1, \qquad t > 0$$
$$e(t) = 0, \qquad t < 0 \tag{10.1}$$

(see Fig. 10.1). That is, $e(t)$ is the *unit step* function $u(t)$. Then by Eq. (9.44) its Fourier transform is

$$E(j\omega) = \int_{-\infty}^{\infty} e(t)\epsilon^{-j\omega t}\, dt = \int_{0}^{\infty} 1\epsilon^{-j\omega t}\, dt = \frac{\epsilon^{-j\omega t}}{-j\omega}\bigg|_{0}^{\infty}.$$

But $\epsilon^{-j\omega t} = \cos \omega t - j \sin \omega t$ and as t approaches infinity, $\epsilon^{-j\omega t}$ oscillates indefinitely. Thus $E(j\omega)$ does not exist. We are therefore left with the embarrassing fact that even so simple a function as the unit step function $u(t)$ does not have a Fourier transform. Similarly, neither such a simple function as the sine nor the cosine has a Fourier transform. It appears, therefore, that some generalization of the Fourier transform is in order.

Toward this end, consider the function

$$\begin{aligned} x(t,\sigma) &= \epsilon^{-\sigma t}, & t &> 0 \\ &= 0, & t &< 0 \end{aligned}$$

where σ is a positive real number. Its Fourier transform is

$$X(j\omega,\sigma) = \int_{-\infty}^{\infty} x(t,\sigma)\epsilon^{-j\omega t}\, dt = \int_{0}^{\infty} \epsilon^{-\sigma t}\,\epsilon^{-j\omega t}\, dt$$

$$= \int_{0}^{\infty} \epsilon^{-(\sigma+j\omega)t}\, dt = \frac{\epsilon^{-(\sigma+j\omega)t}}{-(\sigma + j\omega)}\Big|_{0}^{\infty} = \frac{1}{\sigma + j\omega}. \qquad (10.2)$$

Hence the Fourier transform of $X(t,\sigma)$ exists (remember, $\sigma > 0$). Since

$$\lim_{\sigma \to 0} \epsilon^{-\sigma t} = 1$$

we see that

$$\lim_{\sigma \to 0} x(t,\sigma) = u(t),$$

the unit step function. Thus one might be tempted to write

$$U(j\omega) = X(j\omega,0) = \lim_{\sigma \to 0} X(j\omega,\sigma) = \lim_{\sigma \to 0} \frac{1}{\sigma + j\omega} = \frac{1}{j\omega} \qquad (10.3)$$

where $U(j\omega)$ is the transform of the unit step function. The only difficulty with the above manipulations is that the operation of interchanging the integral and limit, viz.,

$$\lim_{\sigma \to 0} \int_{0}^{\infty} x(t,\sigma)\epsilon^{-j\omega t}\, dt = \int_{0}^{\infty} \lim_{\sigma \to 0} x(t,\sigma)\epsilon^{-j\omega t}\, dt, \qquad (10.4)$$

is not valid.

Let us see, though, in the light of the above example what can be salvaged from this argument. We note that if in the formula

$$E(j\omega) = \int_{-\infty}^{\infty} e(t)\epsilon^{-j\omega t}\, dt$$

the exponent $j\omega$ were replaced by a complex number $\sigma + j\omega$, where $\sigma > 0$, we could write

$$E(j\omega,\sigma) = \int_{-\infty}^{\infty} e(t)\epsilon^{-(\sigma+j\omega)t}\, dt \qquad (10.5)$$

or

$$E(j\omega,\sigma) = \int_{-\infty}^{\infty} [e(t)\epsilon^{-\sigma t}]\epsilon^{-j\omega t}\, dt. \qquad (10.5a)$$

Now it may be that, by introducing the *convergence factor* $\epsilon^{-\sigma t}$, the function $e(t)\epsilon^{-\sigma t}$ *does* have a Fourier transform. If this is the case, it seems plausible that perhaps the concept of Fourier transform could be generalized so as to obtain a transform which includes a larger class of functions. We shall exploit this viewpoint.

Let $e(t)$ be a function defined for all nonnegative t and zero for negative t. The significance of assuming $e(t) = 0$ for $t < 0$ will be discussed below. Now it may be that $e(t)$ does not have a Fourier transform. However, it may be possible to find a positive number σ such that $e(t)\epsilon^{-\sigma t}$ *does* meet the conditions of Theorem 2 of Sec. 9.6. Thus $e(t)\epsilon^{-\sigma t}$ *will* have a Fourier transform. Let us designate this by

$$E(j\omega,\sigma) = \int_0^\infty e(t)\epsilon^{-\sigma t}\,\epsilon^{-j\omega t}\,dt$$
$$= \int_0^\omega e(t)\epsilon^{-(\sigma+j\omega)t}\,dt. \tag{10.6}$$

The inverse transform is given by the second of Eqs. (9.46) as

$$e(t)\epsilon^{-\sigma t} = \frac{1}{2\pi}\int_{-\infty}^\infty E(j\omega,\sigma)\epsilon^{j\omega t}\,d\omega.$$

Multiplying both sides of the above equation by $\epsilon^{\sigma t}$ yields

$$e(t) = \frac{1}{2\pi}\int_{-\infty}^{''} E(j\omega,\sigma)\epsilon^{(\sigma+j\omega)t}\,d\omega. \tag{10.7}$$

(Since $\epsilon^{\sigma t}$ does not depend on ω it may be taken under the integral sign.) Now the only way that σ appears in the integrals of Eqs. (10.6) and (10.2) is in the form $\sigma + j\omega$. Let us therefore make the change of variable

$$s = \sigma + j\omega \tag{10.8}$$

where s, of course, is a complex number. Since $E(j\omega,\sigma)$ depends only on $\sigma + j\omega$, let us define $E(j\omega,\sigma)$ as $E(\sigma + j\omega)$ or $E(s)$. Equation (10.6) then becomes

$$E(s) = \int_0^\infty e(t)\epsilon^{-st}\,dt, \tag{10.9}$$

and Eq. (10.7) becomes

$$e(t) = \frac{1}{2\pi j}\int_{\sigma-j\infty}^{\sigma+j\infty} E(s)\epsilon^{st}\,ds \tag{10.10}$$

since $j\,d\omega = ds$.

Equation (10.9) represents the *Laplace transform* of $e(t)$ and is also written as

$$E(s) = \mathcal{L}[e(t)]. \tag{10.11}$$

Equation (10.10) is called the *inverse Laplace transform* of $e(t)$ and is also written as

$$e(t) = \mathcal{L}^{-1}[E(s)]. \tag{10.12}$$

We shall have very little occasion to use Eq. (10.10) in this chapter.

Let us now find the Laplace transform of the unit step function $u(t)$. It is

$$U(s) = \int_0^\infty 1\epsilon^{-st}\, dt = -\left.\frac{\epsilon^{-st}}{s}\right|_0^\infty = \frac{1}{s} \tag{10.13}$$

provided that Re $[s] = \sigma > 0$.

As another simple example, the Laplace transform of $\cos \alpha t$ is

$$\mathcal{L}[\cos \alpha t] = \int_0^\infty \cos \alpha t\, \epsilon^{-st}\, dt = \left.\frac{\epsilon^{-st}}{\alpha^2 + s^2}[-s \cos \alpha t + \alpha \sin \alpha t]\right|_0^\infty$$

$$= 0 - \frac{1}{\alpha^2 + s^2}(-s) = \frac{s}{s^2 + \alpha^2} \tag{10.14}$$

provided that Re $[s] > 0$.

Similarly we can find transforms of other elementary functions. We leave it to the reader to verify that

$$\mathcal{L}[t] = \frac{1}{s^2} \qquad\qquad \sigma_0 = 0 \tag{10.15}$$

$$\mathcal{L}[t^n] = \frac{n!}{s^{n+1}} \qquad\qquad \sigma_0 = 0 \tag{10.16}$$

$$\mathcal{L}[\epsilon^{-\alpha t}] = \frac{1}{s + \alpha} \qquad\qquad \sigma_0 = -\alpha \tag{10.17}$$

$$\mathcal{L}[\sin \alpha t] = \frac{\alpha}{s^2 + \alpha^2} \qquad\qquad \sigma_0 = 0. \tag{10.18}$$

(See below for the significance of σ_0.)

Before proceeding with more general properties of the Laplace transform, there are two points worthy of elaboration. The first relates to the value of $e(t)$ for $t < 0$. By the way in which the Laplace transform was defined [Eq. (10.6)] it is influenced only by values of $e(t)$ for $t > 0$. Thus, the Laplace transform herein used is more properly designated the *one-sided* Laplace transform. A two-sided Laplace transform may also be defined, but we shall not do so. Two functions having the same values for $t > 0$ and different values for $t < 0$ have the same Laplace transform. Formally, the inverse Laplace transform yields the value zero for $t < 0$; but this is not generally meaningful, for the Laplace transform only encompasses values of t greater than zero. In practical cases this is not too great a restriction, for if we wish to consider functions occurring before $t = 0$ we can make the change of variable $\tau = t - t_0$ in formulating the Laplace transform and thus encompass negative values of t. In such instances, for example, $\mathcal{L}^{-1}[a/(s^2 + a^2)] = \sin a(t - t_0)$ is meaningful for $t > t_0$.

The other point to be discussed is the convergence factor $\epsilon^{-\sigma t}$. It plays an important, though not a forward, role. When we write the Laplace transform $\int_0^\infty x(t)\epsilon^{-st}\, dt$ of a function $x(t)$, it will always be assumed that

Re $[s] = \sigma$ is such that $x(t)\epsilon^{-\sigma t}$ is absolutely integrable, that is, $x(t)\epsilon^{-\sigma t}$ has a Fourier transform. Note that σ can be negative. For example, if $x(t) = \epsilon^{-3t}$, one could take any number greater than -3 as the value of σ. Also, note that not every function has a Laplace transform. For example, ϵ^{t^2} does not have a Laplace transform since there exists no number σ such that $\int_0^\infty \epsilon^{t^2}\epsilon^{-\sigma t}\, dt$ exists. If $x(t)\epsilon^{-\sigma t}$ has a Fourier transform for some value of σ, then there exists a number σ_0 with the property that $x(t)\epsilon^{-\sigma t}$ is Fourier-transformable if $\sigma > \sigma_0$ and is not Fourier-transformable if $\sigma < \sigma_0$. If $\sigma = \sigma_0$, $x(t)\epsilon^{-\sigma_0 t}$ may or may not be Fourier-transformable. The number σ_0 is called the *abscissa of convergence* of $x(t)$. It can be shown that it always exists and is unique. In Eqs. (10.15) to (10.18) we have indicated the abscissa of convergence.

10.2. The Laplace Transform of Derivatives and Integrals. In the previous section we defined the Laplace transform and computed the transforms of some elementary functions. We shall now discuss some general properties of the transform. First, we note that $\mathcal{L}$ is a *linear operator*, that is,

$$\mathcal{L}[ax(t) + by(t)] = a\mathcal{L}[x(t)] + b\mathcal{L}[y(t)], \qquad (10.19)$$

as can be verified by a direct application of Eq. (10.9).

Two of the most important properties of the Laplace transform are

$$\mathcal{L}[x'(t)] = s\mathcal{L}[x(t)] - x(0), \qquad (10.20)$$

where $x'(t)$ signifies differentiation with respect to time, and

$$\mathcal{L}\left[\int_a^t x(t)\, dt\right] = \frac{1}{s}\mathcal{L}[x(t)] - \frac{1}{s}\int_0^a x(t)\, dt. \qquad (10.21)$$

To prove Eq. (10.20) let $x(t)$ be a function which has a Laplace transform and let the derivative of $x(t)$ exist and have a Laplace transform. Then by definition

$$\mathcal{L}[x'(t)] = \int_0^\infty x'(t)\epsilon^{-st}\, dt = \int_0^\infty \epsilon^{-st}\, dx(t)$$

$$= x(t)\epsilon^{-st}\Big|_0^\infty + s\int_0^\infty x(t)\epsilon^{-st}\, dt$$

where we have integrated by parts. Now, $\lim_{t\to\infty} x(t)\epsilon^{-st} = 0$ since we are assuming that Re $[s]$ is greater than the abscissa of convergence of $x(t)$; and $\lim_{t\to 0} x(t)\epsilon^{-st} = x(0).$† Thus

$$\mathcal{L}[x'(t)] = -x(0) + sX(s) \qquad (10.20a)$$

where $X(s)$ is the Laplace transform of $x(t)$.

† Since t is always greater than or equal to zero we should write $x(0+)$ (see footnote on page 71) rather than $x(0)$. However, if $x(t)$ has no discontinuity at $t = 0$ or if $x(t)$ is considered zero for $t < 0$ (rather than for $t \leq 0$) it is immaterial which we use (see Sec. 10.7)

One can easily generalize this formula to the transform of higher derivatives. Let

$$x'(t) = y(t).$$

Then by repeated applications of Eq. (10.20a),

$$\mathcal{L}[x''(t)] = \mathcal{L}[y'(t)] = s\mathcal{L}[y(t)] - y(0)$$
$$= s\mathcal{L}[x'(t)] - x'(0)$$
$$= s\{s\mathcal{L}[x(t)] - x(0)\} - x'(0)$$
$$\mathcal{L}[x''(t)] = s^2 X(s) - sx(0) - x'(0). \qquad (10.20b)$$

In general,

$$\mathcal{L}[x^{(n)}(t)] = s^n X(s) - s^{n-1}x(0) - s^{n-2}x'(0) - \cdots$$
$$- sx^{(n-2)}(0) - x^{(n-1)}(0) \qquad (10.20c)$$

where $X(s) = \mathcal{L}[x(t)]$. Of course we have tacitly assumed that the higher derivatives exist and are Laplace-transformable.

To prove Eq. (10.21), where $a \geqq 0$, we write, again by definition of the Laplace transform, that

$$\mathcal{L}\left[\int_a^t x(t)\, dt\right] = \int_0^\infty \left[\int_a^t x(\xi)\, d\xi\right] \epsilon^{-st}\, dt$$

$$= \int_0^\infty \left[\int_a^t x(\xi)\, d\xi\right] d\left(-\frac{1}{s}\,\epsilon^{-st}\right)$$

$$= -\frac{1}{s}\,\epsilon^{-st} \int_a^t x(\xi)\, d\xi \Big|_0^\infty + \frac{1}{s}\int_0^\infty x(t)\epsilon^{-st}\, dt$$

where we have integrated by parts.   Thus

$$\mathcal{L}\left[\int_a^t x(t)\, dt\right] = \frac{1}{s}\int_a^0 x(\xi)\, d\xi + \frac{1}{s}\,X(s) \qquad (10.21a)$$

where $X(s)$ is the Laplace transform of $x(t)$.

Even with the few formulas we have derived so far we can solve some important practical problems.

Example 10.1. Consider the circuit examined in Sec. 3.1 (see Fig. 10.2). The equilibrium equation is [Eq. (3.1)]

$$L\frac{di}{dt} + Ri = E, \qquad t > 0\dagger \qquad (a)$$

and the initial current is i_0,

$$i(0) = i_0.$$

Determine the response $i(t)$ by the Laplace-transform method.

---

† If the condition $t > 0$ were replaced by $t > t_0$, and $t_0 < 0$, we could reduce it to our form by making the change of variable $\tau = t - t_0$.   Then Eq. (a) would become

$$L\frac{di}{d\tau} + Ri = E, \qquad \tau > 0.$$

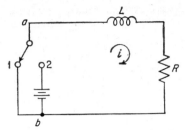

FIG. 10.2. Circuit for Example 10.1.

Solution. To determine the response we shall first transform both sides of the equilibrium equation. If we let $I(s)$ be the Laplace transform of $i(t)$, then by Eq. (10.20*a*),

$$\mathcal{L}\left[\frac{di}{dt}\right] = sI(s) - i(0)$$
$$= sI(s) - i_0.$$

Taking the Laplace transform of both sides of Eq. (*a*) results in

$$L[sI(s) \quad i_0] + RI(s) - \frac{E}{s}$$

since $\mathcal{L}[E] = E/s$ by Eq. (10.13). The above equation is an *algebraic equation* on $I(s)$ which can be easily solved to yield

$$I(s) = \frac{E + Lsi_0}{s(Ls + R)} = \frac{E}{s(Ls + R)} + \frac{Li_0}{Ls + R}.$$

Thus $i(t)$ is nothing more than the inverse transform of the above equation. To compute $\mathcal{L}^{-1}[I(s)]$ we first write $1/s(Ls + R)$ as

$$\frac{1}{s(Ls + R)} = \frac{1}{R}\left(\frac{1}{s} - \frac{L}{Ls + R}\right), \tag{b}$$

that is, we develop $1/s(Ls + R)$ into *partial fractions.*† Then $I(s)$ becomes

$$I(s) = \frac{E}{R}\frac{1}{s} - \frac{E}{R}\frac{1}{s + R/L} + i_0 \frac{1}{s + R/L}$$

and by Eqs. (10.13) and (10.17),

$$i(t) = \frac{E}{R} - \frac{E}{R}\epsilon^{-(R/L)t} + i_0\epsilon^{-(R/L)t}, \quad t > 0$$

or, equivalently,

$$i(t) = \left[\frac{E}{R} - \frac{E}{R}\epsilon^{-(R/L)t} + i_0\epsilon^{-(R/L)t}\right]u(t).$$

Observe in the above example how the natural and forced responses are determined directly from the inverse transform. The term E/Rs is the transform of the forced response, whereas $-(E/R - i_0)/(s + R/L)$ is the transform of the natural response. Here we clearly see that the amplitude of the step forcing function affects the magnitude, but not the form, of the natural-response term.

† See Appendix B.

Example 10.2. As a second example consider the circuit of Sec. 3.2 (Fig. 10.3). The equilibrium equation is given by Eq. (3.23) as

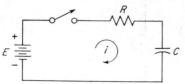

$$Ri + \frac{1}{C}\int_0^t i\, dt + v_{c0} = E, \qquad t > 0.$$

FIG. 10.3. Circuit for Example 10.2.

Solution. To solve this problem, let $I(s)$ be the Laplace transform of $i(t)$. Then by Eq. (10.21a),

$$\mathcal{L}\left[\int_0^t i\, dt\right] = \frac{1}{s}I(s).$$

Thus the transform of the equilibrium equation is

$$RI(s) + \frac{1}{Cs}I(s) + \frac{v_{c0}}{s} = \frac{E}{s}$$

since v_{c0} and E are effectively applied at $t = 0$ and so may be considered step functions. The above equation is an algebraic equation which can be solved for $I(s)$. It is

$$I(s) = \frac{E/s - v_{c0}/s}{R + 1/Cs} = \frac{E - v_{c0}}{R}\,\frac{1}{s + 1/RC}.$$

The current $i(t)$ is, therefore, given by the inverse transform [see Eq. (10.17)],

$$i(t) = \frac{E - v_{c0}}{R}\,\epsilon^{-t/RC}.$$

Note how direct and simple the Laplace-transform technique is. There is no "replace $\int_0^t i(t)\, dt$ by i/s" type of vague argument. Also we did not have first to calculate what the initial current was [see Eq. (3.27)]. All this is taken care of automatically by the Laplace-transform technique. Even at this stage the reader should appreciate the systematic way in which the Laplace transform approaches the solution of network problems.

Before turning to other properties of the Laplace transform we point out one generalization. Suppose that in some complicated network problem we had to solve the equilibrium equation

$$a\frac{d^2i}{dt^2} + b\frac{di}{dt} + ci + d\int_0^t i\, dt + v_{c0} = f(t), \qquad t > 0 \qquad (10.22)$$

where $i(0) = i_0$, $i'(0) = i_0'$ were the given initial current and its derivative. Furthermore, suppose that $f(t)$ is an arbitrary function of t, that is, not necessarily a step function or a sinusoid. Then if we merely assume that $f(t)$ has a Laplace transform, say $F(s)$, Eq. (10.22) can, in principle, be solved just as readily as the simple problems of Examples 10.1 and 10.2. For if we take the transform of both sides of Eq. (10.22) there results

$$a[s^2I(s) - si_0 - i_0'] + b[sI(s) - i_0] + cI(s) + \frac{d}{s}I(s) + \frac{v_{c0}}{s} = F(s)$$

$$(10.23)$$

where $I(s) = \mathcal{L}[i(t)]$.   Now Eq. (10.23) is a linear algebraic equation on $I(s)$.   Thus

$$I(s) = \frac{sF(s) + s^2 a i_0 + s(a i_0' + b i_0) - v_{c0}}{as^3 + bs^2 + cs + d}. \tag{10.24}$$

Since $F(s)$ is known [because $f(t)$ is given] the right-hand side of Eq. (10.24) is an explicit function of s.   Thus $i(t)$ is the inverse transform of Eq. (10.24).   Of course our ability to evaluate an inverse transform depends on how extensive a table of transforms† we have, just as our ability to integrate a complicated integral depends on how extensive a table of integrals we have.   Nevertheless, in principle, we have solved Eq. (10.22).

10.3. Translated Functions.   Other important properties of the Laplace transform express the transform of a function shifted to the right in terms of the transform of the original function, and the transform of an exponential times an arbitrary function.

When shifting functions, one must be careful to recall that when a function $x(t)$ is transformed it is assumed, in effect, to be zero for negative values of t.   Thus, referring to Fig. 10.4, shifting the function of Fig. 10.4a to the right by an amount α results in the new function of Fig. 10.4b. However, shifting to the left by an amount β leads to the different function illustrated in Fig. 10.4c.   Now shifting $x(t + \beta)$ to the right by an amount β will lead to the function $y(t)$ of Fig. 10.4d, which is *not* the same as $x(t)$.   Thus to avoid difficulty when shifting functions it is well to express functions in the form $x(t)u(t)$ to emphasize the one-sided nature of the Laplace transform.   This function shifted to the right α units is $x(t - \alpha)u(t - \alpha)$.   Calling this $z(t)$, we find its transform to be

$$\mathcal{L}[z(t)] = \int_0^\infty x(t - \alpha)u(t - \alpha)\epsilon^{-st}\, dt = \int_\alpha^\infty x(t - \alpha)\epsilon^{-st}\, dt$$

since $u(t - \alpha) = 0$ for $t < \alpha$.   Making the change of variable $\xi = t - \alpha$ leads to

$$\mathcal{L}[z(t)] = \int_0^\infty x(\xi)\epsilon^{-s(\xi+\alpha)}\, d\xi = \epsilon^{-s\alpha} \int_0^\infty x(\xi)\epsilon^{-s\xi}\, d\xi$$

or

$$\mathcal{L}[x(t - \alpha)u(t - \alpha)] = \epsilon^{-s\alpha}\, X(s) \tag{10.25}$$

where $X(s) = \mathcal{L}[x(t)]$.   Observe that this is not the same as $\mathcal{L}[x(t - \alpha)]$, for $x(t)$ may be nonzero for $t < 0$, even though the one-sided Laplace transform truncates the function at $t = 0$.   It might be useful to have an

---

† A brief table is furnished by Eqs. (10.13) to (10.21).   These and other transforms developed later in this chapter are summarized in Appendix C.   More extensive tables may be found in "Standard Mathematical Tables," 10th ed., Chemical Rubber Publishing Company, Cleveland, 1954, and in M. F. Gardner and J. L. Barnes, "Transients in Linear Systems," John Wiley & Sons, Inc., New York, 1945.

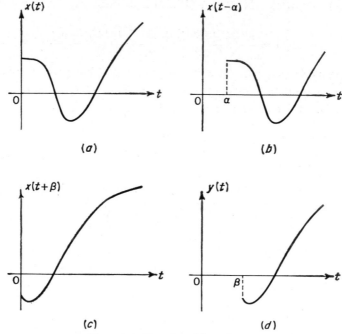

Fig. 10.4. Translated functions.

expression for $\mathcal{L}[x(t - \alpha)]$, but this cannot be obtained in terms of $\mathcal{L}[x(t)]$ because $\mathcal{L}[x(t)]$ does not account for values of $x(t)$ prior to $t = 0$.

Shifting functions to the left (α negative) must be done with great care. Equation (10.25) applies, but only under limited conditions. Generally, if $x(t) = 0$ for $t > t_0$ we may freely shift to the left by an amount less than or equal to t_0, but a greater shift involves difficulties requiring care-ful changes of variables.

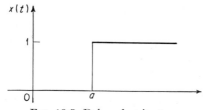

Fig. 10.5. Delayed unit step.

As a simple application of the translation theorem of the Laplace-transform theory, the transform of the delayed step $u(t - a)$ shown in Fig. 10.5 is

$$X(s) = \epsilon^{-sa}U(s) = \frac{1}{s}\,\epsilon^{-sa} \qquad (10.26)$$

where $U(s)$ is the transform of the unit step $u(t)$.

We now consider shifting in the s domain. If we multiply $x(t)$ by an exponential, say $\epsilon^{-\beta t}$, then by definition

$$\mathcal{L}[x(t)\epsilon^{-\beta t}] = \int_0^\infty x(t)\epsilon^{-\beta t}\epsilon^{-st}\,dt = \int_0^\infty x(t)\epsilon^{-(\beta+s)t}\,dt.$$

Making the change of variable $\beta + s = v$ leads to

$$\mathcal{L}[x(t)\epsilon^{-\beta t}] = \int_0^\infty x(t)\epsilon^{-vt}\,dt = X(v) = X(\beta + s) \qquad (10.27)$$

where $X(s)$ is the Laplace transform of $x(t)$.

From Eqs. (10.25) and (10.27) we see that translation in the time domain results in multiplication by an exponential in the s (frequency) domain, while translation in the frequency domain results in multiplication by an exponential in the t (time) domain.

Example 10.3. Determine the Laplace transform of the function shown in Fig. 10.6

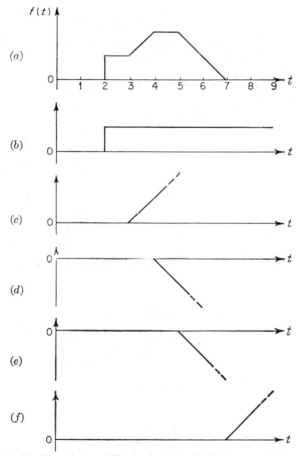

Fig. 10.6. (a) Waveform of Example 10.3; (b–f) component waveforms.

Solution. The function may be decomposed into the sum of functions, as shown in Fig. 10.6b to f. This sum may be written

$$e(t) = u(t-2) + (t-3)u(t-3) - (t-4)u(t-4) - (t-5)u(t-5) + \\ (t-7)u(t-7).$$

(The function $\tau u(\tau)$ is called a *ramp function*. It is seen to be the integral of a unit step.)

It should be noted that the decomposition is not as obvious as might first appear. The Laplace transform is then given by

$$\mathcal{L}[e(t)] = \frac{1}{s}\,\epsilon^{-2s} + \frac{1}{s^2}\,\epsilon^{-3s} - \frac{1}{s^2}\,\epsilon^{-4s} - \frac{1}{s^2}\,\epsilon^{-5s} + \frac{1}{s^2}\,\epsilon^{-7s}$$

$$= \frac{1}{s}\,\epsilon^{-2s}\left[1 + \frac{1}{s}\,(\epsilon^{-s} - \epsilon^{-2s} - \epsilon^{-3s} - \epsilon^{-5s} + \epsilon^{-7s})\right].$$

One can use Eq. (10.27) to deduce certain additional elementary transforms in a simple manner. For example,

$$\mathcal{L}[\epsilon^{-\beta t}\sin\alpha t] = \frac{\alpha}{(s+\beta)^2 + \alpha^2} \tag{10.28}$$

$$\mathcal{L}[\epsilon^{-\beta t}\cos\alpha t] = \frac{s+\beta}{(s+\beta)^2 + \alpha^2} \tag{10.29}$$

where all we have done is to replace s by $s + \beta$ in the expressions [see Eqs. (10.18) and (10.14)] for the Laplace transform of the sine and cosine, respectively. Similarly,

$$\mathcal{L}[\epsilon^{-\beta t}t^n] = \frac{n!}{(s+\beta)^{n+1}}. \tag{10.30}$$

Example 10.4. Consider the important RLC series circuit of Sec. 3.3 (see Fig. 10.7).

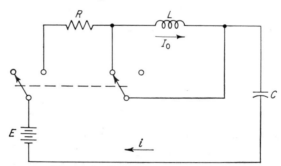

FIG. 10.7. Circuit for Example 10.4.

The equilibrium equation of this network is [see Eq. (3.39)]

$$L\frac{di}{dt} + Ri + \frac{1}{C}\int_0^t i\,dt + v_{c0} = E, \qquad t > 0$$

and the initial current is

$$i(0) = i_0.$$

Assuming that $R = 1\ \Omega$, $L = 1$ henry, $C = 1$ farad, determine the response $i(t)$ by the Laplace-transform technique.

Solution. Letting $I(s) = \mathcal{L}[i(t)]$ we have from Eqs. (10.20), (10.21), and (10.13) that the transform of the equilibrium equation is

$$L[sI(s) - i_0] + RI(s) + \frac{1}{C}\frac{1}{s}I(s) + \frac{v_{c0}}{s} = \frac{E}{s}.$$

Introducing the numerical values for L, R, C, we may solve this algebraic equation for $I(s)$:

$$I(s) = \frac{si_0 + (E - v_{c0})}{s^2 + s + 1}.$$

Upon completing the square in the denominator we may write

$$I(s) = \frac{si_0 + (E - v_{c0})}{(s + \frac{1}{2})^2 + \frac{3}{4}}.$$

Now the above equation is almost of the form of Eqs. (10.28) and (10.29). Just as in the theory of integration we manipulate integrands so that they become standard forms, we must manipulate the equation for $I(s)$. First we write

$$I(s) = i_0 \frac{s}{(s + \frac{1}{2})^2 + \frac{3}{4}} + (E - v_{c0}) \frac{1}{(s + \frac{1}{2})^2 + \frac{3}{4}}.$$

Now if we had $s + \frac{1}{2}$ instead of s in the numerator of the first fraction, it would be exactly the transform of $\epsilon^{-t/2} \cos \frac{\sqrt{3}}{2} t$. Let us therefore add and then subtract this term:

$$I(s) = i_0 \frac{s + \frac{1}{2}}{(s + \frac{1}{2})^2 + \frac{3}{4}} - i_0 \frac{\frac{1}{2}}{(s + \frac{1}{2})^2 + \frac{3}{4}} + (E - v_{c0}) \frac{1}{(s + \frac{1}{2})^2 + \frac{3}{4}}$$

or

$$I(s) = i_0 \frac{s + \frac{1}{2}}{(s + \frac{1}{2})^2 + \frac{3}{4}} + (E - v_{c0} - \frac{1}{2}i_0) \frac{1}{(s + \frac{1}{2})^2 + \frac{3}{4}}.$$

Now if in the second fraction we had $\sqrt{3}/2$ instead of 1, it would be precisely the Laplace transform of $\epsilon^{-t/2} \sin \frac{\sqrt{3}}{2} t$. Let us therefore multiply and divide this second fraction by $\sqrt{3}/2$ to obtain

$$I(s) = i_0 \frac{s + \frac{1}{2}}{(s + \frac{1}{2})^2 + \frac{3}{4}} + \frac{2}{\sqrt{3}} (E - v_{c0} - \frac{1}{2}i_0) \frac{\sqrt{3}/2}{(s + \frac{1}{2})^2 + \frac{3}{4}}.$$

Equations (10.28) and (10.29) then immediately yield

$$i(t) = \mathcal{L}^{-1}[I(s)] = i_0\epsilon^{-t/2} \cos \frac{\sqrt{3}}{2} t + \frac{2\sqrt{3}}{3} (E - v_{c0} - \frac{1}{2}i_0)\epsilon^{-t/2} \sin \frac{\sqrt{3}}{2} t$$

by virtue of the linearity of the Laplace-transform operator $\mathcal{L}$ [see Eq. (10.19)]. If desired, the above response may also be written in phase-angle form as described in Sec. 3.3.

10.4. Transfer Functions. In Sec. 7.11 we introduced the notion of *frequency response*. We showed, for instance, in Example 7.4 that the ratio of input to output voltage for the simple RC circuit of Fig. 10.8 was

$$\frac{E_2(j\omega)}{E_1(j\omega)} = \frac{1}{1 + j\omega RC}. \quad (10.31)$$

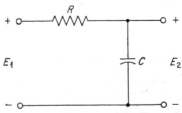

Fig. 10.8. Circuit used in Example 7.4.

We then proceeded to compute the amplitude response

$$A(\omega) = \frac{1}{\sqrt{1 + \omega^2 R^2 C^2}} \qquad (10.32)$$

and the phase response

$$\theta(\omega) = -\arctan \frac{\omega RC}{1}. \qquad (10.33)$$

Now let us apply Laplace-transform techniques to the circuit of Fig. 10.8. Then (see Example 10.2) the equilibrium equation is

$$Ri + \frac{1}{C} \int_0^t i \, dt = e_1(t) \qquad (10.34)$$

where we have assumed that the initial voltage v_{c0} across the capacitor is zero. Transforming both sides of Eq. (10.34) yields

$$RI(s) + \frac{1}{Cs} I(s) = E_1(s) \qquad (10.35)$$

where $I(s) = \mathcal{L}[i(t)]$ and $E_1(s)$ is the Laplace transform of $e_1(t)$. The output voltage $e_2(t)$ may be written

$$e_2(t) = \frac{1}{C} \int_0^t i(t) \, dt \qquad (10.36)$$

and, by Eq. (10.21),

$$E_2(s) = \mathcal{L}[e_2(t)] = \frac{1}{Cs} I(s).$$

Equation (10.35) then becomes, in terms of E_1 and E_2,

$$CRsE_2(s) + E_2(s) = E_1(s)$$

or

$$\frac{E_2(s)}{E_1(s)} = \frac{1}{1 + RCs}. \qquad (10.37)$$

Thus the ratio of the transform of the output voltage to the transform of the input voltage is simply the frequency response with $j\omega$ replaced by s. We shall call this ratio the *transfer function* or *system function* of the RC circuit and denote it by $H(s)$,

$$H(s) = \frac{E_2(s)}{E_1(s)}. \qquad (10.38)$$

It is important to note that this definition holds only for *relaxed* networks, i.e., those in which there is initially no energy stored in inductance or capacitance.

The concept of transfer function can also be extended to multimesh networks. It is a very important tool in advanced network theory.

Example 10.5. Determine the transfer function of the network in Fig. 10.9, assuming that there is no mutual inductance between the coils.

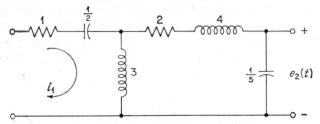

FIG. 10.9. Circuit for Example 10.5.

Solution. Since we are interested in steady-state conditions, we can assume no initial current through the coils and no initial voltage across the capacitors. The equilibrium equations for this two-loop network are

$$i_1 + 2 \int_0^t i_1 \, dt + 3 \frac{d}{dt} i_1 - 3 \frac{d}{dt} i_2 = e_1(t)$$

$$3 \frac{d}{dt} i_2 - 3 \frac{d}{dt} i_1 + 2i_2 + 4 \frac{d}{dt} i_2 + 5 \int_0^t i_2 \, dt = 0.$$

The transformed equations are

$$I_1(s) + \frac{2}{s} I_1(s) + 3sI_1(s) - 3sI_2(s) = E_1(s)$$

$$3sI_2(s) - 3sI_1(s) + 2I_2(s) + 4sI_2(s) + \frac{5}{s} I_2(s) = 0.$$

Collecting terms, we have

$$I_1(s) \left[1 + \frac{2}{s} + 3s \right] - I_2(s)[3s] = E_1(s)$$

$$-I_1(s)[3s] + I_2(s) \left[7s + 2 + \frac{5}{s} \right] = 0$$

and by Cramer's rule

$$I_2(s) = \frac{\begin{vmatrix} 3s + 1 + 2/s & E_1(s) \\ -3s & 0 \end{vmatrix}}{\begin{vmatrix} 3s + 1 + 2/s & -3s \\ -3s & 7s + 2 + 5/s \end{vmatrix}}$$

$$= \frac{3sE_1(s)}{21s^2 + 13s + 31 + 9/s + 10/s^2}. \qquad (a)$$

But

$$e_2(t) = 5 \int_0^t i_2(t) \, dt$$

and

$$E_2(s) = \frac{5}{s} I_2(s).$$

Replacing $I_2(s)$ by $\frac{s}{5} E_2(s)$, Eq. (a) becomes

$$\frac{s}{5} E_2(s) = \frac{3sE_1(s)}{21s^2 + 13s + 31 + 9/s + 10/s^2}$$

or the transfer function $H(s)$ is

$$H(s) = \frac{E_2(s)}{E_1(s)} = \frac{15s^2}{21s^4 + 13s^3 + 31s^2 + 9s + 10}. \qquad (b)$$

Note that $H(s)$ is a *rational function* of s.   This is always the case in circuits involving only resistance, inductance, and capacitance.

10.5. Impulse Functions and Impulsive Responses.   In the previous section we introduced the reader to the *transfer function* of a network and remarked that it was a useful tool in network theory.   There are other important ideas that are also useful in analyzing circuits which we would like to discuss in this and the next section.   Fortunately the motivation

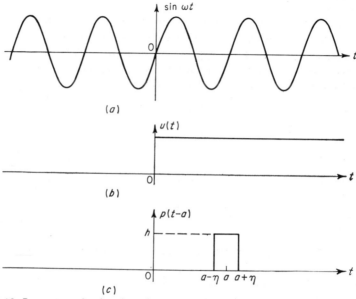

FIG. 10.10. Important forcing functions.   (*a*) Sinusoid; (*b*) step function; (*c*) pulse.

and derivations of these new results are readily understood.   More important, though, is the insight that they give into the structure of general networks.   We hope that this discussion will also whet the student's appetite so that he will pursue the subject more deeply.

We have considered networks where the forcing function was a sinusoid, $\sin \omega t$, or a step function $u(t)$ (Fig. 10.10).   Another important type of exciting function is a pulse, say $p(t - a)$, as illustrated in Fig. 10.10c. Even more important is the limiting case of the pulse as η approaches zero and h approaches infinity in such a manner that the area under the pulse remains finite.   If we let $h = 1/2\eta$ in Fig. 10.10c then clearly

$$p(t - a) = 0, \qquad |t - a| > a$$

$$p(t - a) = \frac{1}{2\eta}, \qquad |t - a| < a \qquad (10.39)$$

$$\int_{-\infty}^{\infty} p(t - a)\, dt = 1.$$

Now if we let η approach zero, then, since $2\eta h = 1$, h will approach infinity and the limiting form of $p(t - a)$ is called the *delta function*, or *unit impulse function*,

$$\lim_{\substack{\eta \to 0 \\ 2\eta h = 1}} p(t - a) = \delta(t - a). \tag{10.40}$$

The idea of a function having no width but infinite height and a fixed area may at first seem strange. Nevertheless, this function ·closely fits many practical situations. For example, consider an uncharged capacitor suddenly connected across a voltage source. An infinite current will flow for zero time, delivering a charge Q ($= CE$) to the capacitor. Or, take the voltage across an inductor suddenly connected to a current source. The voltage will be an impulse, since the current is a step function.

From Eqs. (10.39) it appears that, formally,

$$\begin{aligned} \delta(t - a) &= 0, & t &\neq a \\ \delta(t - a) &= \infty, & t &= a \end{aligned} \tag{10.41}$$

$$\int_{-\infty}^{\infty} \delta(t - a)\, dt = 1.$$

Equations (10.41) express the characteristic properties of the delta function. However, in our formal derivation we have assumed that

$$\lim_{\eta \to 0} \int_{-\infty}^{\infty} p(t - a)\, dt = \int_{-\infty}^{\infty} \lim_{\eta \to 0} p(t - a)\, dt \tag{10.42}$$

which is not true. Even though Eq. (10.42) is not true, the delta function has proved to be a very useful tool in analyzing electric networks. By invoking certain advanced mathematical theories (the theory of distributions) the formal use of the delta function *can* be justified. We shall assume† this justification and formally use the delta function as defined by Eqs. (10.41).

Let us examine a few elementary properties of the delta function. Consider

$$\int_{-\infty}^{\infty} \delta(t - a)x(t)\, dt. \tag{10.43}$$

Since $\delta(t - a) = 0$ for $t \neq a$, we may write Eq. (10.43) as

$$\int_{-\infty}^{\infty} \delta(t - a)x(t)\, dt = \int_{a-\epsilon}^{a+\epsilon} \delta(t - a)x(t)\, dt$$

for any $\epsilon > 0$. Now if $x(t)$ is continuous at $t = a$, its value in a small neighborhood of $t = a$ will be close to $x(a)$. Thus

$$\int_{a-\epsilon}^{a+\epsilon} \delta(t - a)x(t)\, dt \doteq x(a) \int_{a-\epsilon}^{a+\epsilon} \delta(t - a)\, dt = x(a),$$

† Actually, the theory of distributions does not justify the mathematical treatment used here, but the results obtained by our treatment prove to be identical with those obtained when regularly executed in the framework of distribution theory.

and in the limit we have

$$\int_{-\infty}^{\infty} \delta(t - a)x(t)\, dt = \int_{a-\epsilon}^{a+\epsilon} \delta(t - a)x(t)\, dt = x(a). \qquad (10.44)$$

Thus $\delta(t - a)$ *reproduces* the integrand. We also note that

$$\int_{-\infty}^{a} \delta(t - a)\, dt = \int_{a-\epsilon}^{a} \delta(t - a)\, dt = \int_{a}^{a+\epsilon} \delta(t - a)\, dt$$
$$= \int_{a}^{\infty} \delta(t - a)\, dt = \tfrac{1}{2} \qquad (10.45)$$

for any $\epsilon > 0$ since only half the delta function is contained in any of the above four ranges of integration.

Let us now compute the Laplace transform of $\delta(t - a)$. By definition of the Laplace transform,

$$\mathcal{L}[\delta(t - a)] = \int_{0}^{\infty} \delta(t - a)\epsilon^{-st}\, dt = \epsilon^{-as} \qquad (10.46)$$

by Eqs. (10.44), provided that $a > 0$. If $a = 0$,

$$\mathcal{L}[\delta(t)] = \int_{0}^{\infty} \delta(t)\epsilon^{-st}\, dt = \tfrac{1}{2}\epsilon^{-0s} = \tfrac{1}{2} \qquad (10.47)$$

by Eq. (10.45). One sometimes writes, changing the lower limit to $0-$,

$$\Delta(s) = \mathcal{L}[\delta(t)] = \int_{0-}^{\infty} \delta(t)\epsilon^{-st}\, dt \qquad (10.48)$$

where $\Delta(s)$ is the Laplace transform of the impulse function. In this case, of course,

$$\Delta(s) = 1 \qquad (10.49)$$

(see footnote on page 71 for a discussion of the significance of $0-$). It will be convenient to use this definition of the Laplace transform when talking about delta functions. Clearly, $\int_{0}^{\infty} x(t)\epsilon^{-st}\, dt = \int_{0-}^{\infty} x(t)\epsilon^{-st}\, dt$ for any smooth function. That is, $\int_{0-}^{0} x(t)\epsilon^{-st}\, dt = 0$ for any function other than a delta function. Hence all the previous formulas for the Laplace transform which we have developed will still be true if the lower limit, 0, of the integral is replaced by $0-$. This, of course, does not imply that $x(0-)$ must be the same as $x(0+)$.

A consideration of Eq. (10.49) indicates that the impulse is the derivative of a unit step, for $1/s$ is the transform of a step, and Eq. (10.20) shows that the transform of the derivative of a step is s times the transform of the step, or $s/s = 1$. That this is so may be seen from Fig. 10.11, wherein the step function is approximated by one which changes not abruptly but in a short period of time Δt. The derivative of this approximation is a pulse of duration Δt and of height $1/\Delta t$. As the approximation approaches the step function, the derivative approaches an impulse.   We may also take successive derivatives of impulses (doublets, triplets, etc.) by extending the procedures discussed, but the details need not concern us here.

As an application of the delta function let us consider the response of a network $\mathfrak{N}$ (see Fig. 10.12) to a unit impulse function input.   The voltage transfer function or system function $H(s)$ of the network, defined as the ratio of the transform of the voltage response of the (relaxed) network to the transform of the input voltage, is given by

$$H(s) = \frac{E_2(s)}{E_1(s)} \qquad (10.50)$$

where $E_1(s)$ is the Laplace transform of the input $e_1(t)$ and $E_2(s)$ is the transform of the output $e_2(t)$.   But if $e_1(t)$ is a delta function, $E_1(s) = 1$, by Eq. (10.49).   Thus we have the result that

$$H(s) = E_2(s), \qquad (10.51)$$

that is, the transform of the response $e_2(t)$ of a network to a delta function is the system function for the network under consideration.   If we take the inverse transform of Eq. (10.51), we obtain

$$h(t) = e_2(t), \qquad (10.52)$$

where $h(t) = \mathcal{L}^{-1}[H(s)]$ is called the

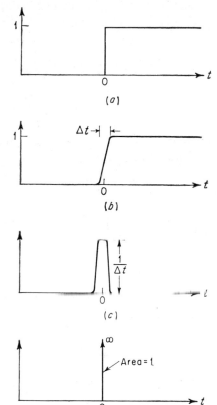

Fig. 10.11. Development of impulse. (a) Step function; (b) approximation to step function; (c) derivative of approximation; (d) derivative of step (impulse).

impulsive response of the network.   In almost all advanced applications of network theory, a network is classified by its impulsive response (a time function) rather than by its system function.   Of course the two are intimately related, one simply being the Laplace transform of the other.

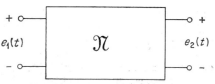

Fig. 10.12. Two-port network.

10.6.   The Superposition Integral. The impulsive response $h(t)$ of a network $\mathfrak{N}$ is also called the *weighting function*.   The reason for this terminology will be made clear in the following application.   Suppose that $e_1(t)$ is a function of time starting at $t = 0$ (see Fig. 10.13). Let us divide the interval 0 to t into n pieces by the points of subdivision $t_0, t_1, \ldots, t_n$ and let $\Delta t_k = t_k - t_{k-1}$. Then an elementary rectangle, such as is illustrated in Fig. 10.13, can be approximated by the number

$$[e_1(t'_k) \, \Delta t_k] \delta(t - t'_k).$$

The function $e_1(t)$ is therefore approximately

$$e_1(t) \doteq \sum_{k=1}^{n} e_1(t'_k) \, \Delta t_k \, \delta(t - t'_k). \tag{10.53}$$

Now the response of $\mathfrak{N}$ to a delta function $\delta(t - t')$ is the impulsive response $h(t - t')$† and the response of $\mathfrak{N}$ to $e_1(t)$ is, by definition, $e_2(t)$.

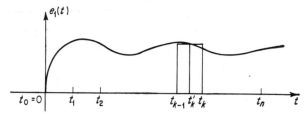

FIG. 10.13. Illustration of superposition integral.

Thus Eq. (10.53) implies

$$e_2(t) \doteq \sum_{k=1}^{n} e_1(t'_k) h(t - t'_k) \, \Delta t_k \tag{10.54}$$

and, if we take the limit as max $\Delta t_k \to 0$, Eq. (10.54) becomes

$$e_2(t) = \int_0^t e_1(\tau) h(t - \tau) \, d\tau. \tag{10.55}$$

The above integral is called the *superposition integral* since it was obtained by superimposing the responses of many delta functions. It is also known as the *convolution integral*. From Eq. (10.54) we see that $e_2(t)$ is a *weighted sum* of the inputs $e_1(t'_k)$, the weighting functions being $h(t - t'_k)$. This is the reason why the impulsive response is also termed the weighting function of the network.

The superposition integral allows us to express the response of a network in terms of the input as an *integral equation* [Eq. (10.55)], where the *kernel* of the integral equation is the impulsive response $h(t - \tau)$.

† The system function to an impulse delayed by an amount t_0 is $\epsilon^{-t_0 s} H(s)$. To preserve mathematical rigor we should denote the response to a delayed impulse by $h(t - t_0)u(t - t_0)$. However, in real networks $h(t - t_0)$ must be zero for $t < t_0$, for otherwise an output would exist before the input was applied. Thus, we may neglect the $u(t - t_0)$.

10.7. Frequency and Time Domain Interpretation of the Laplace Transform.   Just as the Fourier transform enables us to represent functions of time as functions of the imaginary frequency $j\omega$ in the form of frequency spectra, the Laplace transform enables us to represent functions of time in the complex frequency plane.   We might imagine that we could construct spectra in the s plane by plotting the magnitude and phase of the transforms as functions of s.   Such is permissible but is not much used because the s plane is two-dimensional and the plots would comprise three-dimensional contour maps.   Fortunately, a method of circumventing this difficulty exists.

This method is essentially similar to the mapping of impedance functions explained in Sec. 6.8.   If $P(s)$ is a polynomial of the nth degree in s, it is known that $P(s) = 0$ has precisely n roots or zeros.   Thus any rational function $R(s)$,

$$R(s) = \frac{a_0 s^m + a_1 s^{m-1} + \cdots + a_m}{b_0 s^n + b_1 s^{n-1} + \cdots + b_n}, \qquad a_0 \neq 0,\ b_0 \neq 0,$$

may be written in the form

$$R(s) = K \frac{(s - s_{01})(s - s_{02}) \cdots (s - s_{0m})}{(s - s_{p1})(s - s_{p2}) \cdots (s - s_{pn})},$$

where the s_{0i} are the zeros of the rational function and the s_{pi} are its poles. [$R(s)$ may also have poles or zeros at infinity.]   Clearly the s_{0i} and the s_{pi} together with K completely characterize $R(s)$.   Note that all the transforms considered in this chapter can be written as rational functions. Thus we may transform any time function that usually arises in lumped-parameter system analysis and represent the transform not as spectra but as a pole-zero configuration in the s plane.

To emphasize the close relation which exists between a time function and its transform, we shall prove two important theorems, the *initial-value theorem* and the *final-value theorem*, which, in addition to being important in their own right, also provide us with simple checks on the validity of certain parts of our computations.

Initial-value Theorem.   Let $x(t)$ have a Laplace transform $X(s)$ and let the derivative of $x(t)$ exist and also have a transform.   Then if $\lim_{s \to \infty} sX(s)$ exists,

$$\lim_{\substack{t \to 0 \\ t > 0}} x(t) = \lim_{s \to \infty} sX(s). \qquad (10.56)$$

Roughly speaking, this means that values of $x(t)$ near zero correspond to values of $sX(s)$ near infinity.

To prove the initial-value theorem we start with the formula

$$\int_0^\infty x'(t) \epsilon^{-st}\, dt = sX(s) - x(0+)$$

and take the limit of both sides as s approaches infinity.   Since

$$\lim_{s \to \infty} \int_0^\infty x'(t) \epsilon^{-st} \, dt = 0$$

we infer

$$0 = \lim_{s \to \infty} [sX(s) - x(0+)] \tag{10.57}$$

which proves the theorem, for $x(0+)$ is but $\lim_{\substack{t \to 0 \\ t > 0}} x(t)$.

Final-value Theorem.   Let $x(t)$ have a Laplace transform $X(s)$ and let the derivative of $x(t)$ exist and also have a transform.   Then if $\lim_{t \to \infty} x(t)$ exists and $x'(t)$ decreases exponentially,

$$\lim_{t \to \infty} x(t) = \lim_{s \to 0} sX(s). \tag{10.58}$$

This theorem enables us to determine the behavior of $x(t)$ for large t (final value) without actually taking the inverse transform of $X(s)$.

To prove this theorem, we start with the relation

$$\int_0^\infty x'(t) \epsilon^{-st} \, dt = sX(s) - x(0+).$$

Since $x'(t)$ decreases exponentially, the interchange of limits, viz.,

$$\lim_{s \to 0} \int_0^\infty x'(t) \epsilon^{-st} \, dt = \int_0^\infty x'(t) \, dt \tag{10.59}$$

can be shown to be justified, and we may write

$$\int_0^\infty x'(t) \, dt = \lim_{s \to 0} [sX(s) - x(0+)] = \lim_{s \to 0} sX(s) - x(0+). \tag{10.60}$$

The left-hand side of Eq. (10.60) may be written, by definition of the infinite integral, as†

$$\lim_{t \to \infty} \int_0^t x'(\xi) \, d\xi = \lim_{t \to \infty} [x(t) - x(0+)]. \tag{10.61}$$

Equations (10.60) and (10.61) imply the theorem.

10.8. Transform Networks.   It is sometimes useful in simplifying analyses, but more important it is quite illuminating, to introduce the notion of transform networks.   A transform network is one in which the functions of time have been replaced by transforms, or functions of s, and the differential equations representing the impedance elements have been replaced by the operational impedances (that is, impedances as functions of s) of these elements.   Thus, Fig. 10.14*b* is the transform network of Fig. 10.14*a*.   This seems like a fairly obvious and trivial definition, but there is more involved than that.   Suppose that we consider elements in

† The term $x(0+)$ rather than $x(0)$ is used because of the possible existence of a discontinuity at the origin.

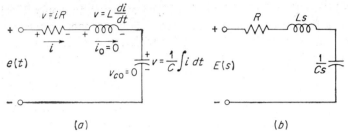

FIG. 10.14. Illustration of transform network.

which there is initial energy storage.   Take first a capacitor.   The current-voltage relation is

$$e_c = \frac{1}{C} \int_0^t i(t)\, dt + v_{c0}. \tag{10.62}$$

Transforming both sides, using Eq. (10.21) yields

$$E_c(s) = \frac{1}{Cs} I(s) + \frac{v_{c0}}{s}. \tag{10.63}$$

Observe that the initial voltage must be treated as a step applied at

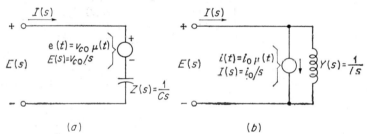

FIG. 10.15. Transform networks showing treatment of initial conditions.   (a) Capacitor; (b) inductance.

$t = 0-$, by the definition of the Laplace transform.†   This should cause no difficulty, however, as we are interested only in results for $t > 0$.   Now, Eq. (10.63) may be represented by the circuit shown in Fig. 10.15a, which is an uncharged capacitor in series with a step-voltage source, corresponding to the initial voltage on the capacitor.   We may proceed similarly for an inductor, writing

$$i = \frac{1}{L} \int_0^t e(t)\, dt + i_{L0}. \tag{10.64}$$

Transforming both sides leads to

$$I(s) = \frac{1}{Ls} E(s) + \frac{i_{L0}}{s} \tag{10.65}$$

which may be represented by Fig. 10.15b.

† For the use of $0-$ rather than 0 as the lower limit of the Laplace transform, see the comments following Eq. (10.49).

Some interesting difficulties arise if we attempt to apply Norton's or Thévenin's theorem to these circuits to obtain a capacitor in parallel with a current source, or an inductor in series with a voltage source.   In dealing with the capacitor, for example, the natural (but incorrect) approach is to place it in parallel with a current source which is also a step function. However, let us recall the precise statement of Norton's theorem: "The current source is equal to the short-circuit current."   What is the short-circuit current of Fig. 10.15a?   Its transform is given by

$$I_0(s) = \frac{v_{c0}/s}{1/Cs} = v_{c0}C. \qquad (10.66)$$

This equation, however, is a delta function of weight $v_{c0}C$.   There may appear, here, to exist an error in units.   We appear to have current

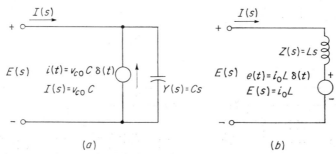

(a)   (b)

FIG. 10.16. (a) Norton's equivalent of capacitor transform network; (b) Thévenin's equivalent of inductor transform network.

(amperes) equated to charge (volt-farads, or coulombs).   However, the current is a delta function, and the strength of a delta function is measured by its area.   Thus, a delta function of current is measured by ampere-seconds, or coulombs.   Moreover, $I_0(s)$ has the dimensions of ampere-seconds.   Consequently, Eq. (10.66) is dimensionally correct.

Since the impedance of Fig. 10.15a remains $1/Cs$, the current-source equivalent is that shown in Fig. 10.16a.   Physically, what has happened is this: Since the Laplace transform requires that the variables all equal zero for $t < 0$, the initial voltage must be placed on the capacitor instantly, at $t = 0$.   This is done by applying a delta function of current, carrying a charge Cv_{c0}, to the capacitor C.

A similar line of reasoning is required when we apply Thévenin's theorem to the inductor of Fig. 10.15b.   The transform of the open-circuit voltage is given by

$$E_0(s) = -\frac{i_{L0}}{s} Ls = -i_{L0}L. \qquad (10.67)$$

Hence, the equivalent circuit is that of Fig. 10.16b.   Dimensionally, the impulse has the form of ampere-henrys, which, since henrys equal flux linkage per ampere, become flux linkages.   That is, volt-seconds and flux linkages are dimensionally equivalent.   Physically, an impulse of voltage (infinite voltage) is required to cause the initial current to flow instantly in the inductance.

Transform networks may be used in network analysis—indeed, we often are tacitly using them.   However, their principal merit is that they may be used as above, to bring out some of the more general methods of handling initial conditions.

10.9. Switching Transients.   The methods discussed above can be applied to all transient problems which one may reasonably be expected to encounter in practice.   However, there is a class of problems involving

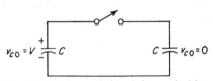

FIG. 10.17. Network involving switching transient.

FIG. 10.18. Final equivalent circuit of Fig. 10.17.

certain idealizations (usually neglecting small resistances) known as *switching transients*, which can be treated more readily in a different fashion.   Typical of these is that shown in Fig. 10.17.   The switch is closed at $t = 0$.   What current flows?   If we ignore the resistance of the connecting wires we come to an impasse.   One approach is to assume finite resistance, find a solution, and let R approach zero in the solution. This generally gives the correct result but is rather roundabout.

A more direct approach is to make use of the principle of conservation of charge, which states that charge can be neither created nor destroyed (we must be careful in applying this principle, since positive charge may nullify negative charge).   To apply the principle of conservation of charge, we observe that after the switch is thrown the circuit appears as in Fig. 10.18.   Before throwing the switch, the total charge on the system was $CV + 0$; the same charge exists after the switch is thrown.   Thus the final voltage V_C is given by

$$V_C = \frac{CV + 0}{2C} = \frac{V}{2}. \tag{10.68}$$

Half the charge has been transferred from the capacitor which was originally charged to that originally uncharged.   Since the transfer took place instantly, a delta function of current, of strength $CV/2$, exists, and so

$$i(t) = \frac{CV}{2} \delta(t). \tag{10.69}$$

This may appear to conclude the problem, but further thought discloses a seeming paradox which must be explained.   The energy in the system before closing the switch was

$$\tfrac{1}{2}C(v_{c0})^2 + 0 = \tfrac{1}{2}CV^2. \tag{10.70}$$

After closing the switch, the energy is

$$\frac{1}{2}\,2C\left(\frac{V}{2}\right)^2 = \frac{1}{4}\,CV^2. \tag{10.71}$$

What happened to half the energy? The almost infinite current flowing through the almost-zero resistance has dissipated exactly half the energy. This can be shown by considering the circuit with a small series resistance and allowing the resistance to approach zero. It is found that exactly half the energy is dissipated, regardless of the size of the resistor.†

The situation here is directly analogous to the case of one steel sphere striking another. This problem is treated by the principle of the conservation of momentum rather than the conservation of energy, for when the spheres strike, part of the kinetic energy is used to set the spheres vibrating and is eventually lost.

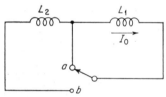

Fig. 10.19. Inductive circuit involving switching transient.

A less familiar principle which may be used in the solution of switching transients involving inductances is the principle of conservation of flux linkages. The statement of this principle is as follows: In any closed circuit containing only pure inductance, the sum of the magnetic flux linkages remains constant at the value it had when the circuit was closed. This principle may be proved by applying Kirchhoff's voltage law to the closed circuit. We have

$$e_1 + e_2 + \cdots + e_n = 0 \tag{10.72}$$

and, since in an inductor $e = d(Li)/dt = d\Lambda/dt$,

$$\frac{d}{dt}\Lambda_1 + \frac{d}{dt}\Lambda_2 + \cdots + \frac{d}{dt}\Lambda_n = 0. \tag{10.73}$$

Hence $\Sigma\Lambda$ is constant. This principle may be applied to the circuit of Fig. 10.19, wherein the switch is thrown from a to b at $t = 0$. Before throwing the switch the total flux linkages are given by

$$\Lambda = L_1 I_0. \tag{10.74}$$

After throwing the switch the total flux linkages are

$$\Lambda = (L_1 + L_2)I \tag{10.75}$$

† If the student is worried about energy being dissipated in a resistanceless wire, the whole problem may be approached on a higher degree of subtlety by noting that the wire has inductance, merely by virtue of its occupying space. The current which flows is oscillatory, with a very high frequency of oscillation. However, the wires then act as an antenna, radiating the energy.

whence

$$I = \frac{L_1}{L_1 + L_2} I_0. \tag{10.76}$$

The sudden change in flux linkages in each coil requires an impulse of voltage across each coil, which is given by

$$e(t) = \left(L_1 - \frac{L_1^2}{L_1 + L_2}\right) I_0 \delta(t) = \frac{L_1 L_2}{L_1 + L_2} I_0 \delta(t). \tag{10.77}$$

Now, we may extend the principle to circuits containing R and C, provided that no impulses of current and charge exist. For example, consider an RLC circuit, the equilibrium equation for which is

$$\frac{d\Lambda}{dt} + Ri + \frac{1}{C} \int_0^t i\, dt + v_{c0} = 0 \tag{10.78}$$

$$\frac{d\Lambda}{dt} + Ri + \frac{q}{C} + v_{c0} = 0. \tag{10.78a}$$

Integrating from 0 to T yields

$$\Lambda(T) - \Lambda(0) + \int_0^T Ri\, dt + \int_0^T \frac{q}{C}\, dt + \int_0^T v_{c0}\, dt = 0. \tag{10.79}$$

Allowing T to approach zero, we see, if no impulses exist,

$$\Lambda(T) = \Lambda(0). \tag{10.80}$$

Example 10.6. Find the currents which exist in the circuit of Fig. 10.20 just after the switch is opened at $t = 0$.

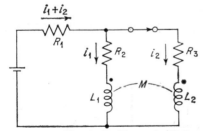

FIG. 10.20. Circuit for Example 10.6.   FIG. 10.21. Equivalent circuit of Fig. 10.20 after a long time has elapsed.

Solution. The solution proceeds as follows:

$$\Sigma\Lambda(0-) = L_1 i_1(0-) + M i_2(0-) + L_2 i_2(0-) + M i_1(0-)$$
$$\Sigma\Lambda(0+) = L_1 i_1(0+) + M i_2(0+) + L_2 i_2(0+) + M i_1(0+).$$

But $i_2(0+)$ must be zero, since loop 2 is open, and therefore

$$\Sigma\Lambda(0-) = L_1 i_1(0+) + M i_1(0+).$$

Now $\Sigma\Lambda(0-) = \Sigma\Lambda(0+)$, and therefore

$$L_2 i_2(0-) + M i_1(0-) + L_1 i_1(0-) + M i_2(0-) = L_1 i_1(0+) + M i_1(0+)$$

or

$$i_1(0+) = i_1(0-) + \frac{M + L_2}{M + L_1} i_2(0-).$$

Now, assuming that the voltage source has been connected for a long period of time, we can find $i_1(0-)$ and $i_2(0-)$ by a simple analysis of Fig. 10.21.

EXERCISES

10.1. If $F(s)$ is the Laplace transform of $f(t)$, prove that
(a) $\mathcal{L}[tf(t)] = -F'(s)$.

(b) $\mathcal{L}\left[\dfrac{f(t)}{t}\right] = \displaystyle\int_s^\infty F(\varsigma)\, d\varsigma$.

(c) $\mathcal{L}[\epsilon^{-at}f(t)] = F(s+a)$.

10.2. Prove that $\mathcal{L}[t^n] = n!/s^{n+1}$, $\sigma_0 = 0$.

10.3. Prove Eq. (10.18).

10.4. Show that

$$\mathcal{L}^{-1}\left[\frac{1}{s(s+\alpha)}\right] = \frac{1}{\alpha}\left(1 - \epsilon^{-\alpha t}\right).$$

10.5. Verify that

$$\mathcal{L}\left[\frac{\epsilon^{-\alpha t} - \epsilon^{-\beta t}}{\beta - \alpha}\right] = \frac{1}{(s+\alpha)(s+\beta)}.$$

10.6. Solve the following differential equations by the Laplace-transform technique:
(a) $\ddot{x} + 5\dot{x} + 6x = t$, $\quad x(0) = 0 = \dot{x}(0)$, $\quad t > 0$.
(b) $4\ddot{x} - 7\dot{x} + 3x = \sin t$, $\quad \dot{x}(0) = 1$, $\quad x(0) = 0$, $\quad t > 0$.
(c) $4\ddot{x} + 4\dot{x} + x = t^2 - 1$, $\quad \dot{x}(0) = 0$, $\quad x(0) = 1$, $\quad t > 0$.
(d) $\ddot{x} - x = \cos t$, $\quad x(0) = \dot{x}(0) = \ddot{x}(0) = 0$, $\quad t > 0$.
(e) $\dddot{x} + \ddot{x} + \dot{x} + x = 1$, $\quad x(0) = \dot{x}(0) = 0$, $\quad \ddot{x}(0) = -2$, $\quad t > 0$.

10.7. A fixed voltage of 10 volts is suddenly impressed on a series RL circuit at $t = 0$. If $R = 5$ ohms and $L = 10$ mh, find the current in the circuit by the Laplace-transform method.

10.8. In the circuit shown in Fig. 10.22 the switch is closed at $t = 0$.
(a) Find the current i by the Laplace-transform technique when the initial conditions are zero.
(b) Find the current when $i_L(0) = 1$ amp, $v_c(0) = 3$ volts.

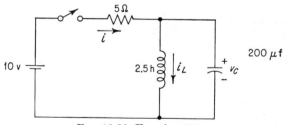

FIG. 10.22. Exercise 10.8.

10.9. Determine the system functions for the two-port networks of (a) Exercise 7.17; (b) Exercise 7.18; (c) Exercise 7.24; (d) Exercise 7.25.

10.10. Establish the following properties of the delta function:

(a) $\displaystyle\int_{-\infty}^{\infty} \epsilon^{j\omega t}\, d\omega = 2\pi\delta(t)$.

(b) $\displaystyle\int_{-\infty}^{\infty} \cos \omega t\, d\omega = 2\pi\delta(t)$.

(c) $\int_{-\infty}^{\infty} x(t)\, \delta^{(k)}(t - \xi)\, dt = (-1)^k x^{(k)}(\xi).$

(d) $\int_{-\infty}^{\infty} \delta(t - \xi)\delta(\xi - u)\, d\xi = \delta(t - u).$

(e) $\delta(t) = \delta(-t).$

(f) $\delta(t) - a\delta(at) = 0, \qquad a > 0.$

(g) $\int_{0}^{\infty} \cos \omega t \cos \omega\xi\, d\omega = \dfrac{\pi}{2}\, \delta(t - \xi), \qquad t > 0, \qquad \xi > 0.$

10.11. Let $x(t)$ be a periodic function of period T. Show that the Laplace transform of $x(t)u(t)$ is

$$X(s) = \frac{Y(s)}{1 - \epsilon^{-sT}}$$

where $Y(s)$ is the Laplace transform of $x(t)[u(t) - u(t - T)]$.

10.12. Find the Laplace transform of $|\sin t|u(t)$.

10.13. Using the convolution theorem, show that

$$x(t) = \tfrac{1}{2} \int_{0}^{t} f(\xi)\epsilon^{-(t-\xi)} \sin 2(t - \xi)\, d\xi$$

is the solution of

$$\ddot{x} + 2\dot{x} + 5x = f(t), \qquad x(0) = 0 = \dot{x}(0), \qquad t > 0.$$

10.14. Apply the convolution theorem to find the solution of the *integral equation*

$$f(t) = t + \int_{0}^{t} (t - \xi)f(\xi)\, d\xi.$$

10.15. With the aid of the convolution theorem find the Laplace transform of

$$t^{-3/2}\epsilon^{-a/4t}, \qquad a > 0.$$

10.16. An important property of linear networks is the following: If $y(t)$ is the response of a network to a signal $x(t)$, then the response of that network to a signal of the form $\int_{0}^{t} x(t)\, dt$ is $\int_{0}^{t} y(t)\, dt$. Precisely formulate the initial conditions and prove the foregoing statement.

10.17. Use the initial- and final-value theorems to determine the initial and final values of x in Exercise 10.16.

10.18. Determine the initial and final values of current in Exercises 10.7 and 10.8 by means of the initial- and final-value theorems. Show that the same results can be obtained by assuming initially that inductors are open circuits and capacitors short circuits and by assuming finally that inductors are short circuits and capacitors open circuits. (This result holds in general, but the proof requires some care.)

CHAPTER 11

MATRIX ANALYSIS OF ELECTRIC NETWORKS

In previous discussions of electric networks we have alluded occasionally to the fact that all the essential information about a network was contained in the set of network impedances. This array of impedances is called a *matrix*. In this chapter we present this concept on a unified basis, showing how matrices may be used in analyzing the general properties of networks. As is often the case with advanced techniques of analysis, matrices are more suitable for studying the general behavior of networks than for solving particular numerical problems; but their use also gives one a depth of understanding which differentiates true knowledge from routine application of formulas.

11.1. Matrices. A matrix is a rectangular array of elements. Thus, the following are examples of matrices:

$$\mathfrak{R} = \begin{Vmatrix} R_{11} & R_{12} \\ R_{21} & R_{22} \end{Vmatrix} \tag{11.1a}$$

$$\mathfrak{A} = \begin{Vmatrix} a_{11} & a_{12} \\ a_{21} & a_{22} \\ a_{31} & a_{32} \end{Vmatrix} \tag{11.1b}$$

$$\mathfrak{Z} = \begin{Vmatrix} 1 + j\omega & \dfrac{1}{j\omega} & 2 \\ 2j + \dfrac{3}{j\omega} & 4 + j\omega & 7 + \dfrac{3}{j\omega} \end{Vmatrix} \tag{11.1c}$$

$$\mathfrak{X} = \|x^2\|. \tag{11.1d}$$

The double bars† are used to differentiate matrices from determinants. A matrix is *not* a determinant, nor does it have a value. A matrix need not be square. Its *order*, therefore, is specified as $n \times m$, where n is the number of rows and m the number of columns. For example, $\mathfrak{R}$ of Eq. (11.1a) is a 2 × 2 matrix, $\mathfrak{A}$ of Eq. (11.1b) is a 3 × 2 matrix, $\mathfrak{Z}$ is a 2 × 3

---

† Parentheses are also commonly used in place of double bars to indicate matrices, and square brackets are sometimes seen. For example, $\mathfrak{R}$ of Eq. (11.1a) could also be written as

$$\begin{pmatrix} R_{11} & R_{12} \\ R_{21} & R_{22} \end{pmatrix} \quad \text{or} \quad \begin{bmatrix} R_{11} & R_{12} \\ R_{21} & R_{22} \end{bmatrix}$$

306

matrix, and $\mathfrak{X}$ is a 1×1 matrix. Two very important special classes of matrices are the *row matrices* (or *row vectors*) which contain but a single row of elements; and the *column matrices* (or *column vectors*) which contain but a single column of elements.

A matrix may be designated by its general term in double bars. Thus we write $\mathfrak{R}$ of Eq. (11.1a) as

$$\mathfrak{R} = \|R_{ij}\|$$

and $\mathfrak{A}$ of Eq. (11.1b) as

$$\mathfrak{A} = \|a_{ij}\|.$$

Of course, in using such compact notation it is tacitly assumed that the context makes clear what the order of the matrix is. Column matrices are sometimes indicated by an open vertical bracket:

$$\mathfrak{B}] = \begin{bmatrix} b_1 \\ b_2 \\ \cdot \\ \cdot \\ \cdot \\ b_n \end{bmatrix} \tag{11.2}$$

and row matrices by an open horizontal bracket:

$$\underline{\mathfrak{C}} = [c_1 \quad c_2 \quad \ldots \quad c_m]. \tag{11.3}$$

These notations, while used in electrical engineering, are not common in the mathematical literature.

If $\mathfrak{A} = \|a_{ij}\|$ and $\mathfrak{B} = \|b_{ij}\|$ are both $n \times m$ matrices, then we say $\mathfrak{A} = \mathfrak{B}$ if and only if

$$a_{ij} = b_{ij}, \qquad i = 1, 2, \ldots, n; j = 1, 2, \ldots, m.$$

The sum of $\mathfrak{A}$ and $\mathfrak{B}$ is defined as the matrix $\mathfrak{C}$:

$$\mathfrak{C} = \mathfrak{A} + \mathfrak{B}$$

where $\mathfrak{C} = \|c_{ij}\|$ is the matrix whose elements c_{ij} are

$$c_{ij} = a_{ij} + b_{ij}, \qquad i = 1, 2, \ldots, n; j = 1, 2, \ldots, m.$$

Clearly, equality of matrices and sums of matrices are meaningful only if both are of the same order.

If $\mathfrak{A} = \|a_{ij}\|$ is an $n \times m$ matrix and k a constant, then multiplication of $\mathfrak{A}$ by k, written $k\mathfrak{A}$, is the $n \times m$ matrix $\mathfrak{K}$:

$$\mathfrak{K} = k\mathfrak{A}$$

where the elements k_{ij} of $\mathfrak{K}$ are

$$k_{ij} = ka_{ij}, \qquad i = 1, 2, \ldots, n; j = 1, 2, \ldots, m.$$

If $\mathfrak{S} = \|s_{ij}\|$ is a square $n \times n$ matrix, then we define the *determinant* of

S as det S or $|S|$. Thus

$$|S| = \det S = |s_{ij}|.$$

It is meaningless to speak of the determinant of a nonsquare matrix. If k is a constant, then

$$\det kS = k^n \det S.$$

Thus the definition of multiplication of matrices and determinants by constants is *not* the same. (Neither is the definition of equality or sum, as we have seen above.)

The multiplication of two matrices is defined in a manner which may appear quite cumbersome but is, in fact, very useful. Thus if $\mathfrak{a}$ is an $n \times m$ matrix and $\mathfrak{B}$ an $m \times p$ matrix, we define their product $\mathfrak{a} \times \mathfrak{B}$ as the $n \times p$ matrix $\mathfrak{C} = \|c_{ij}\|$, where

$$c_{ij} = \sum_{r=1}^{m} a_{ir}b_{rj}, \qquad \begin{array}{l} i = 1, 2, \ldots, n \\ j = 1, 2, \ldots, p. \end{array} \tag{11.4}$$

We see that multiplication is defined only for matrices which have the property that the number of columns of the first is equal to the number of rows of the second.† Some simple examples illustrate the application of Eq. (11.4).

$$\left\| \begin{array}{cc} a_{11} & a_{12} \\ a_{21} & a_{22} \end{array} \right\| \left\| \begin{array}{cc} b_{11} & b_{12} \\ b_{21} & b_{22} \end{array} \right\| = \left\| \begin{array}{cc} a_{11}b_{11} + a_{12}b_{21} & a_{11}b_{12} + a_{12}b_{22} \\ a_{21}b_{11} + a_{22}b_{21} & a_{21}b_{12} + a_{22}b_{22} \end{array} \right\| \tag{11.5}$$

$$\left\| \begin{array}{ccc} a_{11} & a_{12} & a_{13} \\ a_{21} & a_{22} & a_{23} \end{array} \right\| \left\| \begin{array}{cc} b_{11} & b_{12} \\ b_{21} & b_{22} \\ b_{31} & b_{32} \end{array} \right\|$$

$$= \left\| \begin{array}{cc} a_{11}b_{11} + a_{12}b_{21} + a_{13}b_{31} & a_{11}b_{12} + a_{12}b_{22} + a_{13}b_{32} \\ a_{21}b_{11} + a_{22}b_{21} + a_{23}b_{31} & a_{21}b_{12} + a_{22}b_{22} + a_{23}b_{32} \end{array} \right\| \tag{11.6}$$

$$\left\| \begin{array}{cc} 1 & 2 \\ 3 & 4 \end{array} \right\| \left\| \begin{array}{cc} 2 & 4 \\ 1 & 3 \end{array} \right\| = \left\| \begin{array}{cc} 4 & 10 \\ 10 & 24 \end{array} \right\| \tag{11.7}$$

$$\left\| \begin{array}{cc} 2 & 4 \\ 1 & 3 \end{array} \right\| \left\| \begin{array}{cc} 1 & 2 \\ 3 & 4 \end{array} \right\| = \left\| \begin{array}{cc} 14 & 20 \\ 10 & 14 \end{array} \right\| \tag{11.8}$$

$$\left\| \begin{array}{cc} Z_{11} & Z_{12} \\ Z_{21} & Z_{22} \end{array} \right\| \left\| \begin{array}{c} I_1 \\ I_2 \end{array} \right\| = \left\| \begin{array}{c} Z_{11}I_1 + Z_{12}I_2 \\ Z_{21}I_1 + Z_{22}I_2 \end{array} \right\|. \tag{11.9}$$

† A student of determinant theory will recall that if $A = |a_{ij}|$ and $B = |b_{ij}|$ are $n \times n$ determinants, then AB may be written as the $n \times n$ determinant $C = |c_{ij}|$, where $c_{ij} = \sum_{r=1}^{n} a_{ir}b_{rj}, i, j = 1, 2, \ldots, n$. The definition of matrix multiplication is thus the same as for determinants. As a consequence of these facts, if $\mathfrak{a} = \|a_{ij}\|$ and $\mathfrak{B} = \|b_{ij}\|$ are square matrices, then

$$\det \mathfrak{a}\mathfrak{B} = (\det \mathfrak{a}) \times (\det \mathfrak{B}).$$

The existence of a matrix $\mathfrak{a} \times \mathfrak{B}$ does not necessarily imply the existence of a matrix $\mathfrak{B} \times \mathfrak{a}$, for this latter product requires also that the number of columns of $\mathfrak{B}$ be the same as the number of rows of $\mathfrak{a}$. Thus $\mathfrak{a} \times \mathfrak{B}$ and $\mathfrak{B} \times \mathfrak{a}$ can only *both* be defined when $\mathfrak{a}$ and $\mathfrak{B}$ are square matrices of the same order. However, even if both $\mathfrak{a} \times \mathfrak{B}$ and $\mathfrak{B} \times \mathfrak{a}$ are defined, they are not necessarily equal, that is,

$$\mathfrak{a} \times \mathfrak{B} \neq \mathfrak{B} \times \mathfrak{a}. \tag{11.10}$$

We use the term *noncommutative* to express this fact. An example of this phenomenon is furnished by Eqs. (11.7) and (11.8).

Other useful matrix operations are *transposition* and *inversion*. A matrix may be transposed by interchanging its rows and columns. The *transpose* of a matrix may be designated by the subscript T. Thus if $\mathfrak{a} - \|a_{ij}\|$ is an $n \times m$ matrix, the transpose $\mathfrak{B} = \|b_{ij}\|$ is an $m \times n$ matrix and is related to $\mathfrak{a}$ by the equations

$$a_{ij} = b_{ji} \tag{11.11}$$

or $\mathfrak{a}_T = \mathfrak{B}$, $\|a_{ij}\|_T = \|b_{ij}\|$, $(a_T)_{ij} = b_{ij}$. Thus, for example,

$$\left\| \begin{array}{ccc} 2 & 3 & 1 \\ 4 & 7 & 6 \end{array} \right\|_T = \left\| \begin{array}{cc} 2 & 4 \\ 3 & 7 \\ 1 & 6 \end{array} \right\|. \tag{11.12}$$

While division by matrices is not defined, the *inverse matrix* accomplishes essentially the same result. We shall investigate this topic in Sec. 11.3.

11.2. Elementary Applications of Matrices. One of the important uses of matrix theory is as a powerful shorthand. Consider, for example, the following mesh equations:

$$\begin{aligned} E_1 &= Z_{11}I_1 + Z_{12}I_2 + Z_{13}I_3 \\ E_2 &= Z_{21}I_1 + Z_{22}I_2 + Z_{23}I_3 \\ E_3 &= Z_{31}I_1 + Z_{32}I_2 + Z_{33}I_3. \end{aligned} \tag{11.13}$$

In matrix notation this may be written

$$\left\| \begin{array}{c} E_1 \\ E_2 \\ E_3 \end{array} \right\| = \left\| \begin{array}{ccc} Z_{11} & Z_{12} & Z_{13} \\ Z_{21} & Z_{22} & Z_{23} \\ Z_{31} & Z_{32} & Z_{33} \end{array} \right\| \left\| \begin{array}{c} I_1 \\ I_2 \\ I_3 \end{array} \right\| \tag{11.14}$$

for carrying out the indicated multiplication leads to the column matrix

$$\left\| \begin{array}{c} Z_{11}I_1 + Z_{12}I_2 + Z_{13}I_3 \\ Z_{21}I_1 + Z_{22}I_2 + Z_{23}I_3 \\ Z_{31}I_1 + Z_{32}I_2 + Z_{33}I_3 \end{array} \right\|$$

and equating this, termwise, to the column matrix on the left of Eq. (11.14) leads by definition of equality of matrices to Eqs. (11.13).

Equation (11.14) may also be written in the more compact form

$$\mathcal{E} = Z\mathcal{I}. \tag{11.15}$$

where $\mathcal{E}$ is the column matrix of the E's, Z is the square matrix of the Z's, and $\mathcal{I}$ is the column matrix of the I's. This equation is much more general than Eqs. (11.13) for as written it has no constraints on the number of meshes.

The power of this shorthand is not merely in the saving of space permitted. Rather, by expressing complicated relationships concisely, we are enabled to focus attention on general properties of networks. This will be done in a subsequent section.

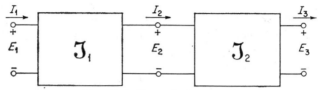

FIG. 11.1. Networks in cascade.

There also exist some direct applications of matrix analysis to circuit theory. Such an application is the cascade connection of two-port networks. Consider a two-port described by $ABCD$ constants:

$$\begin{aligned} E_1 &= AE_2 + BI_2 \\ I_1 &= CE_2 + DI_2. \end{aligned} \tag{11.16}$$

This may be expressed as

$$\left\| \begin{matrix} E_1 \\ I_1 \end{matrix} \right\| = \left\| \begin{matrix} A & B \\ C & D \end{matrix} \right\| \left\| \begin{matrix} E_2 \\ I_2 \end{matrix} \right\| \tag{11 17}$$

or

$$x_1 = \mathfrak{I}x_2 \tag{11.17a}$$

where

$$x_i = \left\| \begin{matrix} E_i \\ I_i \end{matrix} \right\|, \qquad i = 1, 2, 3; \tag{11.18}$$

and $\mathfrak{I}$, the *transfer matrix* of the two-port, is

$$\mathfrak{I} = \left\| \begin{matrix} A & B \\ C & D \end{matrix} \right\|. \tag{11.19}$$

Thus, if two two-ports are cascaded as in Fig. 11.1,

$$x_1 = \mathfrak{I}_1 x_2 \tag{11.20}$$

and

$$x_2 = \mathfrak{I}_2 x_3. \tag{11.21}$$

Substituting the value of x_2 from Eq. (11.21) into Eq. (11.20) yields

$$x_1 = \mathfrak{I}_1 \mathfrak{I}_2 x_3 \tag{11.22}$$

whence the over-all transfer function $\mathfrak{J}_0$ is

$$\mathfrak{J}_0 = \mathfrak{J}_1\mathfrak{J}_2. \tag{11.23}$$

This result may be compared with Example 7.1.

Similar applications may be made to other simple network connections.

11.3. Some Elementary Properties of Matrices. The $n \times n$ *unit*, or *identity matrix* $\mathfrak{U}$, is defined as the square matrix $\|\delta_{ij}\|$, where δ_{ij} is the Kronecker delta,

$$\delta_{ij} = \begin{cases} 1 & \text{if } i = j \\ 0 & \text{if } i \neq j \end{cases} \quad i, j = 1, 2, \ldots, n. \tag{11.24}$$

From our definition of matrix multiplication it is readily verified that if $\mathfrak{A}$ is any $n \times n$ square matrix, then

$$\mathfrak{A} \times \mathfrak{U} = \mathfrak{U} \times \mathfrak{A} = \mathfrak{A} \tag{11.25}$$

(where, of course, $\mathfrak{A}$ and $\mathfrak{U}$ have the same number of rows and columns).

The *inverse* of $\mathfrak{A}$, written $\mathfrak{A}^{-1}$, is a matrix with the property

$$\mathfrak{A}^{-1} \times \mathfrak{A} = \mathfrak{A} \times \mathfrak{A}^{-1} = \mathfrak{U}. \tag{11.26}$$

A matrix may not have an inverse. To show the conditions under which a matrix has an inverse we return to our experience in circuit theory. Let us write a set of n loop equations as

$$\mathcal{E} = \mathfrak{Z}\mathcal{I}. \tag{11.27}$$

Thus $\mathfrak{Z}$ is an $n \times n$ matrix. Premultiplying† both sides of the equation by $\mathfrak{Z}^{-1}$ leads to

$$\mathfrak{Z}^{-1}\mathcal{E} = \mathfrak{Z}^{-1}\mathfrak{Z}\mathcal{I} = \mathfrak{U}\mathcal{I} = \mathcal{I}$$

or

$$\mathcal{I} = \mathfrak{Z}^{-1}\mathcal{E}. \tag{11.28}$$

Now, we know from Chap. 5 that the loop currents are related to the loop voltages by an admittance matrix, the elements of which are

$$y_{ij} = \frac{A_{ji}}{\det \mathfrak{Z}}, \quad i, j = 1, 2, \ldots, n \tag{11.29}$$

where, if $\mathfrak{Z} = \|Z_{ij}\|$, the term A_{ji} is the cofactor of Z_{ji}. Thus

$$\mathfrak{Z}^{-1} = \left\| \frac{A_{ji}}{\det \mathfrak{Z}} \right\| = \frac{\|A_{ji}\|}{\det \mathfrak{Z}}.‡ \tag{11.30}$$

---

† Because multiplication is not commutative, it is necessary to specify the order of the terms. This may be done by using the terms *premultiplication* and *postmultiplication*.

‡ The matrix $\|A_{ji}\|$ of cofactors is termed the *adjoint* of $\mathfrak{Z}$ and is sometimes written $\tilde{\mathfrak{Z}}$.

From Eqs. (11.29) and (11.30) it is seen that in order that Z have an inverse it must be square, and the determinant of Z must not be zero. Such a matrix is termed *nonsingular*. A necessary and sufficient condition for a matrix to have an inverse is that it be nonsingular.

11.4. Network Topology. One of the very interesting applications of matrix theory is to network topology. This application permits a fascinating generalization of the relations which exist between the individual elements of a circuit and the circuit equations, node and loop, which describe the circuit. Properly speaking, network topology refers only to the manner in which the elements are interconnected. We shall later, however, extend this analysis to include the actual element values, thereby unifying the whole theory.

Many of the terms used in network topology such as node, branch, and circuit were defined as early as Chap. 1. Some of these need to be modified slightly or defined more precisely in order to prevent confusion. For example, a *branch* is defined as two distinct points with a line connecting them—from a topological point of view it matters not whether the branch consists of resistors, inductors, capacitors, or merely a piece of wire. The end points of the branch are *nodes*. It is also helpful to consider an *oriented branch*, which is merely a branch to which an arrow is affixed. A *graph* is defined as a collection of elements connected at nodes. We say a branch is *incident* on a node if the node is an end point of the branch.

In considering graphs, we number the branches $a, b, c, \ldots, B$ and designate the nodes $A, \ldots, N$, where B is the number of branches and N the number of nodes.

A *path* is defined as the set of elements traversed by starting at a node and following branches, never leaving subsequent nodes by the same branch by which the node was reached, and never meeting a node more than once. (Meeting a node means reaching and leaving the node. Thus, paths may be open or closed.) A graph is *connected* if a path exists between every pair of nodes. Connected graphs are those which, unlike some in Sec. 5.3, have only one separate part. Only connected graphs are considered herein because the consideration of separated graphs adds unnecessary inconvenience without adding to the substance of the discussion.

A *circuit* or *loop* is a path which begins and ends on the same node, or, simply, a closed path. An oriented loop is one to which an arrow is attached.

The foregoing definitions are quite straightforward. Less obvious, not in its definition, perhaps, but in its implications, is a tree. A *tree* is a connected subgraph (that is, a subset of a graph) which contains no loops. A particular form of tree which figures importantly in topology is the *complete tree*, one which contains all the nodes of a graph. Examples of trees and complete trees are shown in Fig. 11.2. It is clear that there are many possible trees and complete trees for any graph.†

With respect to a particular complete tree, a branch of the original graph either is in the complete tree, in which case it is termed a *tree branch*, or is not in the complete tree, in which case it is termed a *link*.

Every tree has one more node than branches, for each branch, except the first, adds one node, and the first branch adds two nodes. As a

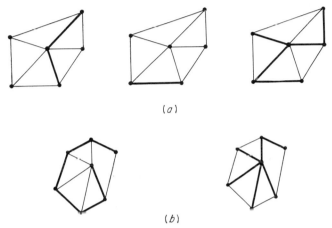

(*a*)

(*b*)

Fig. 11.2. (*a*) Examples of trees; (*b*) complete trees.

corollary, a complete tree contains $N - 1$ tree branches. Consequently, the number of links in a B-branch graph is $B - (N - 1)$ or $B - N + 1$.

The structure of a graph can be described in matrix form by the use of the *node matrix* or *incidence matrix*. The node matrix α, of order $B \times N$, is defined by

$$\alpha = \|a_{pQ}\| \tag{11.31}$$

where

$a_{pQ} = 1$ if node Q is the terminal node of the pth branch,
$= -1$ if node Q is the initial node of the pth branch,
$= 0$ if node Q is not incident on the pth branch.

(It is observed in this definition that all branches are oriented.)   The node matrix has exactly two nonzero elements ($+1$ and -1) in each row and at least two nonzero elements in each column.   ("Dangling" branches are not permitted in a graph.)   For example, the node matrix of the

† In particular, every (connected) graph has at least one complete tree.   For, each branch in a network either is or is not a member of a loop.   Remove one branch which is a member of a loop (leaving, of course, the nodes).   Repeat.   Eventually all loops are removed, but all nodes remain, and the remaining graph is a complete tree of the original graph.

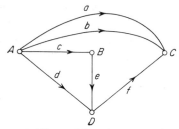

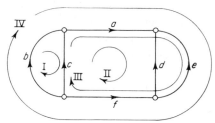

Fig. 11.3. Network for demonstration of node matrix.

Fig. 11.4. Network for demonstration of circuit matrix.

graph in Fig. 11.3 is given by

$$
\mathfrak{a} =
\begin{Vmatrix}
-1 & 0 & 1 & 0 \\
-1 & 0 & 1 & 0 \\
-1 & 1 & 0 & 0 \\
-1 & 0 & 0 & 1 \\
0 & -1 & 0 & 1 \\
0 & 0 & 1 & -1
\end{Vmatrix}
\begin{matrix}
a \\ b \\ c \\ d \\ e \\ f
\end{matrix}
. \qquad (11.32)
$$
$$
 A \quad B \quad C \quad D
$$

Loops may be described in matrix form by the *circuit matrix* $\mathfrak{B}$. This is defined for oriented branches and oriented loops:

$$
\mathfrak{B} = \|b_{pq}\| \qquad (11.33)
$$

where

b_{pq} = 1 if branch p is in loop q and has the same sense,
$\phantom{b_{pq}}$ = −1 if branch p is in loop q and has the opposite sense,
$\phantom{b_{pq}}$ = 0 if branch p is not in loop q.

As an example, the circuit matrix of the graph in Fig. 11.4 is given by

$$
\mathfrak{B} =
\begin{Vmatrix}
0 & 1 & 1 & 1 \\
1 & 0 & 0 & 1 \\
-1 & 1 & 1 & 0 \\
0 & -1 & 0 & 0 \\
0 & 0 & -1 & -1 \\
0 & -1 & -1 & -1
\end{Vmatrix}
\begin{matrix}
a \\ b \\ c \\ d \\ e \\ f
\end{matrix}
. \qquad (11.34)
$$
$$
 I \quad II \quad III \quad IV
$$

The choice of meshes is completely arbitrary. In the example given, there is already one more loop than necessary to solve the usual circuit equations, and two more loops may be selected. It is ordinarily important to work only with those loops which completely define the circuit behavior, particularly in the case of complicated circuits. We wish, therefore, to find *basic loops*. Our previous experience has shown us that for simple circuits there are many sets of basic loops (in dealing with mappable circuits, the meshes constitute a set of basic loops).   A set of basic loops may be uniquely determined by selecting a complete tree of the graph.   A basic loop is formed by a link and its unique tree path (by the definition of a tree, there is only one path).   Each loop has an orientation coinciding with the sense of its link.   The set of basic loops is that formed by repeating this procedure singly for each link.

Each of the loops so formed contains at least one branch (the link) which is part of no other loop, yet every branch is part of at least one loop. Furthermore, since there are $B - N + 1$ links, there will be $B - N + 1$ basic loops, and the required number of Kirchhoff's loop equations may be written.   The basic loops so formed are not always the most convenient to manipulate (for example, meshes form the basic loops only in very simple circuits) but they always lead to independent loop equations, which is more important in a general theory.

The circuit matrix for a set of basic loops is termed the *basic circuit matrix* and is designated by the symbol $\mathcal{C}$.   Because each link is in one and only one basic loop, the basic circuit matrix takes on an interesting appearance when the branches which are links are numbered lower than the tree branches, and the basic loops are numbered the same as the corresponding links.   Namely, the matrix in the upper left-hand corner is the identity matrix.   For example, the matrix corresponding to Fig. 11.4 would look like

$$\mathcal{C} = \left\| \begin{array}{cccc} 1 & 0 & 0 & \epsilon_1 \\ 0 & 1 & 0 & \epsilon_2 \\ 0 & 0 & 1 & \epsilon_3 \\ \epsilon_4 & \epsilon_5 & \epsilon_6 & \epsilon_7 \\ \epsilon_8 & \epsilon_9 & \epsilon_{10} & \epsilon_{11} \\ \epsilon_{12} & \epsilon_{13} & \epsilon_{14} & \epsilon_{15} \end{array} \right\| \left. \begin{array}{c} \\ \\ \\ \end{array} \right\} \text{links} \left. \begin{array}{c} \\ \\ \\ \end{array} \right\} \text{tree branches}$$

(11.35)

where the ϵ_i are $+1$, 0, or -1.

In this discussion of topology we have limited ourselves essentially to some basic definitions.   Some of the implications of these definitions are obvious, but many interesting properties of graphs and of the various matrices are left unmentioned.   We have only laid sufficient groundwork for subsequent discussions.

11.5. The First Fundamental Theorem of Electric Circuits.   We now apply matrix methods to a unified discussion of both the topological laws and Kirchhoff's laws of electric circuits.

With each branch we associate a number I.   The numbers are called currents, and they are assumed to be directed in the direction of the branch orientation.   These are represented by the matrix $\mathcal{I}$, of order $B \times 1$. Similarly, we associate a loop current I' with each loop.   These we represent by the matrix $\mathcal{I}'$, of order $(B - N + 1) \times 1$. Each loop current generates a branch current in all its branches, I' if the senses agree and $-I'$ if the senses disagree. The total branch current in any branch is the algebraic sum of the loop currents.

The branch currents are related to the loop currents by

$$\mathcal{I} = \mathcal{C}\mathcal{I}'. \tag{11.36}$$

This is seen by considering the definition of the basic circuit matrix. Each row in that matrix essentially shows what loops traverse the branch corresponding to that row, and so Eq. (11.36) is but a formal statement of the previous paragraph.

A branch emf E is a complex number associated with a branch of a network. The set of these emf's for the whole network is a $B \times 1$ matrix $\mathcal{E}$. Similarly, we have loop emf's $\mathcal{E}'$, a $(B - N + 1) \times 1$ matrix. If branch emf's are assigned in all branches, they generate a loop emf equal to the sum of the branch emf's of the branches contained in the loop, positive or negative polarity being affixed to the branch emf according to whether the senses of the branch and loop agree or disagree. Assuming a set of basic loops, we may write

$$\mathcal{E}' = \mathcal{D}\mathcal{E} \tag{11.37}$$

which is

$$E_q' = \sum_1^B D_{qp} E_p \tag{11.37a}$$

where

$D_{qp} = 1$ if branch p is in loop q and has the same sense,
$\quad\ = -1$ if branch p is in loop q and has the opposite sense,
$\quad\ = 0$ if branch p is not in loop q.

It is seen by comparing the definitions of $\mathcal{C}$ and $\mathcal{D}$ that $\mathcal{D}$ is merely the transpose of $\mathcal{C}$. Thus,

$$\mathcal{D} = \mathcal{C}_T \tag{11.38}$$

and

$$\mathcal{E}' = \mathcal{C}_T \mathcal{E}. \tag{11.39}$$

Since we ultimately wish to relate the currents in the circuit to the voltages, we must introduce the circuit impedances into the analysis. To that end we consider the *network impedance matrix* $\mathcal{Z}$. This is a $B \times B$ matrix whose terms along the principal diagonal are the self-impedances of each branch, and whose term in the i, j position is the mutual impedance coupling the potential drop in the ith branch to the current in the jth branch. *These are branch, not loop, impedances.*

The branch potential rise V is equal to the emf less the IZ drops (self and mutual).   This relationship may be generalized in matrix form to

$$\mathcal{V} = \mathcal{E} - \mathcal{Z}\mathcal{I}. \tag{11.40}$$

Now, Kirchhoff's voltage law† states that the sum of the branch potential rises for the branches of any loop is zero, the polarity of each potential rise being positive or negative according to the orientation of branch and loop agreeing or disagreeing.   This may be expressed, recalling the definition of $\mathcal{D}$, as

$$\mathcal{D}\mathcal{V} = 0 \tag{11.41}$$

and, since $\mathcal{D} = \mathcal{C}_T$,

$$\mathcal{C}_T\mathcal{V} = 0. \tag{11.42}$$

Let us premultiply Eq. (11.40) by $\mathcal{C}_T$:

$$\mathcal{C}_T\mathcal{V} = \mathcal{C}_T\mathcal{E} - \mathcal{C}_T\mathcal{Z}\mathcal{I} \tag{11.43}$$

or by applying Eq. (11.42):

$$\mathcal{C}_T\mathcal{E} = \mathcal{C}_T\mathcal{Z}\mathcal{I} \tag{11.44}$$

which, since $\mathcal{E}' = \mathcal{C}_t\mathcal{E}$ and $\mathcal{I} = \mathcal{C}\mathcal{I}'$, becomes

$$\mathcal{E}' = \mathcal{C}_T\mathcal{Z}\mathcal{C}\mathcal{I}'. \tag{11.45}$$

Let us define $\mathcal{Z}'$ as

$$\mathcal{Z}' = \mathcal{C}_T\mathcal{Z}\mathcal{C}. \tag{11.46}$$

Then from Eq. (11.45)

$$\mathcal{E}' = \mathcal{Z}'\mathcal{I}'. \tag{11.47}$$

From this last equation we recognize $\mathcal{Z}'$ as the long-familiar loop impedance matrix.

In the general problem of loop analysis the emf's are specified and we wish to find the currents.   To do this we must determine the inverse of $\mathcal{Z}'$.   This requires that $\mathcal{Z}'$ be nonsingular.   In more physical terms, this means that the emf's uniquely determine the currents.   This at first appears to be clearly the case; however, it is not, in general, true.   Initial charges on capacitors and currents in inductors give rise to transient currents which are not determined by the emf's.   Furthermore, in lossless circuits the "transients" may persist indefinitely.   However, in dissipative circuits in the steady state the emf's do uniquely determine the currents.   Rather than become involved in lengthy considerations of the conditions under which $\mathcal{Z}'$ is nonsingular we shall postulate it to be so. That is, the subsequent discussion applies to that (undefined) class of networks for which $\mathcal{Z}'$ is nonsingular.

Since $\mathcal{Z}'$ is nonsingular, $\mathcal{Z}'^{-1}$ exists.   Accordingly we may premultiply

† We have not explicitly mentioned Kirchhoff's current law because, by selecting loop currents, as much current enters a node as leaves it, and so the current law is satisfied.

Eq. (11.47) by $\mathbb{Z}'^{-1}$:

$$\mathbb{Z}'^{-1}\mathcal{E}' = \mathbb{Z}'^{-1}\mathbb{Z}'\mathcal{J}' = \mathcal{J}'. \tag{11.48}$$

Again, premultiplying by $\mathbb{C}$ yields

$$\mathbb{C}\mathcal{J}' = \mathbb{C}\mathbb{Z}'^{-1}\mathcal{E}' \tag{11.49}$$

or

$$\mathcal{J} = \mathbb{C}\mathbb{Z}'^{-1}\mathcal{E}' \tag{11.50}$$

which, on substituting expressions for $\mathbb{Z}'$ and $\mathcal{E}'$, becomes

$$\mathcal{J} = \mathbb{C}[\mathbb{C}_T\mathbb{Z}\mathcal{J}]^{-1}\mathbb{C}_T\mathcal{E}. \tag{11.51}$$

This last equation is known as the *first fundamental theorem of electric networks*.[†] It relates the branch currents to the branch emf's and branch impedances through a basic circuit matrix. Nowhere do the particular loops used appear, although they are implicit in the choice of $\mathbb{C}$. However, any appropriate $\mathbb{C}$ may be used.

A similar theorem, the second fundamental theorem of electric networks,[‡] may be derived by attacking the networks on a node basis. It is

$$\mathcal{V} = \mathbb{C}_1[\mathbb{C}_{1T}\mathcal{Y}\mathbb{C}_1]^{-1}\mathbb{C}_{1T}\mathcal{J} \tag{11.52}$$

where $\mathbb{C}_1$ is the *basic node matrix* (obtained from $\mathbb{C}$ by striking out the column corresponding to the reference node), $\mathcal{Y}$ is the branch admittance matrix, and $\mathcal{J}$ is the current-source matrix representing the current sources in parallel with each branch.

The curious reader may inquire of these last results: "Of what use are they?" The answer is: In practical cases, little. However, as an intellectual achievement they are really quite remarkable as a synthesis of topological and electromagnetic aspects of circuits.

EXERCISES

11.1. If A, B, and C are square matrices, prove that
(a) $A(BC) = (AB)C$.
(b) $A(B + C) = AB + AC$.

11.2. If A and B are nonsingular square matrices, prove that AB is nonsingular. Show that

$$(AB)^{-1} = B^{-1}A^{-1}.$$

11.3. The zero matrix is defined as a matrix all of whose elements are zero. We write this as

$$0 = \|0_{ij}\| \qquad i, j = 1, 2, \ldots, n.$$

[†] J. L. Synge, The Fundamental Theorem of Electric Networks, *Quart. Appl. Math.,* **9**:113–127 (1951).

[‡] C. Saltzer, The Second Fundamental Theorem of Electrical Networks, *Quart. Appl. Math.,* **11**:119–123 (1953).

Show that matrices have "divisors of zero." That is, show that, if A and B are nonzero square matrices, their product may be zero. Thus we cannot conclude from the matrix equation $AB = 0$ that either A or B or both are zero.

11.4. Prove that there exist no square matrices A and B such that

$$AB - BA = U$$

where U is the identity matrix.

11.5. Find the following matrix products:

(a) $\begin{Vmatrix} 4 & 8 \\ 9 & 0.7 \end{Vmatrix} \times \begin{Vmatrix} 3 & -2 \\ 5 & \sqrt{6} \end{Vmatrix}$

(b) $\begin{Vmatrix} 3 & -2 \\ 5 & \sqrt{6} \end{Vmatrix} \times \begin{Vmatrix} 4 & 8 \\ 9 & 0.7 \end{Vmatrix}$

(c) $\begin{Vmatrix} 1 & 3\pi & 2 \\ 4 & -9 & 11 \end{Vmatrix} \times \begin{Vmatrix} 6\sqrt{2} & -8 \\ 7 & \sqrt{7} \\ 4 & 9 \end{Vmatrix}$

(d) $\begin{Vmatrix} 2 & \sqrt{3} & -6 \\ 1 & 50 & 9 \end{Vmatrix} \times \begin{Vmatrix} 8 & -6 \\ 5 & 7 \\ 3 & 11 \end{Vmatrix} \times \begin{Vmatrix} 10 & 1 \\ 4 & -3 \end{Vmatrix}$

(e) $\begin{Vmatrix} 2 & -1 & 1 & -1 \\ 3 & \sqrt{2} & 7 & 3 \end{Vmatrix} \times \begin{Vmatrix} 2 & 5 & 30 \\ -1 & -1 & 4 \\ 6 & 9 & 0.4 \\ 7 & -2 & 6 \end{Vmatrix}$

11.6. Find the inverses of the following matrices:

(a) $\begin{Vmatrix} 4 & 6 \\ 7 & 9 \end{Vmatrix}$

(b) $\begin{Vmatrix} 5\sqrt[3]{2} & 6 \\ 7 & 7 \end{Vmatrix}$

(c) $\begin{Vmatrix} 1.03 & -0.47 \\ 0.96 & 0.88 \end{Vmatrix}$

11.7. The resistance matrix of a circuit is

$$\begin{Vmatrix} 90 & 22 & 17 & 6 \\ 22 & 40 & 15 & 0 \\ 17 & 15 & 45 & -8 \\ 6 & 0 & -8 & 32 \end{Vmatrix}.$$

Find the loop-current matrix when the voltage matrix is

$$\begin{Vmatrix} 10 \\ 7 \\ 6 \\ 4 \end{Vmatrix}.$$

11.8. In a certain vacuum-tube circuit the resistance matrix is

$$\begin{Vmatrix} 17 & 2 & 1 \\ 2 & 16 & -5 \\ 0 & -5 & 3 \end{Vmatrix}.$$

Find the loop currents when the voltage matrix is

$$\begin{Vmatrix} 5 \\ 4 \\ 8 \end{Vmatrix}.$$

11.9. Find the loop-current matrix in a circuit whose impedance matrix is

$$\left\| \begin{array}{cc} 4\underline{|45°} & 6\underline{|30°} \\ 3\underline{|27°} & 8\underline{|80°} \end{array} \right\|$$

and whose voltage matrix is

$$\left\| \begin{array}{c} 10\underline{|\;0°} \\ 15\underline{|-40°} \end{array} \right\|.$$

DETERMINANTS

We have seen (Chaps. 1 and 5, for example) that one of the mathematical problems associated with electric circuits is that of solving systems of *linear algebraic equations*. For example,

$$
\begin{aligned}
a_{11}x_1 + a_{12}x_2 + \cdots + a_{1n}x_n &= b_1 \\
a_{21}x_1 + a_{22}x_2 + \cdots + a_{2n}x_n &= b_2 \\
\cdots \cdots \cdots \cdots \cdots \cdots \cdots \cdots \\
a_{n1}x_1 + a_{n2}x_2 + \cdots + a_{nn}x_n &= b_n
\end{aligned}
\tag{A.1}
$$

is a system of n equations on the n unknowns $x_1, x_2, \ldots, x_n$. It is presumed that the a_{ij}, $i, j = 1, 2, \ldots, n$, and the b_k, $k = 1, 2, \ldots, n$, are known constants. This system of equations is similar to Eqs. (1.16) where we were given the resistances R_{ij} and voltages E_k and were required to find the currents $I_1, I_2, \ldots, I_n$. We prefer to use the notation indicated in Eqs. (A.1) above to emphasize that the results which we obtain apply to any system of linear equations and not just to one where the coefficients a_{ij} are resistances and the unknowns are currents. For example, when we treated a-c circuits the coefficients were not just resistances, but complex impedances.

It is, of course, possible to solve Eqs. (A.1) by a "brute force" calculation. For example, eliminate x_1 between the first and second of Eqs. (A.1), eliminate x_1 between the first and third of Eqs. (A.1), eliminate x_1 between the first and fourth of Eqs. (A.1), etc. Continuing this process we shall obtain a system of $n - 1$ equations on the $n - 1$ unknowns $x_2, \ldots, x_n$. We can then eliminate x_2 from the first and second equations of this new set and eventually reduce the problem to $n - 2$ equations on the $n - 2$ unknowns $x_3, \ldots, x_n$. Repeated applications of this technique will eventually reduce the system of Eqs. (A.1) to one equation on x_n, which, of course, gives x_n. Substituting x_n back into either of the pair of equations on x_{n-1} and x_n yields x_{n-1}, and repeated applications of this technique eventually will yield the numerical values of all the unknowns.

For example, consider the following system of equations:

$$
\begin{aligned}
x_1 - 2x_2 + x_3 &= 4 \\
3x_1 + 4x_2 - x_3 &= 6 \\
-0.5x_1 + 5x_2 + 2x_3 &= 12.
\end{aligned}
\tag{A.2}
$$

If we multiply the first equation by 3 and subtract from the second we obtain

$$10x_2 - 4x_3 = -6, \tag{A.3}$$

while multiplying the last equation by 2 and adding to the first we obtain

$$8x_2 + 5x_3 = 28. \tag{A.4}$$

Now we may eliminate x_2 from Eqs. (A.3) and (A.4) by multiplying Eq. (A.3) by 4 and Eq. (A.4) by 5 and subtracting:

$$41x_3 = 164.$$

Hence we see that

$$x_3 = 4.$$

Substituting $x_3 = 4$ into Eq. (A.3) or (A.4) yields

$$x_2 = 1$$

and substituting $x_3 = 4$ and $x_2 = 1$ into any of Eqs. (A.2) yields

$$x_1 = 2.$$

Thus we have solved the system of Eqs. (A.2). However, one must admit that the above process is lengthy, and if we had more than three equations, the method would be very laborious.

A systematic technique which enables us to solve systems of linear algebraic equations is the method of *determinants* which we shall develop in the following sections. Not only is it of some practical use in solving problems, but more important it enables us to study general properties of systems of linear algebraic equations, which prove extremely useful in the more advanced study of circuit theory.

A.1. Determinants. If we have *two* equations in *two* unknowns, for example,

$$\begin{aligned} a_{11}x_1 + a_{12}x_2 &= b_1 \\ a_{21}x_1 + a_{22}x_2 &= b_2, \end{aligned} \tag{A.5}$$

then we can solve for x_1 and x_2 by the elimination process discussed above to obtain†

$$x_1 = \frac{b_1 a_{22} - b_2 a_{12}}{a_{11}a_{22} - a_{12}a_{21}}, \qquad x_2 = \frac{b_2 a_{11} - b_1 a_{21}}{a_{11}a_{22} - a_{12}a_{21}}. \tag{A.6}$$

Let us now introduce some new mathematical notation. We define the array of four numbers

$$\begin{vmatrix} A & B \\ C & D \end{vmatrix} \tag{A.7}$$

---

† Of course we must assume that $a_{11}a_{22} - a_{12}a_{21} \neq 0$. If $a_{11}a_{22} - a_{12}a_{21} = 0$, then the reader may readily verify that one of Eqs. (A.5) is just a constant times the other. In other words, we effectively have only *one* equation instead of a *pair* of equations.

as the number $AD - BC$. Then, for example,

$$\begin{vmatrix} 1 & 3 \\ 2 & 4 \end{vmatrix} = 4 - 6 = -2$$

and

$$\begin{vmatrix} 0.5 & -7 \\ -6 & 12 \end{vmatrix} = 6 - 42 = -36.$$

In terms of this new notation, Eqs. (A.6) may be written

$$x_1 = \frac{\begin{vmatrix} b_1 & a_{12} \\ b_2 & a_{22} \end{vmatrix}}{\begin{vmatrix} a_{11} & a_{12} \\ a_{21} & a_{22} \end{vmatrix}} \tag{A.8}$$

and

$$x_2 = \frac{\begin{vmatrix} a_{11} & b_1 \\ a_{21} & b_2 \end{vmatrix}}{\begin{vmatrix} a_{11} & a_{12} \\ a_{21} & a_{22} \end{vmatrix}}, \tag{A.9}$$

respectively. Note that the denominator in both x_1 and x_2 is simply the array of the coefficients of Eqs. (A.5) and the numerator is the same array with the coefficients of x_1 replaced by b_1 and b_2 in Eq. (A.8) while the coefficients of x_2 are replaced by b_1 and b_2 in Eq. (A.9). Thus the form of the solution of Eqs. (A.5) is easy to remember.

For example, the solution of the pair of simultaneous equations

$$2x_1 - 3x_2 = 7$$
$$x_1 + 4x_2 = 6$$

may be written down by inspection as

$$x_1 = \frac{\begin{vmatrix} 7 & -3 \\ 6 & 4 \end{vmatrix}}{\begin{vmatrix} 2 & -3 \\ 1 & 4 \end{vmatrix}} = \frac{28 + 18}{8 + 3} = \frac{46}{11}$$

and

$$x_2 = \frac{\begin{vmatrix} 2 & 7 \\ 1 & 6 \end{vmatrix}}{\begin{vmatrix} 2 & -3 \\ 1 & 4 \end{vmatrix}} = \frac{12 - 7}{11} = \frac{5}{11}.$$

The symbol

$$\begin{vmatrix} A & B \\ C & D \end{vmatrix} = AD - BC$$

of Eq. (A.7) is called a *second-order determinant*, or a *two-by-two determinant*.

An nth order or $n \times n$ determinant is written

$$\begin{vmatrix} a_{11} & a_{12} & \cdots & a_{1n} \\ a_{21} & a_{22} & \cdots & a_{2n} \\ \cdot & \cdot & \cdots & \cdot \\ a_{n1} & a_{n2} & \cdots & a_{nn} \end{vmatrix}. \tag{A.10}$$

The first subscript on the a_{ij} refers to the *row* in which the element lies; the second subscript refers to the *column* in which the element lies. Thus a_{ij} is the element in the ith row and jth column. We sometimes abbreviate Eq. (A.10) by the symbol $|a_{ij}|$. Of course this is the same symbol for the absolute value of the *element* a_{ij}. However, the context will make clear whether we are talking about the *determinant* of the a_{ij}'s or the absolute value of the particular *coefficient* a_{ij}.

We have yet to define the *value* of a determinant. If $n = 2$ in Eq. (A.10), then by Eq. (A.7)

$$|a_{ij}| = \begin{vmatrix} a_{11} & a_{12} \\ a_{21} & a_{22} \end{vmatrix} = a_{11}a_{22} - a_{12}a_{21}.$$

If $n > 2$, then the value of the symbol of Eq. (A.10) is as yet undefined. To define the value of the determinant in these cases we introduce a new definition. Consider the array of Eq. (A.10) and strike out the row and column containing the element a_{ij}. There results an $(n - 1) \times (n - 1)$ array (called a *minor*) which is identical with the array of Eq. (A.10) except that the ith row and jth column have been deleted. The determinant of this array is called the *complement* of a_{ij} and will be denoted by D_{ij}. Now if $n = 3$ we define $|a_{ij}|$ as

$$|a_{ij}| = \begin{vmatrix} a_{11} & a_{12} & a_{13} \\ a_{21} & a_{22} & a_{23} \\ a_{31} & a_{32} & a_{33} \end{vmatrix} = a_{11}D_{11} - a_{21}D_{21} + a_{31}D_{31}, \tag{A.11}$$

or in expanded notation

$$|a_{ij}| = a_{11}\begin{vmatrix} a_{22} & a_{23} \\ a_{32} & a_{33} \end{vmatrix} - a_{21}\begin{vmatrix} a_{12} & a_{13} \\ a_{32} & a_{33} \end{vmatrix} + a_{31}\begin{vmatrix} a_{12} & a_{13} \\ a_{22} & a_{23} \end{vmatrix}. \tag{A.12}$$

Note that the D_{ij} in Eq. (A.11) are *second-order determinants* and hence may be evaluated by Eq. (A.7). Thus

$$|a_{ij}| = a_{11}(a_{22}a_{33} - a_{23}a_{32}) - a_{21}(a_{12}a_{33} - a_{13}a_{32}) + a_{31}(a_{12}a_{23} - a_{13}a_{22})$$
$$= a_{11}a_{22}a_{33} - a_{11}a_{23}a_{32} - a_{21}a_{12}a_{33} + a_{21}a_{13}a_{32} + a_{31}a_{12}a_{23} - a_{31}a_{13}a_{22}.$$

For example,

$$\begin{vmatrix} 1 & 2 & -1 \\ 6 & 3 & 0 \\ 7 & 5 & -2 \end{vmatrix} = 1 \times \begin{vmatrix} 3 & 0 \\ 5 & -2 \end{vmatrix} - 6 \times \begin{vmatrix} 2 & -1 \\ 5 & -2 \end{vmatrix} + 7 \times \begin{vmatrix} 2 & -1 \\ 3 & 0 \end{vmatrix}.$$
$$= 1(-6 - 0) - 6(-4 + 5) + 7(0 + 3) = 9.$$

If $n = 4$, we define the value of the determinant as

$$|a_{ij}| = \begin{vmatrix} a_{11} & a_{12} & a_{13} & a_{14} \\ a_{21} & a_{22} & a_{23} & a_{24} \\ a_{31} & a_{32} & a_{33} & a_{34} \\ a_{41} & a_{42} & a_{43} & a_{44} \end{vmatrix} = a_{11}D_{11} - a_{21}D_{21} + a_{31}D_{31} - a_{41}D_{41}. \quad \text{(A.13)}$$

In the above equation the D_{ij} are all 3×3 determinants which we can expand by the methods indicated above. In general, we define the value of the determinant of Eq. (A.10) as

$$|a_{ij}| = a_{11}D_{11} - a_{21}D_{21} + a_{31}D_{31} - \cdots + (-1)^{n+1}a_{n1}D_{n1}$$

where the D_{ij} are $(n-1) \times (n-1)$ determinants. Thus we see that an nth-order determinant can be written as the sum of n determinants, each of $(n-1)$st order. Each of the $(n-1) \times (n-1)$ determinants may in turn be written as the sum of $n-1$ determinants, each of $(n-2)$nd order. In this way we can continually reduce an nth-order determinant to the sum of lower-order determinants. For example,

$$\begin{vmatrix} 1 & 0.5 & 0 & 2 \\ -1 & 3 & 4 & 0.3 \\ 0 & -0.6 & 0 & 6 \\ 3 & 0 & 2 & 0 \end{vmatrix} = 1 \times \begin{vmatrix} 3 & 4 & 0.3 \\ -0.6 & 0 & 6 \\ 0 & 2 & 0 \end{vmatrix} + 1 \times \begin{vmatrix} 0.5 & 0 & 2 \\ -0.6 & 0 & 6 \\ 0 & 2 & 0 \end{vmatrix}$$

$$+ 0 \times \begin{vmatrix} 0.5 & 0 & 2 \\ 3 & 4 & 0.3 \\ 0 & 2 & 0 \end{vmatrix} - 3 \times \begin{vmatrix} 0.5 & 0 & 2 \\ 3 & 4 & 0.3 \\ -0.6 & 0 & 6 \end{vmatrix}$$

$$= 1[3(-12) + 0.6(-0.6)] + 1[0.5(-12) + 0.6(-4)]$$
$$- 3[0.5(24) - 0.6(-8)] = -36.36 - 8.4 - 50.4$$
$$= -95.16.$$

A.2. Properties of Determinants. Before returning to the solution of systems of algebraic equations, we wish to prove a number of theorems that will facilitate our manipulation of determinants. We shall state all our theorems in the general case but, for simplicity in notation, prove the theorems using 3×3 determinants. Our methods will be general. We shall use no special properties that apply only to 3×3 determinants (as is frequently done in some college algebra texts). All our proofs may be written immediately for $n \times n$ determinants by a simple change in *notation* but with *no* change in *method*.

Theorem 1. If the rows and columns of a determinant are interchanged, then the value of the determinant remains the same.

Proof. Let

$$D = \begin{vmatrix} a_{11} & a_{12} & a_{13} \\ a_{21} & a_{22} & a_{23} \\ a_{31} & a_{32} & a_{33} \end{vmatrix} \quad \text{(A.14)}$$

and let D' be the determinant with rows and columns interchanged, namely,

$$D' = \begin{vmatrix} a_{11} & a_{21} & a_{31} \\ a_{12} & a_{22} & a_{32} \\ a_{13} & a_{23} & a_{33} \end{vmatrix}.$$

(The determinant D' is called the *transpose* of D.) By definition of a determinant,

$$D = a_{11}a_{22}a_{33} - a_{11}a_{23}a_{32} - a_{21}a_{12}a_{33} + a_{21}a_{13}a_{32} + a_{31}a_{12}a_{23} - a_{31}a_{13}a_{22}$$

$$(A.15)$$

and

$$D' = a_{11}a_{22}a_{33} - a_{11}a_{23}a_{32} - a_{12}a_{21}a_{33} + a_{12}a_{23}a_{31} + a_{13}a_{21}a_{32} - a_{13}a_{22}a_{31}.$$

Comparing the expansions for D and D' we see that they are identical and thus the theorem is proved.

Our definition of the value of a determinant was obtained by "expanding by minors of the first column." That is, we took the first column and multiplied each element by its complement and alternately added and subtracted terms. By virtue of the above theorem we can also write a determinant by "expanding by minors of the first row." An even more general result can be obtained by use of the next theorem.

Theorem 2. If any two columns of a determinant are interchanged, the sign of the determinant is changed.

Proof. Let D be as given by Eq. (A.14) and let D^* be the same as D with (say) its first and third columns interchanged:

$$D^* = \begin{vmatrix} a_{13} & a_{12} & a_{11} \\ a_{23} & a_{22} & a_{21} \\ a_{33} & a_{32} & a_{31} \end{vmatrix}.$$

Then, by definition of determinant,

$$D^* = a_{13}a_{22}a_{31} - a_{13}a_{21}a_{32} - a_{23}a_{12}a_{31} + a_{23}a_{11}a_{32} + a_{33}a_{12}a_{21} - a_{33}a_{11}a_{22}.$$

Comparison of this expansion with Eq. (A.15) shows that

$$D = -D^*.$$

The reader may readily verify that if the first and second or second and third columns are interchanged the value of the resulting determinant will still be $-D$.

Let us examine a few consequences of this theorem. If we are given an $n \times n$ determinant, then if we interchange, say, the first and tenth columns, the resulting determinant (which is minus the old one) can be expanded by minors† of the first column. This, of course, is equivalent

---

† If we strike out any k rows and any k columns in an $n \times n$ determinant, the determinant of the resulting $(n - k) \times (n - k)$ array is called a *minor*. For example, the complement of an element in a determinant is a minor.

to expanding the original determinant by minors of the tenth column. Thus if we define the *cofactor* A_{ij} of the element a_{ij} in the $n \times n$ determinant a_{ij} as

$$A_{ij} = (-1)^{i+j} D_{ij},$$

we may write

$$D = \begin{vmatrix} a_{11} & a_{12} & \cdots & a_{1n} \\ a_{21} & a_{22} & \cdots & a_{2n} \\ \cdot & \cdot & \cdots & \cdot \\ a_{n1} & a_{n2} & \cdots & a_{nn} \end{vmatrix} = \sum_{i=1}^{n} a_{i\mu} A_{i\mu} \qquad (A.16)$$

for any μ, $\mu = 1, 2, \ldots, n$. If $\mu = 1$ we have the original definition of the value of a determinant. Now by virtue of Theorem 1, we have the corollary to Theorem 2 that the sign of the determinant is changed if any two rows are interchanged. And as a consequence of this remark, Eq. (A.16) may be written

$$D = \sum_{j=1}^{n} a_{\nu j} A_{\nu j} \qquad (A.17)$$

for *any* ν, $\nu = 1, 2, \ldots, n$. That is, Eq. (A.17) represents an expansion of a determinant by minors of the νth row.

As an illustration, consider the determinant

$$D = \begin{vmatrix} -10 & 0 & 1 & -2 \\ \sqrt{2} & 3 & 9 & 7 \\ 1 & 0 & -5 & 0 \\ 4 & 0 & \pi & -1 \end{vmatrix}.$$

Since the second column contains three zeros, it would be more convenient to expand the determinant by minors of the second column than by any other row or column. Thus

$$D = 3 \times \begin{vmatrix} -10 & 1 & -2 \\ 1 & -5 & 0 \\ 4 & \pi & -1 \end{vmatrix}. \qquad (A.18)$$

Again this resulting determinant is most readily evaluated by expanding by minors of the second row or third column since this row and column contains a zero. Expanding, for example, by minors of the second row we have

$$D = 3[-1(-1 + 2\pi) - 5(10 + 8)] = -(267 + 6\pi).$$

The sign before the 3 in Eq. (A.18) is $(-1)^{2+2} = +1$ since 3 lies in the second row and second column. A convenient mnemonic scheme to determine the sign quickly is given by the checkerboard array illustrated below,

$$\begin{vmatrix} + & - & + & - & + & \cdot & \cdot & \cdot \\ - & + & - & + & - & \cdot & \cdot & \cdot \\ + & - & + & - & + & \cdot & \cdot & \cdot \\ - & + & - & + & - & \cdot & \cdot & \cdot \\ \cdot & \cdot & \cdot & \cdot & \cdot & \cdot & \cdot & \cdot \\ \cdot & \cdot & \cdot & \cdot & \cdot & \cdot & \cdot & \cdot \end{vmatrix}.$$

Additional theorems for manipulating determinants follow.

Theorem 3. If all the elements of a single column (or row) of a determinant are multiplied by a number c then the value of the determinant is multiplied by c.

Proof. Let D be given by Eq. (A.14) and let D_c have (say) the second column of D multiplied by c.

$$D_c = \begin{vmatrix} a_{11} & ca_{12} & a_{13} \\ a_{21} & ca_{22} & a_{23} \\ a_{31} & ca_{32} & a_{33} \end{vmatrix}.$$

Then if we expand D_c it becomes identical with Eq. (A.15) except that every term will be multiplied by c. Thus

$$D_c = cD.$$

Theorem 4. The value of a determinant is zero if any row (column) consists entirely of zeros.

Proof. This follows from Theorem 3 with $c = 0$.

Theorem 5. If a determinant has two identical columns (or rows) its value is zero.

Proof. Let D be a determinant. If the two identical rows are interchanged, the resulting determinant D^* is identical with D,

$$D^* = D.$$

But by Theorem 2,

$$D^* = -D.$$

Thus $D = -D$ or $2D = 0$ and

$$D = 0.$$

Theorem 6. If any column (row) in a determinant is equal to any other column (row) multiplied by a constant c, then the value of the determinant is zero.

Proof. Let D be the determinant. Then by Theorem 3, D is equal to c times a determinant with two identical columns (rows), and by Theorem 5, $D = 0$.

Theorem 7.   The value of a determinant is unchanged if every element in any column (row) is multiplied by a constant and added to the corresponding element of any other column (row).

Proof.   Let D be given by Eq. (A.14).   If we multiply, say, the third row by c and add it to the first row we obtain

$$D_c = \begin{vmatrix} a_{11} + ca_{31} & a_{12} + ca_{32} & a_{13} + ca_{33} \\ a_{21} & a_{22} & a_{23} \\ a_{31} & a_{32} & a_{33} \end{vmatrix}.$$

Expanding D_c we see that it is identical with D as given by Eq. (A.15).

Let us illustrate some of the above theorems† by applying them to the evaluation of the following determinant:

$$D = \begin{vmatrix} 2 & 3 & 1 & 6 & 4 \\ 5 & 1 & 4 & 2 & -1 \\ 4 & 5 & 3 & 1 & 0 \\ 1 & 2 & 0 & 3 & 0 \\ 18 & 6 & 15 & 6 & 24 \end{vmatrix}.$$

If we factor a 3 from the last row, multiply the first row by 2, and subtract it from the last row, and then add four times the second row to the first row we obtain

$$D = 3 \begin{vmatrix} 22 & 7 & 17 & 14 & 0 \\ 5 & 1 & 4 & 2 & -1 \\ 4 & 5 & 3 & 1 & 0 \\ 1 & 2 & 0 & 3 & 0 \\ 2 & -4 & 3 & -10 & 0 \end{vmatrix}.$$

Now expand by minors of the last column:

$$D = 3 \begin{vmatrix} 22 & 7 & 17 & 14 \\ 4 & 5 & 3 & 1 \\ 1 & 2 & 0 & 3 \\ 2 & -4 & 3 & -10 \end{vmatrix}.$$

Subtracting the second row from the last row we obtain

$$D = 3 \begin{vmatrix} 22 & 7 & 17 & 14 \\ 4 & 5 & 3 & 1 \\ 1 & 2 & 0 & 3 \\ -2 & -9 & 0 & -11 \end{vmatrix}$$

which becomes

$$D = 3 \times 17 \begin{vmatrix} 4 & 5 & 1 \\ 1 & 2 & 3 \\ -2 & -9 & -11 \end{vmatrix} - (3 \times 3) \begin{vmatrix} 22 & 7 & 14 \\ 1 & 2 & 3 \\ -2 & -9 & -11 \end{vmatrix}$$

† For other manipulative methods see M. Salvadori and K. S. Miller, "Mathematical Solution of Engineering Problems," Columbia University Press, New York, 1953.

on expanding by minors of the third column. Now add twice the second row to the last row in each of the above determinants, and factor a minus one from the last row of each. There results

$$D = -51 \begin{vmatrix} 4 & 5 & 1 \\ 1 & 2 & 3 \\ 0 & 5 & 5 \end{vmatrix} + 9 \begin{vmatrix} 22 & 7 & 14 \\ 1 & 2 & 3 \\ 0 & 5 & 5 \end{vmatrix}.$$

Finally, subtract the second column from the last column in both the above determinants,

$$D = -51 \begin{vmatrix} 4 & 5 & -4 \\ 1 & 2 & 1 \\ 0 & 5 & 0 \end{vmatrix} + 9 \begin{vmatrix} 22 & 7 & 7 \\ 1 & 2 & 1 \\ 0 & 5 & 0 \end{vmatrix}$$

and expand by minors of the last row:

$$D = -51[-5(4 + 4)] + 9[-5(22 - 7)] = 1365.$$

A.3. Cramer's Rule. We now wish to show how the above results on determinants can be applied to the solution of algebraic equations [see Eqs. (A.1)]. First we recall Eq. (A.16):

$$D = \begin{vmatrix} a_{11} & a_{12} & \cdots & a_{1n} \\ a_{21} & a_{22} & \cdots & a_{2n} \\ \cdot & \cdot & \cdots & \cdot \\ a_{n1} & a_{n2} & \cdots & a_{nn} \end{vmatrix} = \sum_{i=1}^{n} a_{i\mu} A_{i\mu}.$$

Now suppose that we consider

$$\sum_{i=1}^{n} a_{i\mu} A_{i\nu},$$

where $\mu \neq \nu$. That is, we multiply $a_{i\mu}$ by the cofactor of $a_{i\nu}$. But if D^* is a determinant whose μth column is identical with its νth column, then

$$D^* = \sum_{i=1}^{n} a_{i\nu} A_{i\nu} = \sum_{i=1}^{n} a_{i\mu} A_{i\nu},$$

since $a_{i\mu} \equiv a_{i\nu}$, $i = 1, 2, \ldots, n$. But by Theorem 5, $D^* = 0$. Thus

$$\sum_{i=1}^{n} a_{i\mu} A_{i\nu} = 0, \qquad \mu \neq \nu.$$

We may therefore generalize Eq. (A.16) to read

$$\sum_{i=1}^{n} a_{i\mu} A_{i\nu} = \delta_{\mu\nu} D \qquad \qquad \text{(A.19)}$$

where $\delta_{\mu\nu}$ is the Kronecker delta, that is,

$$\delta_{\mu\nu} = \begin{cases} 1 & \text{if } \mu = \nu \\ 0 & \text{if } \mu \neq \nu. \end{cases}$$

Similarly, Eq. (A.17) may be generalized to

$$\sum_{j=1}^{n} a_{\mu j} A_{\nu j} = \delta_{\mu\nu} D. \tag{A.20}$$

Now we are in a position to solve the system of Eqs. (A.1).   Multiply the first of Eqs. (A.1) by the cofactor of a_{11}, the second by the cofactor of a_{21}, the third by the cofactor of a_{31}, etc.   We thus obtain

$$
\begin{aligned}
A_{11}a_{11}x_1 + A_{11}a_{12}x_2 + \cdots + A_{11}a_{1n}x_n &= A_{11}b_1 \\
A_{21}a_{21}x_1 + A_{21}a_{22}x_2 + \cdots + A_{21}a_{2n}x_n &= A_{21}b_2 \\
&\cdots \\
A_{n1}a_{n1}x_1 + A_{n1}a_{n2}x_2 + \cdots + A_{n1}a_{nn}x_n &= A_{n1}b_n
\end{aligned}
$$

or, more compactly,

$$A_{11} \sum_{i=1}^{n} a_{1i}x_i = A_{11}b_1$$

$$A_{21} \sum_{i=1}^{n} a_{2i}x_i = A_{21}b_2$$

$$\cdots$$

$$A_{n1} \sum_{i=1}^{n} a_{ni}x_i = A_{n1}b_n.$$

Now add these equations,

$$\sum_{j=1}^{n} A_{j1} \sum_{i=1}^{n} a_{ji}x_i = \sum_{j=1}^{n} A_{j1}b_j$$

and interchange the order of summation on the left,

$$\sum_{i=1}^{n} \left(\sum_{j=1}^{n} A_{j1}a_{ji} \right) x_i = \sum_{j=1}^{n} A_{j1}b_j. \tag{A.21}$$

But by Eq. (A.19)

$$\sum_{j=1}^{n} A_{j1}a_{ji} = \delta_{1i} D$$

where

$$D = \begin{vmatrix} a_{11} & a_{12} & \cdots & a_{1n} \\ a_{21} & a_{22} & \cdots & a_{2n} \\ \cdot & \cdot & \cdots & \cdot \\ a_{n1} & a_{n2} & \cdots & a_{nn} \end{vmatrix}$$

is the determinant of the coefficients of the system of Eqs. (A.1).   Thus Eq. (A.21) becomes

$$Dx_1 = \sum_{j=1}^{n} A_{j1} b_j$$

and if $D \neq 0$,

$$x_1 = \frac{1}{D} \sum_{j=1}^{n} A_{j1} b_j. \tag{A.22}$$

Thus we have solved the system of Eqs. (A.1) for x_1.   Similarly, if we had multiplied the first of Eqs. (A.1) by the cofactor of $a_{i\mu}$, the second by the cofactor of $a_{2\mu}$, the third by the cofactor of $a_{3\mu}$, etc., and performed the same manipulations as above, we would have obtained

$$x_\mu = \frac{1}{D} \sum_{j=1}^{n} A_{j\mu} b_j. \tag{A.23}$$

The results embodied in Eqs. (A.22) and (A.23) are known as *Cramer's rule* and may be formally stated as follows:
Cramer's Rule.   Let

$$
\begin{aligned}
a_{11}x_1 + a_{12}x_2 + \cdots + a_{1n}x_n &= b_1 \\
a_{21}x_1 + a_{22}x_2 + \cdots + a_{2n}x_n &= b_2 \\
\cdots \cdots \cdots \cdots \cdots \cdots \cdots \cdots \cdots \\
a_{n1}x_1 + a_{n2}x_2 + \cdots + a_{nn}x_n &= b_n
\end{aligned}
\tag{A.24}
$$

be a system of linear algebraic equations on the n unknowns x_1, x_2, $\ldots$, x_n.   If the determinant D of the coefficients,

$$
D = \begin{vmatrix}
a_{11} & a_{12} & \cdots & a_{1n} \\
a_{21} & a_{22} & \cdots & a_{2n} \\
\cdot & \cdot & \cdots & \cdot \\
a_{n1} & a_{n2} & \cdots & a_{nn}
\end{vmatrix},
\tag{A.25}
$$

is unequal to zero, then the solution of Eqs. (A.24) is given by the formula

$$x_\mu = \frac{A_{1\mu} b_1 + A_{2\mu} b_2 + \cdots + A_{n\mu} b_n}{D}, \qquad \mu = 1, 2, \ldots, n. \tag{A.26}$$

We leave it to the reader to show that Eq. (A.26) may also be written in the form

$$
x_\mu = \frac{1}{D}
\begin{vmatrix}
a_{11} & a_{12} & \cdots & a_{1,\mu-1} & b_1 & a_{1,\mu+1} & \cdots & a_{1n} \\
a_{21} & a_{22} & \cdots & a_{2,\mu-1} & b_2 & a_{2,\mu+1} & \cdots & a_{2n} \\
\cdot & \cdot & \cdots & \cdot & \cdot & \cdot & \cdots & \cdot \\
a_{n1} & a_{n2} & \cdots & a_{n,\mu-1} & b_n & a_{n,\mu+1} & \cdots & a_{nn}
\end{vmatrix} .
\tag{A.27}
$$

That is, x_μ is the ratio of two determinants. The denominator is the determinant D of the coefficients a_{ij} and the numerator is the same determinant D with the μth column replaced by the b_i's. This constitutes a generalization of Eqs. (A.8) and (A.9). The form of Eq. (A.27) is, of course, easier to remember than Eq. (A.26).

As an example, we consider Example 1.3,

$$
\begin{aligned}
3I_1 - 2I_2 &= 9 \\
-2I_1 + 9I_2 \quad - 4I_4 &= 0 \\
11I_3 - 5I_4 &= -10 \\
-4I_2 - 5I_3 + 16I_4 &= 6.
\end{aligned}
$$

The determinant D of the coefficients of the unknowns I_1, I_2, I_3, I_4 is

$$
D = \begin{vmatrix}
3 & -2 & 0 & 0 \\
-2 & 9 & 0 & -4 \\
0 & 0 & 11 & -5 \\
0 & -4 & -5 & 15
\end{vmatrix}.
$$

Expanding by minors of the first row,

$$
D = 3 \begin{vmatrix}
9 & 0 & -4 \\
0 & 11 & -5 \\
-4 & 5 & 16
\end{vmatrix} + 2 \begin{vmatrix}
-2 & 0 & -4 \\
0 & 11 & -5 \\
0 & -5 & 16
\end{vmatrix}
$$

$$
= 3[9(176 - 25) - (4 \times 44)] + 2[-2(176 - 25)] = 2945.
$$

Thus

$$
I_1 = \frac{1}{2945} \begin{vmatrix}
9 & -2 & 0 & 0 \\
0 & 9 & 0 & -4 \\
-10 & 0 & 11 & -5 \\
6 & -4 & -5 & 16
\end{vmatrix}
$$

$$
= \frac{1}{2945} \left\{ 9 \begin{vmatrix}
9 & 0 & -4 \\
0 & 11 & -5 \\
-4 & -5 & 16
\end{vmatrix} + 2 \begin{vmatrix}
0 & 0 & -4 \\
-10 & 11 & -5 \\
6 & -5 & 16
\end{vmatrix} \right\}
$$

$$
= \frac{1}{2945} [10{,}647 + 128] = \frac{10{,}775}{2945} = 3.655
$$

and

$$
I_2 = \frac{1}{2945} \begin{vmatrix}
3 & 9 & 0 & 0 \\
-2 & 0 & 0 & -4 \\
0 & -10 & 11 & -5 \\
0 & 6 & -5 & 16
\end{vmatrix} = \frac{2910}{2945} = 0.9881.
$$

Similarly we may evaluate I_3 and I_4.

EXERCISES

A.1. Evaluate the following determinants:

(a)
$$\begin{vmatrix} 1 & -2 & 3 \\ 7 & 0 & 4 \\ -3 & 6 & -2 \end{vmatrix}.$$

(b)
$$\begin{vmatrix} \sqrt{2} & 1 & -7 \\ 0 & \sqrt{3} & \pi \\ -\sqrt{2} & 1 & 17.2 \end{vmatrix}.$$

(c)
$$\begin{vmatrix} 1 & -6 & -3 & 2 \\ 2 & 3 & 5 & 1 \\ 5 & 1 & 2 & 4 \\ 7 & 9 & 7 & 3 \end{vmatrix}.$$

(d)
$$\begin{vmatrix} \sin \phi \cos \theta & \sin \phi \sin \theta & \cos \phi \\ \cos \phi \cos \theta & \cos \phi \sin \theta & -\sin \phi \\ -\sin \phi \sin \theta & \sin \phi \cos \theta & 0 \end{vmatrix}.$$

(e)
$$\begin{vmatrix} 2 & a & 3b \\ 42b & 30ab - 14b & 42 \\ -3b & b & 7 \end{vmatrix}.$$

(f)
$$\begin{vmatrix} 2 - j3 & 4 + 6j & 3 - j \\ 4 - j6 & j^3 - j & 4 - j2 \\ 3 + j & 4 + 2j & 1 \end{vmatrix}.$$

A.2. Evaluate the following determinants, making full use of the theorems developed in the text.

(a)
$$\begin{vmatrix} 10 & 4 & -4 \\ -1 & -5 & 10 \\ 9 & 9 & -15 \end{vmatrix}.$$

(b)
$$\begin{vmatrix} 2 & 1 & 4 & 3 \\ 3 & -2 & 2 & 1 \\ -1 & 2 & 1 & -3 \\ 5 & 3 & 4 & 2 \end{vmatrix}.$$

(c)
$$\begin{vmatrix} 2 & 3 & 5 & 1 \\ 1 & -6 & -3 & 2 \\ 7 & 9 & 7 & 3 \\ 5 & 1 & 2 & 4 \end{vmatrix}.$$

(d)
$$\begin{vmatrix} 1 & 2 & 3 & 4 \\ 2 & 4 & 1 & 5 \\ 6 & 2 & 5 & 4 \\ 1 & 1 & 2 & 2 \end{vmatrix}.$$

$$(e) \qquad \begin{vmatrix} 7 & 10 & -5 & 21 \\ 3 & 5 & -1 & 11 \\ -2 & -4 & 2 & -8 \\ 6 & 10 & -4 & 20 \\ 3 & 4 & -2 & 9 \end{vmatrix}.$$

A.3. Solve for x,

$$\begin{vmatrix} a & a & a \\ x & x & b \\ b & c & d \end{vmatrix} = 0.$$

A.4. For what values of x does the following determinant vanish?

$$\begin{vmatrix} x & 3 & 1 \\ -1+x^2 & -2 & x \\ x^2 & 4 & 3-x \end{vmatrix}.$$

A.5. Show that $x = 1$ is a triple root and $x = 3$ a simple root of

$$\begin{vmatrix} x & 1 & 1 & 1 \\ 1 & x & 1 & 1 \\ 1 & 1 & x & 1 \\ 1 & 1 & 1 & x \end{vmatrix} = 0.$$

A.6. Prove that

$$\begin{vmatrix} 1 & x & x & x & x \\ -x & 1 & x & x & x \\ -x & -x & 1 & x & x \\ -x & -x & -x & 1 & x \\ -x & -x & -x & -x & 1 \end{vmatrix} = \tfrac{1}{2}[(x+1)^5 - (x-1)^5].$$

A.7. Prove that

$$\begin{vmatrix} z^2 + x^2 - y^2 & 2xy & -2yx \\ 2xy & z^2 - x^2 + y^2 & 2xz \\ 2yz & -2xz & z^2 - x^2 - y^2 \end{vmatrix} = (x^2 + y^2 + z^2)^3.$$

A.8. Prove that

$$\begin{vmatrix} 0 & x & x & x & x & x \\ 1 & 0 & x & x & x & x \\ 1 & 1 & 0 & x & x & x \\ 1 & 1 & 1 & 0 & x & x \\ 1 & 1 & 1 & 1 & 0 & x \\ 1 & 1 & 1 & 1 & 1 & 0 \end{vmatrix} = \frac{x - x^6}{x - 1}, \qquad x \neq 1.$$

A.9. If $A = |a_{ij}|$ and $B = |b_{ij}|$ are 3×3 determinants, show that their product $C = AB$ can be expressed as a 3×3 determinant $C = |c_{ij}|$, where

$$c_{ij} = \sum_{\alpha=1}^{3} a_{i\alpha} b_{\alpha j}, \qquad i, j = 1, 2, 3.$$

(This result is also true for $n \times n$ determinants with obvious generalizations of notation.)

A.10. Let $F(x) = |f_{ij}(x)|$, $i, j = 1, 2, 3, 4$. We shall use the temporary notation $|f_{ij}(x)|_\alpha$ to mean a determinant identical with $|f_{ij}(x)|$ except that its α row has been replaced by the *derivatives* of the corresponding elements in $F(x)$. For example,

$$|f_{ij}(x)|_2 = \begin{vmatrix} f_{11}(x) & f_{12}(x) & f_{13}(x) & f_{14}(x) \\ f'_{21}(x) & f'_{22}(x) & f'_{23}(x) & f'_{24}(x) \\ f_{31}(x) & f_{32}(x) & f_{33}(x) & f_{34}(x) \\ f_{41}(x) & f_{42}(x) & f_{43}(x) & f_{44}(x) \end{vmatrix}.$$

Prove that

$$\frac{d}{dx} F(x) = |f_{ij}(x)|_1 + |f_{ij}(x)|_2 + |f_{ij}(x)|_3 + |f_{ij}(x)|_4.$$

A.11. Solve the following systems of equations by Cramer's rule:

(a)
$$\begin{aligned} -2x + 3y - 6z &= -5 \\ 4x + 7y + 2z &= 8 \\ -6x - 5y + 2z &= 1. \end{aligned}$$

(b)
$$\begin{aligned} 2x - 2y + 5z &= -7 \\ x + y &= 3 \\ 5x - 2z &= 7. \end{aligned}$$

(c)
$$\begin{aligned} 3a - 6b - 2c &= 1 \\ -a - 6b - 4c &= 5 \\ -2a + 5b + c &= -3. \end{aligned}$$

(d)
$$\begin{aligned} (a_1 + b)x + a_2 y + a_3 z + a_4 u &= 1 \\ a_1 x + (a_2 + b)y + a_3 z + a_4 u &= 0 \\ a_1 x + a_2 y + (a_3 + b)z + a_4 u &= 0 \\ a_1 x + a_2 y + a_3 z + (a_4 + b)u &= 0. \end{aligned}$$

(e)
$$\begin{aligned} (2 + j)x + jy - 3z + u &= 1 - j \\ \epsilon^{2j} x + 7jz - (1 - j)u &= 7 \\ (-3 + 4j)x + 2y - 3u &= 2 - j \\ (1 + j)y - (3 - j)z &= 0. \end{aligned}$$

A.12. Show that

$$\begin{vmatrix} -a & b & c & d & e & f & g \\ a & -b & c & d & e & f & g \\ a & b & -c & d & e & f & g \\ a & b & c & -d & e & f & g \\ a & b & c & d & -e & f & g \\ a & b & c & d & e & -f & g \\ a & b & c & d & e & f & -g \end{vmatrix} = 320\ abcdefg.$$

A.13. Carefully examine the possibility of solving

$$\begin{aligned} 2x + 5y - 3z &= 0 \\ 5x + 3y - 4z &= 1 \\ 8x + y - 5z &= 2 \end{aligned}$$

for x, y, z.

PARTIAL FRACTIONS

If

$$A(s) = a_0 s^n + a_1 s^{n-1} + \cdots + a_n$$

and

$$B(s) = b_0 s^m + b_1 s^{m-1} + \cdots + b_m$$

are polynomials in s, then we call

$$F(s) = \frac{A(s)}{B(s)} \tag{B.1}$$

a *rational function* of s. If $a_0 \neq 0$, we say that the *degree* of $A(s)$ is n and if $b_0 \neq 0$ we say that the *degree* of $B(s)$ is m. In this discussion we shall limit ourselves to rational functions where the degree of the denominator exceeds the degree of the numerator, viz., $m > n$.

If the zeros of $B(s)$ are all distinct, say $s_1, s_2, \ldots, s_m$, then $F(s)$ may be developed in *partial fractions* in the form

$$F(s) = \frac{A_1}{s - s_1} + \frac{A_2}{s - s_2} + \cdots + \frac{A_m}{s - s_m} \tag{B.2}$$

where the A_i are constants. [Note that the zeros of $B(s)$ are the poles of $F(s)$.] The reader will recall from the calculus that one way to evaluate $A_1, A_2, \ldots, A_m$ is to clear fractions in Eq. (B.2) and equate like powers of s. One obtains in this way a system of linear equations on the A_i. For example, if

$$F(s) = \frac{s + 1}{s^2 - 3s + 2}$$

then we may write

$$F(s) = \frac{A_1}{s - 1} + \frac{A_2}{s - 2} \tag{B.3}$$

since the roots of $s^2 - 3s + 2 = 0$ are $s = 1$ and $s = 2$. If we multiply both sides of Eq. (B.3) by $s^2 - 3s + 2$ there results the identity (in s)

$$s + 1 = A_1(s - 2) + A_2(s - 1).$$

Collecting coefficients, we have

$$(A_1 + A_2 - 1)s - (2A_1 + A_2 + 1) = 0.$$

If this equation is to be identically true in s we must have

$$A_1 + A_2 = 1$$
$$2A_1 + A_2 = -1.$$

Solving this system of equations for A_1 and A_2 gives

$$A_1 = -2, \qquad A_2 = 3.$$

Thus the partial-fraction expansion of $F(s)$ is

$$F(s) = \frac{s + 1}{s^2 - 3s + 2} = \frac{-2}{s - 1} + \frac{3}{s - 2}.$$

While the above straightforward method is often the most convenient, we wish to develop some more general systematic techniques for obtaining partial-fraction expansions. The methods that we shall expound are useful not only in practical applications but in theoretical investigations as well.

For the moment let us return to Eq. (B.2). Later we shall consider the more general case where the poles of $F(s)$ are not distinct. To determine the A_i of Eq. (B.2) when $F(s)$ is given we first multiply both sides of the equation by $s - s_1$:

$$\frac{A(s)(s - s_1)}{B(s)} = A_1 + \frac{A_2(s - s_1)}{s - s_2} + \cdots + \frac{A_m(s - s_1)}{s - s_m} \qquad \text{(B.4)}$$

and then let s approach s_1. If we do so, the right-hand side of Eq. (B.4) becomes A_1, but the left-hand side becomes indeterminate. That is,

$$\lim_{s \to s_1} \frac{A(s)(s - s_1)}{B(s)} = \frac{0}{0} \qquad \text{(B.5)}$$

[since s_1 is a root of $B(s) = 0$].

There are two common methods for evaluating such limits. One is to note that since

$$B(s) = b_0(s - s_1)(s - s_2) \cdots (s - s_m)$$

we may write

$$B(s) = (s - s_1)B_1(s)$$

where

$$B_1(s) = b_0(s - s_2)(s - s_3) \cdots (s - s_m)$$

and

$$B_1(s_1) \neq 0.$$

Substituting in Eq. (B.5) yields

$$\lim_{s \to s_1} \frac{A(s)(s - s_1)}{(s - s_1)B_1(s)} = \frac{A(s_1)}{B_1(s_1)}.$$

Thus

$$A_1 = \frac{A(s_1)}{B_1(s_1)}. \tag{B.6}$$

Similarly,

$$A_k = \frac{A(s_k)}{B_k(s_k)}, \qquad k = 1, 2, \ldots, m, \tag{B.7}$$

where

$$B_k(s) = b_0(s - s_1)(s - s_2) \cdots (s - s_{k-1})(s - s_{k+1}) \cdots (s - s_n). \tag{B.8}$$

The determination of the coefficients in the partial-fraction expansion of $F(s)$ is now complete.

Another method for evaluating the limit of Eq. (B.5) is to use L'Hospital's rule. Thus,

$$\lim_{s \to s_1} \frac{A(s)(s - s_1)}{B(s)} = \lim_{s \to s_1} \frac{\dfrac{d}{ds}[A(s)(s - s_1)]}{\dfrac{d}{ds}[B(s)]}$$

$$- \lim_{s \to s_1} \frac{A'(s)(s - s_1) + A(s)}{B'(s)} = \frac{A(s_1)}{B'(s_1)} \tag{B.9}$$

where the prime denotes differentiation. [Since s_1 is a simple root of $B(s) = 0$, $B'(s_1) \neq 0$.] In general, then,

$$A_k = \frac{A(s_k)}{B'(s_k)}, \qquad k = 1, 2, \ldots, m. \tag{B.10}$$

Thus the A_k coefficients of Eq. (B.2) can be evaluated from either Eq. (B.7) or Eq. (B.10).

Example B.1. Expand

$$F(s) = \frac{s^2 + 3s + 2}{s^3 - 6s^2 + 11s - 6}$$

into partial fractions.

Solution. First we note that the poles of $F(s)$ occur at $s = 1$, $s = 2$, and $s = 3$ since

$$s^3 - 6s^2 + 11s - 6 = (s - 1)(s - 2)(s - 3).$$

We therefore write

$$\frac{s^2 + 3s + 2}{s^3 - 6s^2 + 11s - 6} = \frac{A_1}{s - 1} + \frac{A_2}{s - 2} + \frac{A_3}{s - 3}.$$

Using Eq. (B.7) we find

$$A_1 = \frac{s^2 + 3s + 2}{(s - 2)(s - 3)} \bigg|_{s=1} = \frac{6}{2} = 3$$

$$A_2 = \frac{s^2 + 3s + 2}{(s - 1)(s - 3)} \bigg|_{s=2} = \frac{12}{-1} = -12$$

$$A_3 = \frac{s^2 + 3s + 2}{(s - 1)(s - 2)} \bigg|_{s=3} = \frac{20}{2} = 10.$$

Alternatively, since $B'(s) = 3s^2 - 12s$, Eq. (B.10) yields

$$A_1 = \frac{s^2 + 3s + 2}{3s^2 - 12s + 11}\bigg|_{s=1} = \frac{6}{2} = 3$$

$$A_2 = \frac{s^2 + 3s + 2}{3s^2 - 12s + 11}\bigg|_{s=2} = \frac{12}{-1} = -12$$

$$A_3 = \frac{s^2 + 3s + 2}{3s^2 - 12s + 11}\bigg|_{s=3} = \frac{20}{2} = 10$$

and

$$\frac{s^2 + 3s + 2}{s^3 - 6s^2 + 11s + 6} = \frac{3}{s - 1} - \frac{12}{s - 2} + \frac{10}{s - 3}.$$

Even though the roots of $B(s) = 0$ may be complex, the representation of Eq. (B.2) holds, although some of the A_i coefficients will be complex. Since complex roots occur in conjugate pairs, a partial-fraction expansion which contains the term

$$\frac{A}{s - s_0}$$

must of necessity contain a term of the form

$$\frac{A'}{s - s_0^*}$$

where s_0^* is the conjugate of the root s_0. The reader may verify for himself that A' is actually the conjugate A^* of A. Thus the two complex terms $A/(s - s_0)$ and $A^*/(s - s_0^*)$ can be combined into a single *real quadratic* term, viz.,

$$\frac{A}{s - s_0} + \frac{A^*}{s - s_0^*} = \frac{(A + A^*)s - (s_0 A^* + s_0^* A)}{s^2 - (s_0 + s_0^*) + s_0 s_0^*}$$

$$= \frac{2\,\mathrm{Re}\,[A]s - 2\,\mathrm{Re}\,[s_0 A^*]}{s^2 - 2\,\mathrm{Re}\,[s_0]s + |s_0|^2}$$

and all the coefficients are real.

Now let us consider Eq. (B.1) when $B(s)$ has multiple or repeated roots. Then if s_k is a root of multiplicity m_k, $k = 1, 2, \ldots, r$ and

$$m_1 + m_2 + \cdots + m_r = m,$$

the partial-fraction expansion of $F(s)$ becomes

$$F(s) = \frac{A_{11}}{s - s_1} + \frac{A_{12}}{(s - s_1)^2} + \cdots + \frac{A_{1m_1}}{(s - s_1)^{m_1}}$$

$$+ \frac{A_{21}}{s - s_2} + \frac{A_{22}}{(s - s_2)^2} + \cdots + \frac{A_{2m_2}}{(s - s_2)^{m_2}}$$

$$+ \cdots \qquad \cdots \qquad \cdots \qquad \cdots$$

$$+ \frac{A_{r1}}{s - s_r} + \frac{A_{r2}}{(s - s_r)^2} + \cdots + \frac{A_{rm_r}}{(s - s_r)^{m_r}}. \qquad \text{(B.11)}$$

Let us suppose that $s = s_1$ is a root of multiplicity p of $B(s)$. Then we may write

$$B(s) = (s - s_1)^p P(s) \tag{B.12}$$

where $P(s)$ is a polynomial of degree $m - p$ involving the other zeros of $B(s)$. We then have

$$F(s) = \frac{A(s)}{B(s)} = \frac{A(s)}{(s - s_1)^p P(s)}, \tag{B.13}$$

and in this case

$$F(s) = \frac{A_{11}}{s - s_1} + \frac{A_{12}}{(s - s_1)^2} + \cdots + \frac{A_{1p}}{(s - s_1)^p} + C(s) \tag{B.14}$$

where $C(s)$ represents the partial-fraction expansion corresponding to the other poles of $F(s)$.

We now multiply both sides of Eq. (B.14) by $(s - s_1)^p$ to obtain

$$F(s)(s - s_1)^p = A_{11}(s - s_1)^{p-1} + A_{12}(s - s_1)^{p-2} + \cdots + A_{1,p-1}(s - s_1)$$
$$+ A_{1p} + C(s)(s - s_1)^p. \tag{B.15}$$

For simplicity in notation let

$$G(s) = F(s)(s - s_1)^p = \frac{A(s)}{B(s)}(s - s_1)^p = \frac{A(s)}{P(s)}.$$

Since s_1 is not a root of $P(s) = 0$ we infer that $G(s_1)$ exists and is finite. If we let $s = s_1$ in Eq. (B.15),

$$G(s_1) = A_{1p}$$

and we have evaluated A_{1p}. If we differentiate Eq. (B.15) we obtain

$$G'(s) = (p - 1)A_{11}(s - s_1)^{p-2} + (p - 2)A_{12}(s - s_1)^{p-3}$$
$$+ \cdots + A_{1,p-1} + D'(s) \tag{B.16}$$

where

$$D(s) = C(s)(s - s_1)^p.$$

Since

$$D'(s) = C'(s)(s - s_1)^p + pC(s)(s - s_1)^{p-1}$$

we infer that $D'(s_1) = 0$ and hence, from Eq. (B.16),

$$G'(s_1) = A_{1,p-1}. \tag{B.17}$$

Repeated differentiation of Eq. (B.16) followed by setting s equal to s_1 leads to

$$G^{(k)}(s_1) = k!A_{1,p-k}$$

or

$$A_{1,p-k} = \frac{G^{(k)}(s_1)}{k!}, \qquad k = 0, 1, \ldots, p - 1. \tag{B.18}$$

Example B.2. Express

$$F(s) = \frac{s^2 + 2}{s^2(s + 1)(s + 2)}$$

as the sum of partial fractions.

Solution. According to our general theory,

$$F(s) = \frac{s^2 + 2}{s^2(s + 1)(s + 2)} = \frac{A_{11}}{s} + \frac{A_{12}}{s^2} + \frac{A_2}{s + 1} + \frac{A_3}{s + 2}.$$

In the notation introduced above,

$$G(s) = \frac{s^2 + 2}{(s + 1)(s + 2)}.$$

Thus

$$A_{12} = G(0) = 1.$$

Since

$$G'(s) = \frac{(s + 1)(s + 2)(2s) - (s^2 + 2)(2s + 3)}{(s + 1)^2(s + 2)^2},$$

$$G'(0) = \frac{-6}{4} = -\frac{3}{2}$$

and

$$A_{11} = G'(0) = -\frac{3}{2}.$$

We can use our earlier methods to evaluate A_2 and A_3. Thus

$$A_2 = \frac{(s^2 + 2)(s + 1)}{s^2(s + 1)(s + 2)}\bigg|_{s=-1} = \frac{3}{1} = 3$$

$$A_3 = \frac{(s^2 + 2)(s + 2)}{s^2(s + 1)(s + 2)}\bigg|_{s=-2} = \frac{6}{-4} = -\frac{3}{2}.$$

The partial-fraction decomposition is therefore

$$F(s) = \frac{s^2 + 2}{s^2(s + 1)(s + 2)} = -\frac{3}{2s} + \frac{1}{s^2} + \frac{3}{s + 1} - \frac{3}{2(s + 2)}.$$

For further details, especially as applied to the Laplace transform, we refer the reader to K. S. Miller, "Engineering Mathematics," Rinehart & Company, Inc., New York, 1956, chap. 5; in particular, p. 210ff.

EXERCISES

B.1. Express the following rational functions in terms of partial fractions:

(a) $\dfrac{1}{s^2 - 1}$

(b) $\dfrac{2s + 3}{s^2 + s + 1}$

(c) $\dfrac{2s^2 - 3s + 1}{4s^3 + 16s^2 - s - 4}$

(d) $\dfrac{s + 1}{s^3 + 3s^2 + s - 2}$

(e) $\dfrac{s^3 - 4s + 3}{s^4 + 3s^3 + 5s^2 + 4s + 2}$

B.2. Decompose the following into partial fractions:

(a) $\dfrac{s^2 + 1}{s^3}$

(b) $\dfrac{2s}{(s + 1)^2}$

(c) $\dfrac{s - 1}{s^2(s + 2)}$

(d) $\dfrac{16s + 2}{16s^4 - 8s^2 + 1}$

(e) $\dfrac{s^3 + s}{s^4 - s^3 - 3s^2 + 5s - 2}$

A SHORT TABLE OF LAPLACE TRANSFORMS

$F(s) = \mathcal{L}[f(t)]$	$f(t) = \mathcal{L}^{-1}[F(s)]$
$\int_0^\infty f(t)\epsilon^{-st}\,dt$	$\dfrac{1}{2\pi j}\int_{\sigma-j\infty}^{\sigma+j\infty} F(s)\epsilon^{st}\,ds$
$aF(s) + bG(s)$	$af(t) + bg(t)$
$sF(s) - f(0)$	$f'(t)$
$s^2F(s) - sf(0) - f'(0)$	$f''(t)$
$\dfrac{1}{s}F(s) - \dfrac{1}{s}\int_0^a f(t)\,dt$	$\int_a^t f(t)\,dt \qquad a > 0$
$-F''(s)$	$tf(t)$
$\int_s^\infty F(\xi)\,d\xi$	$\dfrac{f(t)}{t}$
$\epsilon^{-as}F(s)$	$f(t-a)u(t-a) \qquad a > 0$
$F(s+a)$	$\epsilon^{-at}f(t)$
$\dfrac{1}{s}$	$u(t) \qquad \sigma_0 = 0$
$\dfrac{1}{s}\epsilon^{-as}$	$u(t-a) \qquad a > 0 \qquad \sigma_0 = 0$
$\dfrac{1}{s^2}$	$t \qquad \sigma_0 = 0$
$\dfrac{n!}{s^{n+1}}$	$t^n, \qquad n \geqq 0 \qquad \sigma_0 = 0$
$\dfrac{1}{s+a}$	$\epsilon^{-at} \qquad \sigma_0 = -a$
$\dfrac{n!}{(s+a)^{n+1}}$	$\epsilon^{-at}t^n, \qquad n \geqq 0 \qquad \sigma_0 = -a$
$\dfrac{b}{s^2+b^2}$	$\sin bt \qquad \sigma_0 = 0$
$\dfrac{s}{s^2+b^2}$	$\cos bt \qquad \sigma_0 = 0$
$\dfrac{b}{(s+a)^2+b^2}$	$\epsilon^{-at}\sin bt \qquad \sigma_0 = -a$
$\dfrac{s+a}{(s+a)^2+b^2}$	$\epsilon^{-at}\cos bt \qquad \sigma_0 = -a$

INDEX

345